PRE-ALGEBRA

A TEACHING TEXTBOOK

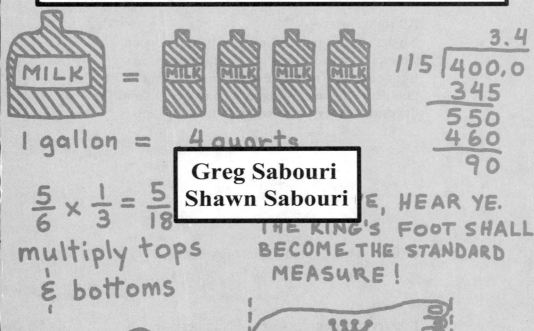

PRE-ALGEBRA
A TEACHING TEXTBOOK

Greg Sabouri
Shawn Sabouri

Teaching Textbooks, Inc.

Pre-Algebra: A Teaching Textbook™
First Edition

Copyright © 2005 by Teaching Textbooks, Inc.

Printed in the United States of America.

Library of Congress Control Number:

ISBN: 0-9749036-4-7

Teaching Textbooks, Inc.
P. O. Box 60529
Oklahoma City, OK 73146
www.teachingtextbooks.com

Table of Contents

2 weeks

A Letter to Parents

Dear Parents,

Finally, there's a Pre-Algebra book designed specifically for independent learners. Let us tell you about it.

Textbook and Teacher Combined

Unlike traditional classroom textbooks, which are meant to be used only with the help of a teacher, the Pre-Algebra Teaching Textbook™ is both a textbook and a teacher combined into one. The print lessons explain each of the concepts in an easy-to-digest conversational tone. Plus, each lesson includes a 10-15 minute audiovisual lecture.

Never Get Stumped Again

But what really makes the Teaching Textbook™ unique is that in addition to the CD-ROM lectures, the program offers **audiovisual step-by-step solutions for every one of the 3,800 problems in the book!** This is far more teaching than is offered by any other product on the market. In fact, it's even more teaching than is available in most traditional classes. With this unprecedented CD-ROM package, the frustration of missing a problem and not being able to figure out what you did wrong is over. A student (or parent) need never get stumped again!

Easy-to-Use CD-ROMs

The Teaching Textbook™ CD-ROMs are also incredibly easy to use. Unlike most software, which often requires wading through detailed instruction manuals, the Teaching Textbook™ is designed to be as easy to use as a videotape. You just set the CD in the tray, click on the lesson and lecture you want and that's it!

Friendly Text and Fun Illustrations

Parents love the Teaching Textbook™ primarily because it gives them a safety net whenever they have to answer a question on a tough problem. But if you ask kids what makes a Teaching Textbook™ the best, they almost always say the same thing: *It's more fun*. Students say that reading the text is like having a friendly tutor or coach gently guiding you through each concept and problem type. They also enjoy the fascinating (and sometimes entertaining) real-world examples and humorous illustrations. Together these features put students at ease and keep them totally engaged in the learning process. Finally, because the problem sets employ the well-known review method, students are more likely to actually retain what they've learned.

Thank you for your purchase of the Pre-Algebra Teaching Textbook™ and for the opportunity to serve you and your family's educational needs.

Greg Sabouri and Shawn Sabouri

Suggestions on How to Use This Product

Please feel free to use this powerful and versatile product as you see fit. However, when families ask us to suggest a "best" method for using the Pre-Algebra Teaching Textbook, here is the advice we give.

How to "Best" Use the Teaching Textbook
1) Read the printed lesson in your book.

2) Watch the lecture on CD.

3) Work any of the five practice problems that seem difficult.

4) Watch the CD lectures that explain those practice problems. These are on the LECTURE & PRACTICE CDs.

5) Work all of the problems in the problem set.

6) Grade the assignment.

7) Watch the step-by-step solutions on CD for any problems that were missed. These are on the STEP-BY-STEP SOLUTIONS CDs.

8) After finishing each chapter, take and grade the chapter test (found in the Answer Key & Test Bank).

Practice Problems
We should also mention a few things about the practice problems and highlighted text. First of all, practice problems are not required. They are additional examples to help the student with the assigned problem set. Each of the five practice problems is labeled with a letter (**a**, **b**, **c**, **d**, or **e**). These problems are very similar to the problems in the problem set that are labeled with those same letters. So if a student is having trouble with number 16, and it's labeled **b**, he or she can see how a very similar problem was solved by referring back to practice problem b. Usually, the hardest problems have a practice problem to match them. So this system gives students a hint for the toughest problems in each problem set.

Highlighted Text
You've already noticed that we use a text highlighter. The purpose of the highlighting is to emphasize the most important points in a lesson. This improves reading comprehension and makes it easier for students to go back and review material that has already been covered. That can be particularly helpful with this book, since every problem set uses the review method. Also, some students may just want to watch the lectures on CD (instead of reading the lessons in the book) and then only read the highlighted text as reinforcement.

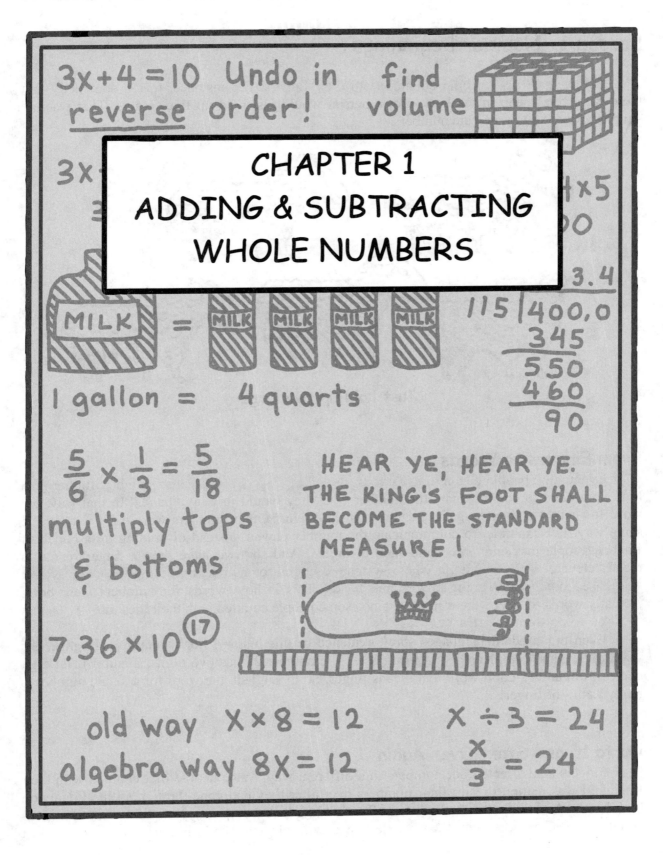

CHAPTER 1
ADDING & SUBTRACTING
WHOLE NUMBERS

Lesson 1—Number Beginnings

A long time ago, people counted with their fingers. For instance, to tell somebody that there were five sheep in the backyard, a person would just hold up five fingers. That was the simplest way to communicate numbers.

Just hold up five fingers.

From Fingers to Words

Eventually, people began to use words instead of fingers to indicate a number. Rather than hold up a hand to communicate the number five, they would just say "hand." In that way, the word for hand (in their language) came to mean "five." Other numbers were dealt with in the same way. For example, to communicate the number eleven, instead of holding up a bunch of fingers, people just said "two hands and a finger." And so "two hands and a finger" came to mean "eleven." After awhile, a whole system of words for numbers grew up. And the system was based on the words for fingers and hands. This is how words for numbers were born. Actually words for feet were also used, since some people counted with their toes too.

Even our modern languages show evidence of this history. For example in English, the word **digit** is used to mean a single number. (The number 25 has two digits: 2 and 5.) But digit comes from an old Latin word that means finger. So in English, the word for a single number is really Latin for finger!

Up to 10 and Start Over Again

Fingers also affected our numbers in a different way. Since people first counted with their fingers, it was natural to start their numbers over after they had gone through all the fingers on both hands. And that's the method we still use today. If that surprises you, think about it. When counting, we first go to ten, then we start over with eleven. That's because eleven really just means ten and one left over. From eleven, we go to twelve, which means ten and two left over and then on to thirteen, which means ten and three ("thir" stands for three and "teen" for ten). Then once we get to twenty, which means two tens, we start over again. Twenty-one means two tens and one, twenty-two means two tens and two, and so on. So our numbers basically start over every time we get to 10. And the reason it works this way is that people used to always count with their fingers! In fact, if humans had seven fingers instead of ten, we might count by starting over after every seventh number instead of after every tenth.

Written Numbers

As time progressed, people needed to do more with numbers than just talk about them. They needed to write numbers down in order to keep records for things like taxes. A lot of different kinds of written number symbols were developed around the world: Roman, Greek, Sumerian, and so on. In fact, Roman numbers (or "numerals") are still used occasionally today, mainly on clocks, buildings, and in book headings. Here are the major Roman number symbols.

I	V	X	L	C	D	M
one	five	ten	fifty	one hundred	five hundred	one thousand

Roman Number Symbols

To show "one" using Roman numerals, we just write the symbol I. To show "two," we write II. Three is III. Since the new symbol V is used as five, the Roman system sort of starts over at 5, except that there's no new symbol after ten until you get to 50, so it's a little confused. In the old days, the Romans would write four as IIII. But later on, people got into the habit of writing four as IV, which is shorter. With the I to the left of the V, you're supposed to subtract one from five to get four. To show six, they would write VI. Since the I is to the right of the V, this means to add five and one to get six. Here are some other examples of Roman numerals.

VIII = eight	XI = eleven	XV = fifteen
LXXV = seventy-five	CCCXXII = three hundred twenty-two	

A Primitive Calculator

The one bad thing about most of the ancient number systems (including the Romans') was that they were really hard to calculate with. That's why people didn't even use them for that purpose. They only used numbers to write down the answer. If they wanted to perform a calculation, they worked with something called an **abacus**, which was really a primitive calculator. The abacus was popular throughout the world. A typical abacus has a set of parallel metal wires, each wire with ten sliding balls on it. Here's what one looks like.

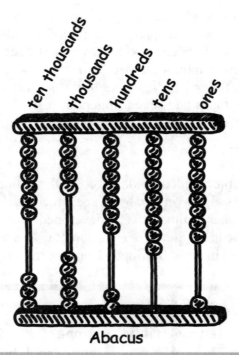

Abacus

Notice that the wire on the far right is for ones, the next wire is for tens, the one after that is for hundreds, and so on.

To put a number in an abacus, we slide the proper number of balls down each wire. For instance, to show the number four hundred thirty-two, we pull down four balls on the hundreds wire, three balls on the tens wire, and two balls on the ones wire, like this.

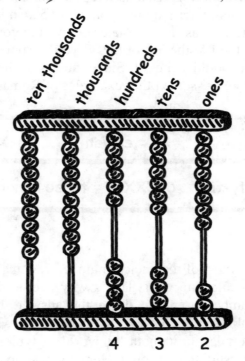

4   3   2

Then let's say we want to use the abacus to add four hundred thirty two to another number like two hundred forty-one. We just pull down two more balls on the hundreds wire, another four balls on the tens wire, and another one ball on the ones wire.

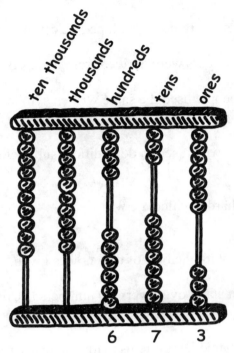

This gives us a total of six balls on the hundreds, seven on the tens, and three on the ones wires, for an answer of six hundred seventy-three. That's how the primitive calculator called an abacus worked.

Practice 1

   a.   Tell what number XXVI represents.   2,6 1

   b.   Tell what number MCVIII represents.   1108

   c.   Write the Roman number for 62.   LX II   →

   d.   Write the Roman number for 2,833.   MM DCCC X xx 111

   e.   Answer the following question: A page in a book is numbered XI. What will the number on the next page be? Write your answer in Roman numbers.

   x11

Problem Set 1

Tell whether each sentence below is True or False.

T 1. Before number systems were developed, people counted on their fingers.

F 2. The first names for numbers were derived from names of animals.

F 3. In ancient times, all people used the same written symbols for numbers throughout the world.

F 4. Early written numbers were used to do addition, subtraction, multiplication, and division.

T 5. Roman numbers are hard to calculate with.

Complete each sentence below with the best of the choices given.

6. A number system that starts over every 10 numbers became popular because ___B___.

    A. it was simpler than other systems mathematically.
    B. humans have 10 fingers
    C. ancient astronomers believed there were 10 planets
    D. 10 was believed to be a divine number
    E. the ancient world was divided into 10 nations

7. A(n) ___E___ is a primitive machine for calculating that was used throughout the world a long time ago.

    A. calculator   B. adding machine   C. slide rule
    D. computer   E. abacus

8. Today, Roman numerals are mainly only used ___B___.

    A. by scientists
    B. on clocks, buildings, and in book headings
    C. in the financial industry
    D. in the metric system
    E. in India

Tell what number each Roman number below represents.

9. III *3*   10. XI *II*   (a) 11. XXVIII *253*   12. CCLXI *261*

13. DCXVII *617* (b) 14. MCCXII *1212*

Write the Roman number for each number below.

15. 36 *XXXVI*   (c) 16. 73 *LXXIII*   17. 206 *CCIII*   (d) 18. 3,721 *MMMDXXCCI*

Answer each question below.

19. The cornerstone of a building shows the date of its construction to be MMI. In what year was it built? *2001*

(e) 20. A page in a book is numbered XXII. What will the number on the next page be? Write your answer in Roman numbers.

XXIII

Lesson 2—Our Modern Numbers

The number symbols we use today actually came all the way from India and were brought to Europe by Arabs. That's why they're called **Hindu-Arabic numbers**. (Many Hindus live in India.) But here's the amazing thing about Hindu-Arabic numbers. Before they were invented, all sorts of different numbers were used throughout the world. But after the Hindu-Arabic numbers became widely known, all the other kinds of numbers practically went away. In other words, the Hindu-Arabic numbers worked so well that they drove all the other numbers almost completely out of existence. Compare that to what has happened with languages. We still have lots of different languages (English, German, Japanese, French, Chinese, Russian, and so on). No one language has driven all the others out.

Place Value

Why were Hindu-Arabic numbers (or "modern numbers," as we'll call them) so popular? Well, it's because they worked just like an abacus. An abacus has different wires, remember, and each one contains balls that have a certain value. Modern numbers work the same way. They use only ten symbols (0, 1, 2, 3, 4, 5, 6, 7, 8, 9), and each symbol has a different value. A symbol on the far right represents ones. A symbol just to the left of it represents tens. A symbol one more place to the left represents hundreds, and so on. This is called **the place-value system**, because a symbol's place or position determines its value. Using place value, here's how we represent the number four hundred thirty-two.

See, writing the number 432 is like pulling 4 balls down on the hundreds wire, 3 on the tens wire, and 2 on the ones wire. So modern numbers are really just an abacus on paper!

Because the value of a symbol depends on its position, we can write numbers as large as we want with the same ten symbols (0, 1, 2, 3, 4, 5, 6, 7, 8, 9).[1] Compare that with the Roman numerals. Using them, if we wanted to write a number very far above 1,000, we would need to use lots of different letters.

You may remember that the abacus also made adding and subtracting really easy. All we had to do was move balls on wires. Well, modern numbers work almost exactly the same way. We just add up columns of numbers instead of counting balls on wires. So with modern numbers adding and subtracting is as easy as it was with an abacus. Of course, none of this is new to you. But we just want you to see how similar modern numbers are to the abacus.

---

[1] As you know, when writing larger numbers, we put a comma after every third number starting from the right: 2,345,211,018.

Representing the Empty Wire

We're making modern numbers sound great, but it actually took a long time to get them to work as smoothly as an abacus. The reason was that no one could figure out how to represent an empty wire. You see, with an abacus, if a number has no tens, then the tens wire remains empty. That's simple enough. But with numbers on paper, just leaving a position empty could create confusion. Does the number 2 2 represent twenty-two or two hundred two or even two thousand, two? It's hard to tell how many empty spaces there are between the 2s, especially if your handwriting is sloppy.

2 2

Is it twenty two or two hundred two or two thousand, two?

Fortunately, a symbol for an empty wire was invented, and that ended all the confusion. As you know, the symbol is 0 (for zero). With 0, it's easy to show an empty column. Twenty-two is written as 22 and two hundred two is written as 202, and two thousand two as 2,002.

22	202	2,002
twenty-two	two hundred two	two thousand, two

Writing Numbers in Words

Finally, we should mention that sometimes it's necessary to write a number out in words, and it turns out that there's a whole system of rules for doing this. Fortunately, they aren't too complicated. There are really only two things to remember. First, when we write a number in words, we should put the commas in the same places that they appear in the number. For example, if we wanted to write 45,238 in words, we'd write it like this.

Forty-five thousand, two hundred thirty-eight

Another way to think about this rule is just to remember that we should always put commas after the words "trillion," "billion," "million," and "thousand." One more thing. Did you notice that the "forty-five" had a dash between the forty and the five and "thirty-eight" also had a dash? That's because we're supposed to use a dash on all numbers between 20 and 100 that have two words (fifty-six is another example).

Practice 2

a. Rewrite 5238446395042 with commas in the proper places.

b. Write five million, six hundred thirty thousand, two (using modern numbers).

c. Write the number 150,088,341 in words.

d. Rearrange the digits in 2,548,796 so that the number is as large as possible.

e. Rearrange the digits in 6,340,905 so that the number is as small as possible.

Problem Set 2

Tell whether each sentence below is True or False.

1. With only ten symbols, Hindu-Arabic (modern) numbers can be used to represent any number, no matter how large.

2. The greatest advantage of the Hindu-Arabic (modern) numbers is that they work like an abacus.

Complete each sentence below with the best of the choices given.

3. Our modern numbers were invented in _____.

    A. America   B. Greece   C. India
    D. Rome   E. England

4. Our modern numbers were transmitted to Europe by the _____.

    A. Greek philosophers   B. Israelites   C. Vikings
    D. Chinese mandarins   E. Arabs

5. Hindu-Arabic numbers use the following symbols:_____.

    A. ▲ ▶ ◀ ▪ ■ —
    B. א ב ג ד ה ו ז ח ט י
    C. A B Γ Δ E F Z H Θ
    D. 1 2 3 4 5 6 7 8 9 0
    E. ق ف غ غ غ غ ف

6. Under the _____, the value of a number symbol depends on its position.

    A. place value system   B. binary system
    C. Greek alphabet   D. latest scientific discoveries
    E. Egyptian number system

7. If our modern number system did not have a symbol for _____, it would be easy to confuse one written number with another.

   A. plus   B. zero   C. minus
   D. three   E. equal

Tell what number each Roman number below represents.

8. XIII   9. DCLXXI   10. MCCLXII

Complete the following.

11. 7,891 = ____ thousands ____ hundreds ____ tens ____ ones

12. 4,862,357 = ____ millions ____ hundred thousands ____ ten thousands ____ thousands ____ hundreds ____ tens ____ ones

Rewrite each number below with commas in the proper places.

13. 58162840   (a) 14. 8150276150938

Write each number below (using modern numbers).

15. twenty-seven thousand, six hundred thirty-two

(b) 16. fourteen million, three hundred eleven thousand, four

Write each number below in words.

17. 46,867   (c) 18. 520,075,998

Rearrange the digits in each number below so that it is as large as possible.

19. 204,913   (d) 20. 4,356,872

Rearrange the digits in each number below so that it is as small as possible.

21. 7,146   (e) 22. 1,670,302

Lesson 3—Addition

Now that we've introduced modern numbers, let's go over the methods for calculating with them. We'll start with addition of whole numbers. Even though this will all be review for you (since you've been adding whole numbers for years), you still may be surprised at how much you *don't* know about addition.

Abacus Addition

As we mentioned in the last lesson, the main point about adding with numbers is that it works just like an abacus. Actually, in some ways it's even easier than adding with an abacus. With an abacus, you can't check over your work and see all the steps because the steps disappear as soon as they're performed. When adding with numbers on paper, you can check every step to find mistakes. Also, to add with an abacus, you have to carry one around with you, which can obviously be a pain. But since pencil and paper can be stuffed into even a small pocket, adding with modern numbers is easier in that way too.[2]

Now let's do an addition example.

Teddy   Theodore

All of the stuck-up teddy bears in Happy Valley prefer to be called Theodore. The others just go by Teddy. If 1,235 prefer the name Theodore and 2,041 don't mind being called Teddy, how many Teddy and Theodore bears (combined) are there in Happy Valley?

3276

---

[2] Another advantage is that multiplying and dividing are much easier with modern numbers than they are on an abacus.

Using modern numbers, we can find the answer to this problem by just writing down 1,235, and then putting 2,041 underneath it, making sure that ones are directly under ones, tens under tens, and so on.

$$1,235$$
$$2,041$$

Now imagine that every number column is a wire on an abacus. To figure out the total balls that need to be pulled down on each wire, all we have to do is add the numbers in the columns vertically. That gives us this.

$$1,235$$
$$+2,041$$
$$\overline{\mathbf{3,276}}$$

The answer or "sum"—remember, the answer to an addition problem is called a **sum**—is 3,276 teddy bears (Teddy plus Theodore, actually) in Happy Valley. That's all there is to it.

Only Less than Ten

Here's something really interesting about adding with modern numbers. All we need to know to add any two numbers, no matter how big, is how to add numbers that are less than ten. In our example, we got the answer by adding 5 and 1, then 3 and 4, then 2 and 0, and finally 1 and 2. But as a result of those calculations, we ended up adding two really large numbers (1,235 and 2,041). This is another big advantage of making the value of a number symbol depend on its position or place. You only need to know how to add numbers below ten, and with that knowledge alone you can add numbers that are extremely large. Of course, the abacus works exactly the same way. On an abacus, all you have to do is count the number of balls that need to be pulled down on each wire. And since there are only ten balls per wire, you're able to stay below ten with the abacus too.

Practice 3

12,342,065

a. Write twelve billion, three hundred forty-two million, sixty-five using modern numbers.

b. Write 200,005,885 in words. *two million, 5 thousand, eight hundred eighty-five*

c. Rearrange the digits in 7,502,309 so that it is as small as possible. *23,579*

d. Add these two numbers
$$23,485$$
$$+14,312$$
37,797

e. Add these two numbers
$$346,215$$
$$+223,764$$
569,979

15

Problem Set 3

Complete each sentence below with the best of the choices given.

1. Modern numbers are better than an abacus because ___D___.

    A. you can easily check over your work
    B. it's easier to multiply and divide with them
    C. you don't have to carry an abacus around
    D. all of the above
    E. None of the above

2. In an addition, the answer is called the ___A___.

    A. sum
    B. product
    C. difference
    D. quotient
    E. power

3. With ___D___, we just need to know how to add numbers below ten to add numbers that are extremely large.

    A. the multiplication table
    B. the alphabet
    C. the Pledge of Allegiance
    D. modern numbers
    E. none of the above

Complete the following.

4. 7,321 = __7__ thousands __3__ hundreds __2__ tens __1__ ones

5. 8,032,514 = __8__ millions __0__ hundred thousands __3__ ten thousands __2__ thousands __5__ hundreds __1__ tens __4__ ones

Write each number below (using modern numbers).

6. four hundred thousand, twenty   400,020

7. two million, six thousand   2,006,000

(a) 8. fourteen billion, eight hundred sixty-one million, forty-seven

    14,861,000,047

16

Write each number below in words.

9. 52,488   **(b) 10.** 600,003,119

fifty two thousand four hundred eighty six hundred million

Rearrange the digits in each number below so that it is as small as possible. *three thousand*

11. 3,278   **(c) 12.** 5,230,104

2,378   *12,345*   *one hundred nineteen.*

Answer each question below.

13. Write a number that is 1 greater than 9,999,999. *10,000,000*

14. Write a number that is 1 greater than 34,589. *34,590*

15. Write a number that is 1 greater than 208,999. *209,000*

Add each pair of numbers below.

16.
23
+51
74

17.
84
+14
98

18.
427
+362
789

19.
307
+682
989

20.
1,125
+7,364
8,489

(d) 21.
54,321
+23,457
77,778

22.
50,002
+34,635
84,637

(e) 23.
883,024
+111,112
994,136

17

Lesson 4—Carrying

We reviewed addition of whole numbers in the last lesson. But we didn't do any problems where one of the columns adds up to more than 9. Here's an example like that.

A school of 125 fish swam up to a school of 438 fish. How many fish were in both schools?

We need to add 125 and 438 here. First, we should write the numbers vertically, so that the ones, tens, and hundreds are directly underneath each other.

$$\begin{array}{r} 125 \\ +438 \\ \hline \end{array}$$

Next, we need to add up the columns. Starting with the ones column, we get $5+8$ which equals 13. The problem is there's only room for one digit below that column, and 13 has two digits.

$$\begin{array}{r} 125 \\ +438 \\ \hline 13? \end{array} \quad \textbf{13 won't fit}$$

Exchanging Balls on Wires

It shouldn't surprise you that this same problem occurs when adding on an abacus. If we tried to add 125 and 438 on an abacus, we would start with 5 balls on the ones wire, 2 balls on the tens wire, and 1 on the hundreds wire. Then to add 438, we'd first need to pull down 8 balls from the ones wire. But there would only be 5 balls left. That's 3 short.

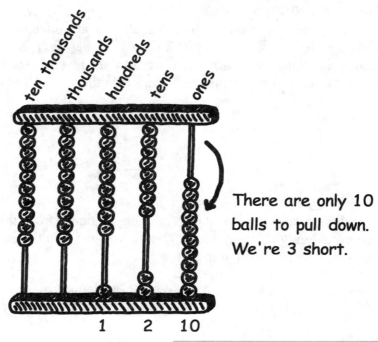

There are only 10 balls to pull down. We're 3 short.

1   2   10

Experts on the abacus got around this problem by exchanging 10 balls on the ones wire for 1 ball on the tens wire. Since these have the same value, that's legal.

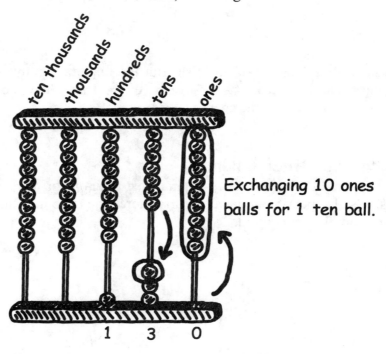

Exchanging 10 ones balls for 1 ten ball.

1   3   0

From here, 3 more balls could be pulled down on the ones wire and the calculation could be finished by pulling down the right number of balls on the other wires.

Carrying = Exchanging Balls

Well, since modern numbers and the abacus are so similar, we do the same kind of exchange when adding on paper. As you know, it's called **carrying**.[3] Since the ones column adds to 13, which is too many, we "carry" ten over to the tens column. This is done by writing a little 1 up at the top of that column. Since the little 1 is in the tens column, it stands for a ten.

$$
\begin{array}{r}
1 \\
125 \\
+\ 438 \\
\hline
3
\end{array}
$$

All we're really doing with this step is trading 10 ones (from the 13) for one ten. Again, it's exactly like exchanging balls on wires. That leaves just 3 in the ones column and an extra ten in the tens column, which is written in on top.

From here, we add up all the tens, including the extra ten on top, giving us a total of 6 tens (or 60). The last step is to add up the hundreds column to get 5 (or 500).

$$
\begin{array}{r}
1 \\
125 \\
+\ 438 \\
\hline
563
\end{array}
$$

We end up with an answer of 563 fish. But the important point is that carrying on paper and exchanging balls on an abacus are the same thing. That's how the carrying technique was first developed. It was based on the abacus.

Carrying into Other Columns

Sometimes it's not the ones column that adds up to more than 9, but one of the other columns. It's also possible to have to carry more than once in a single problem. Let's look at an example where this is required.

---

[3] Some books call it "regrouping."

Leroy, the certified couch potato, changed the channel 1,673 times on Friday and 2,581 times on Saturday (He has trouble deciding which sporting event to watch on weekends.) How many times did Leroy change the channel altogether (both days included)?

To add these two numbers, we write them over each other, as usual. Starting with the ones column, we get this.

$$\begin{array}{r} 1{,}673 \\ +\,2{,}581 \\ \hline \mathbf{4} \end{array}$$

So far, so good. But look at the tens column. Its numbers add to 15, which is too big. We're going to have to carry again.

Now, a lot of people don't really understand what happens when they carry from a larger column. Since we're working in the tens column, we're really adding tens: 7 tens plus 8 tens makes 15 tens. But 15 tens is 150, and that means when we carry over the 1 from 15, we're really taking 100 of the 150 over into the hundreds column and leaving 50 in the tens column. A single hundred in the hundreds column is shown with a 1.

$$\begin{array}{r} \mathbf{1} \\ 1{,}673 \\ +\,2{,}581 \\ \hline \mathbf{54} \end{array}$$

Notice that we just have a 5 below, but since it's in the tens column, that 5 actually stands for 50.

Next, we add the hundreds column: 6 and 5 and another 1 give us a total of 12 hundreds, so, unfortunately, we have too many again. However, since 12 hundreds is the same as 1,200, we can take 1,000 and carry it to the thousands column like this.

$$
\begin{array}{r}
\overset{1\ 1}{1{,}673} \\
+\ 2{,}581 \\
\hline
254
\end{array}
$$

This leaves 200 in the hundreds column, which is shown with just a 2. The final step is to add the numbers in the thousands column. The $1+2$ plus the 1 that was carried comes to 4 thousands, which is shown as a 4 in that column.

$$
\begin{array}{r}
\overset{1\ 1}{1{,}673} \\
+\ 2{,}581 \\
\hline
4{,}254
\end{array}
$$

The answer, then, is 4,254 channel changes (wow!). Of course, other problems may require you to carry in even higher columns, but the process is exactly the same.

Carrying without Understanding

Even though a lot of people don't really understand what they're doing when they carry (especially from a larger column), the great thing about modern numbers is that they don't have to know. In fact, as we showed in the last lesson, modern numbers are designed so that you can add numbers of any size with only a knowledge of how to add numbers smaller than 10. That's why almost everybody in the world knows how to add. Believe-it-or-not, before modern numbers, addition was something that only a few intellectuals knew how to do.

Practice 4

a. Write the number one trillion, four hundred million, six hundred fifty-five (using modern numbers).

b. Write a number that is 10,000 greater than 3,845,965.

c. Write two hundreds, three tens, twelve ones (using modern numbers).

d. Add these two numbers
$$
\begin{array}{r}
74 \\
+\ 216 \\
\hline
\end{array}
$$

e.   Add these two numbers

$$\begin{array}{r} {}^{1\ 1\ 1\ 1} \\ 95,497 \\ +\ 4,876 \\ \hline 100,373 \end{array}$$

Problem Set 4

Tell whether each sentence below is True or False.

1.   When adding two numbers, "carrying" is necessary if the top digit is greater than the bottom digit.   *false*

2.   The method of carrying when adding with modern numbers is very similar to exchanging ten balls for one (on the next higher wire) on an abacus.

true

Complete the following.

3. $1,238 =$ __1__ thousands __2__ hundreds __3__ tens __8__ ones

4. $9,356,488 =$ __9__ millions __3__ hundred thousands __5__ ten thousands __6__ thousands __4__ hundreds __8__ tens __8__ ones

Write each number below (using modern numbers).

5.   eight million, two hundred thousand, three hundred, fifty-seven   *8,200,357*

(a) 6.   nine trillion, three hundred million, seventy-four

9,000,300,000,074

Write each number below in words.

7.   43,799   8.   800,596,025   *eight hundred million five hundred ninty six thousand twety five*

faurty three thousand sevan hundred ninty nine.

Rearrange the digits in each number below so that it is as large as possible.

9.   17,553,421   10.   234,687,810

75,543,211   *887,643,210*

Answer each question below.

11. Write a number that is 10 greater than 5,060,011. 5,060,021

(b) 12. Write a number that is 10,000 greater than 5,060,011.

5070,011

Write each number below (using modern numbers).

13. five tens, fifteen ones 65

(c) 14. four hundreds, five tens, sixteen ones

466

Add each pair of numbers below.

15.
$$\begin{array}{r} 47 \\ +33 \\ \hline \end{array}$$
86

16.
$$\begin{array}{r} 96 \\ +55 \\ \hline \end{array}$$
151

17.
$$\begin{array}{r} 64 \\ +36 \\ \hline \end{array}$$
100

18.
$$\begin{array}{r} 8 \\ +51 \\ \hline \end{array}$$
59

(d) 19.
$$\begin{array}{r} 67 \\ +123 \\ \hline \end{array}$$
190

20.
$$\begin{array}{r} 888 \\ +999 \\ \hline \end{array}$$
1887

21.
$$\begin{array}{r} 2,345 \\ +6,789 \\ \hline \end{array}$$
9,134

(e) 22.
$$\begin{array}{r} 98,799 \\ +1,654 \\ \hline \end{array}$$
100,453

Lesson 5—Addition of Long Strings

In this lesson, we're going to continue our review of arithmetic by adding several numbers at once instead of only two. There's not too much new here, so this should go pretty fast. Here's our first example.

During his long and illustrious career, El Magnifico, the great artist/composer, has produced 2,457 sculptures, 1,973 paintings, 5,081 symphonies, and 652 string quartets. How many works is this in total?

The first step, of course, is to put all the numbers on top of each other, making sure to line up the columns properly (ones over ones, tens over tens, and so on).

$$
\begin{array}{r}
2,457 \\
1,973 \\
5,081 \\
+\,652 \\
\end{array}
$$

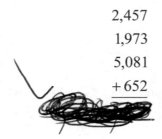

All At Once

Next, we need to do the addition. The fastest and easiest way to add a long string of numbers is just to add all the numbers in each column at once. So let's add up the ones column: $7+3$ is 10, $10+1$ is 11, and $11+2$ is 13. But 13 is too big to fit, which means we're going to have to carry. We carry ten into the tens column (by putting a little 1 on top) and leave 3 at the bottom of the ones column.

$$
\begin{array}{r}
\overset{1}{} \\
2,457 \\
1,973 \\
5,081 \\
+652 \\
\hline
3
\end{array}
$$

Now we add up the numbers in the tens column, including the extra ten that was carried: $1+5$ is 6, $6+7$ is 13, $13+8$ is 21, $21+5$ is 26. This is way over 9, so we're going to need to carry again. But instead of carrying a single ten, we're going to have to carry two tens or 20. That leaves 6, which is small enough to fit down below. To carry 2, though, all we do is put a little 2 on top of the hundreds column.

$$
\begin{array}{r}
\overset{21}{} \\
2,457 \\
1,973 \\
5,081 \\
+652 \\
\hline
63
\end{array}
$$

Keep in mind that the sum of the tens column was actually 26 tens or 260, so we really carried a 200 into the hundreds column and left 60 at the bottom.

The next step is to add up the numbers in the hundreds column, including the 2 that was carried: $2+4$ is 6, $6+9$ is 15, $15+0$ is 15, and $15+6$ is 21. We have to carry again. We put a 2 on top of the next column (the thousands column) and leave a 1 below.

$$
\begin{array}{r}
\overset{2\,21}{} \\
2,457 \\
1,973 \\
5,081 \\
+652 \\
\hline
163
\end{array}
$$

The hundreds column added to equal 21 hundreds or 2,100, so we actually carried a 2,000 and left 100 below.

The last step is to add the numbers in the thousands column, including the extra 2: $2+2$ is 4, $4+1$ is 5, and $5+5$ is 10. This is greater than 9, but since there are no more columns to carry into, we can just put a 10 below, like this.

$$
\begin{array}{r}
\scriptstyle 2\,21 \\
2{,}457 \\
1{,}973 \\
5{,}081 \\
+\quad 652 \\
\hline
10{,}163
\end{array}
$$

Be sure you understand what really happened in the last step. The thousands column added up to 10 thousands or 10,000 and by putting 10 down below, we ended up with a 1 in the ten thousands column and a 0 in the thousands column, which is exactly what we need. See how perfectly our number system works. (Notice also that we put the comma in its proper place.)

The final answer turns out to be 10,163. That's the number of works that El Magnifico has created.

Checking Your Answer

When you're adding long strings of large numbers, as we just did, it's easy to make mistakes. That's why checking over your work is a good idea. Instead of just going back over the same calculation, a good way to check is to add the numbers again in a different order. For instance, you could check the calculation we just did by rearranging the numbers like this and adding again.

$$
\begin{array}{r}
5{,}081 \\
1{,}973 \\
652 \\
+\ 2{,}457 \\
\hline
\end{array}
$$

If you still come out with 10,163, you can be pretty sure that the answer is correct.

This checking method works because of a couple of rules of arithmetic that you probably already know. The first rule is called the **commutative property of addition**, and it just says that the order in which any two numbers are added won't affect the answer. In other words, $7+3$ equals $3+7$. The rule is usually written with the letters a and b to show that it works no matter what two numbers are involved: $a+b=b+a$.

The other rule is called the **associative property of addition**. And it just says that if you add more than two numbers the answer will come out the same. So whether you're adding two numbers or two hundred numbers, feel free to scramble the order and add everything up again, just to make sure that you didn't make a mistake the first time.

Practice 5

a. Write a number that is 200,000 greater than 6,503,155. 6,703,155

b. Write a number that is 700,000 less than 5,849,812. 5,149,812

c. Add
56
81
+23
160

d. Add
22
468
+537
1027

e. Add
6,568
9,345
+8,729
24,642

Problem Set 5

Tell whether each sentence below is True or False.

1. Hindu-Arabic (modern) numbers cannot be used to add more than two numbers at once.
false

2. The commutative property of addition says that the order in which any two numbers are added can be changed without changing the sum (answer).
true

Complete the following.

3. 9,999 = ___a___ thousands ___a___ hundreds ___9___ tens ___9___ ones

4. 8,010,000 = ___8___ millions ___0___ hundred thousands ___1___ ten thousands
___0___ thousands ___0___ hundreds ___0___ tens ___0___ ones

Write each number below (using modern numbers).

5. thirty-one million, four hundred fifty-thousand, eight hundred seventeen
31450817

6. eighty trillion, fourteen billion, thirty-six million, two hundred thousand six
80014,036

Write each number below in words.

7. 88,975

eighty eight thousand, nine hundred seventy-five

8. 936,034,849

nine hundred thirty six million thirtyfour thousand eight hundred fourty nine

Answer each question below.

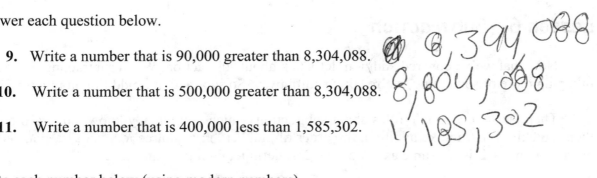

9. Write a number that is 90,000 greater than 8,304,088. 8,394,088

(a) 10. Write a number that is 500,000 greater than 8,304,088. 8,804,088

(b) 11. Write a number that is 400,000 less than 1,585,302. 1,185,302

Write each number below (using modern numbers).

12. six thousands, five hundreds, two tens, four ones 6,524

13. eight ten thousands, three thousands, four hundreds, nine tens, six ones 83,496

14. nine hundred thousands, seven ten thousands, five thousands, three hundreds, two ones

   975,302

Add each group of numbers below.

15. 456
   +878
   1334

16. 3,896
   +6,878
   10774

(c) 17. 42
   58
   +10
   110

18. 389
   274
   +865
   1528

(d) 19. 34
   138
   +857
   1029

20. 238
   45
   +389
   672

(e) 21. 3,858
   +9,365
   16,169

22. 2,946
   209
   +2,583
   2,862

23. 70
   89,456
   23,878
   +34,694
   148,028

Lesson 6—Subtraction

Now that we've covered addition, let's talk about subtraction. When subtracting, instead of piling up more of something, we're taking stuff away. So subtraction is addition in reverse.

There are a few simple rules about subtraction, which you already know, but we'll review them quickly. First, unlike addition, the order of numbers in a subtraction can't be changed. So even though $5+2$ is the same as $2+5$, $5-2$ is definitely not the same as $2-5$.[4]

$$5 + 2 = 2 + 5$$
$$\text{but}$$
$$5 - 2 \neq 2 - 5$$

When you think about it, $2-5$ doesn't even make sense. How can you take 5 donuts away from just 2 donuts? That brings us to our second rule, which says that in arithmetic, you always have to subtract a smaller number from a larger number. Later in the book, you'll find out that this rule doesn't apply to algebra (and higher math). But we'll stick with it for now.

Addition in Reverse

To add numbers, no matter how large, all we need to know is how to add numbers that are less than 10. That's why little kids have to memorize the addition table ($1+1=2$, $1+2=3$, and so on). Does that mean we have to memorize a subtraction table in order to subtract larger numbers? Fortunately, no. Since subtraction is just addition in reverse, we can use a knowledge of the addition table to subtract. For example, we've already memorized the fact that $6+9=15$. Using that knowledge, we can figure out that $15-9$ has to be 6. No new memorization is needed. Just do the addition in reverse and you'll get it right every time.

Back to the Abacus!

The actual process of subtracting with larger numbers is very similar to the way it works on an abacus. On an abacus, the first step is to pull down all of the balls for the first number. If it's 785, then we pull down 7 on the hundreds wire, 8 on the tens wire, and 5 on the ones wire. Then to do the subtraction, we push the balls of the smaller number back up, one wire at a time. The balls left on the bottom will be our answer.

And the neat thing is that it works the same way on paper. Let's start with 785 and then subtract 432.

First, we write down the larger number, 785, and then the smaller one, 432, below it, making sure the ones are lined up with the ones, the tens with the tens, and the hundreds with the hundreds.

$$785$$
$$432$$

---

[4] The symbol $\neq$ means "is not equal to."

Add each group of numbers below.

13.
$$327 \\ +968 \\ \hline$$
1295
~~175~~

14.
$$4{,}786 \\ +5{,}898 \\ \hline$$
10683
1,349

15.
$$26{,}495 \\ +14{,}176 \\ \hline$$
40,671

26,495 ← this is right

16.
$$239 \\ +957 \\ \hline$$
4196

17.
$$9{,}582 \\ +8{,}226 \\ \hline$$
17,808

Subtract each group of numbers below.

(b) 18.
$$69 \\ -11 \\ \hline$$
58

(b) 19.
$$39 \\ -17 \\ \hline$$
22

20.
$$485 \\ -352 \\ \hline$$
133

(c) 21.
$$738 \\ -26 \\ \hline$$
712

22.
$$8{,}657 \\ -5{,}432 \\ \hline$$
3,235

(d) 23.
$$98{,}786 \\ -24{,}332 \\ \hline$$
74454

Translate the word problem below into math; then solve.

(e) 24.   Benjamin decided to give 25 of his 157 sunflower seeds to his pet kookaburra. How many are left now?

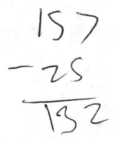

$$157 \\ -25 \\ \hline \\ 132$$

Lesson 7—Regrouping

When subtracting, we have to subtract the numbers in each column. Sometimes, though, the number on bottom is larger than the one on top. Since subtracting a larger number from a smaller number isn't allowed (in arithmetic, at least), that causes a problem.

Exchanging Balls on Paper

To show an example, let's say we want to subtract 435 from 672.

$$
\begin{array}{r}
672 \\
-\ 435 \\
\hline
\end{array}
$$

We would normally start by subtracting in the ones column. But we can't take away 5 from 2. This same thing used to happen when subtracting numbers on an abacus. What they would do is exchange 1 tens ball for 10 ones balls. We can do basically the same thing by taking one of the tens in 672 and moving it to the ones column. That changes 672, which is really $600 + 70 + 2$, to $600 + 60 + 12$. It looks like this.

$$
\begin{array}{r}
6\ 12 \\
672 \\
-\ 435 \\
\hline
\end{array}
$$

Now we have 12 minus 5 in the ones column, and that doesn't give us any trouble.

$$
\begin{array}{r}
6\ 12 \\
672 \\
-\ 435 \\
\hline
7
\end{array}
$$

The tens and hundreds are easy, because the numbers on top are larger than the numbers on bottom in both columns.

$$
\begin{array}{r}
6\ 12 \\
672 \\
-\ 435 \\
\hline
237
\end{array}
$$

That leaves us with an answer of 237.

Moving a number from one column to another is called **regrouping**. It's also called borrowing, because people imagine that the ones column is "borrowing" a ten from the tens column. But regrouping is probably a better name, since we're never going to pay that ten back to the tens column, after all. The interesting thing, though, is that the process on paper works pretty much the same way as it does on the abacus.

Regrouping Twice

Let's go through one more example that involves regrouping twice.

$$823 - 567$$

We should start by subtracting in the ones column, but since 7 is greater than 3, we're going to have to regroup. What we do is take 10 away from the tens column, which leaves us with only 1 ten there. Then we give that 10 to the ones column, which turns 3 into 13.

$$\begin{array}{r} 1\;13 \\ 8\cancel{2}\cancel{3} \\ -\;567 \\ \hline \end{array}$$

Now there's no problem subtracting 7 from 13. That leaves us with 6 in the ones column.

$$\begin{array}{r} 1\;13 \\ 8\cancel{2}\cancel{3} \\ -\;567 \\ \hline 6 \end{array}$$

The next step is to subtract in the tens column. But notice that we have a larger number being subtracted from a smaller number again (6 is being subtracted from 1). That means we'll need to regroup here too. This time, we take 100 from the hundreds column, which changes the 8 in that column to a 7. Then we put that 100 in the tens column, which turns the 1 into an 11. That's because 100 is the same as 10 tens, so 10 tens added to the 1 that's already there gives us 11 tens.

$$\begin{array}{r} 7\;11\;13 \\ \cancel{8}\cancel{2}\cancel{3} \\ -\;567 \\ \hline 6 \end{array}$$

Now we can finish up by subtracting $11-6$ in the tens column, and $7-5$ in the hundreds column.

$$\begin{array}{r} 7\;11\;13 \\ \cancel{8}\cancel{2}\cancel{3} \\ -\;567 \\ \hline 256 \end{array}$$

We end up with an answer of 256.

So by regrouping, which is just moving numbers from one column to another, we're able to avoid the trouble caused from needing to subtract a larger number from a smaller number. And the great thing about regrouping is that we can use it as many times as necessary and in any column.

Practice 7

a. Add
$$\begin{array}{r} 2,888 \\ +4,134 \\ \hline 7,022 \end{array}$$

b. Subtract
$$\begin{array}{r} 72 \\ -36 \\ \hline 36 \end{array}$$

c. Subtract
$$\begin{array}{r} 847 \\ -58 \\ \hline 789 \end{array}$$

d. Subtract
$$\begin{array}{r} 840 \\ -352 \\ \hline 488 \end{array}$$

e. Translate the word problem below into math; then solve.

John owns 432 finger puppets. If he gives away 257 of these to his friend Billy, how many will he have left?

$$\begin{array}{r} 432 \\ -257 \\ \hline 175 \end{array}$$

Problem Set 7

Tell whether each sentence below is True or False.

1. Regrouping is very similar to what is done when subtracting on an abacus.   Flase

2. Regrouping is like changing 50 + 3 to 40 + 13.   True

Complete the following.

3. 28,765 = _2_ ten thousands _8_ thousands _7_ hundreds _6_ tens _5_ ones

4. 45,893,239 = _4_ ten millions _5_ millions _8_ hundred thousands _9_ ten thousands _3_ thousands _2_ hundreds _3_ tens _9_ ones

Write each number below (using modern numbers).

5. four hundred seventy-six thousand, nine hundred ninety-nine 476,999,

6. sixty million, thirty-five thousand, one hundred six 60,035,106,

7. nine hundred trillion, two hundred billion, sixteen million, three hundred thousand, four hundred fifty

900,200,016,300,450

Write each number below in words.

8. 3,578,004

9. 59,001

Answer each question below.

10. Write a number that is 1,000 greater than 104,875.

11. Write a number that is 10,000 greater than 104,875.

12. Write a number that is 1,000 less than 38,285,835.

Add each group of numbers below.

13.
$$\begin{array}{r} 298 \\ +252 \\ \hline \end{array}$$

(a) 14.
$$\begin{array}{r} 3,999 \\ +3,824 \\ \hline \end{array}$$

15.
$$\begin{array}{r} 54,087 \\ +81,890 \\ \hline \end{array}$$

16.
$$\begin{array}{r} 895 \\ 17 \\ +725 \\ \hline \end{array}$$

17.
$$\begin{array}{r} 9,541 \\ 239 \\ +1,083 \\ \hline \end{array}$$

Subtract each group of numbers below.

18.
$$\begin{array}{r} 85 \\ -15 \\ \hline \end{array}$$

19.
$$\begin{array}{r} 99,999 \\ -514 \\ \hline \end{array}$$

(b) 20.
$$\begin{array}{r} 83 \\ -54 \\ \hline \end{array}$$

(b) 21.
$$\begin{array}{r} 75 \\ -38 \\ \hline \end{array}$$

(c) 22.
$$\begin{array}{r} 954 \\ -65 \\ \hline \end{array}$$

(d) 23.
$$\begin{array}{r} 623 \\ -234 \\ \hline \end{array}$$

Translate the word problem below into math; then solve.

(e) 24. The first version of the garbage sculpture weighed 2,653 pounds, but then El Magnifico, the great artist/composer, decided to eliminate another 385 pounds (this time for good). How much does the sculpture weigh now?

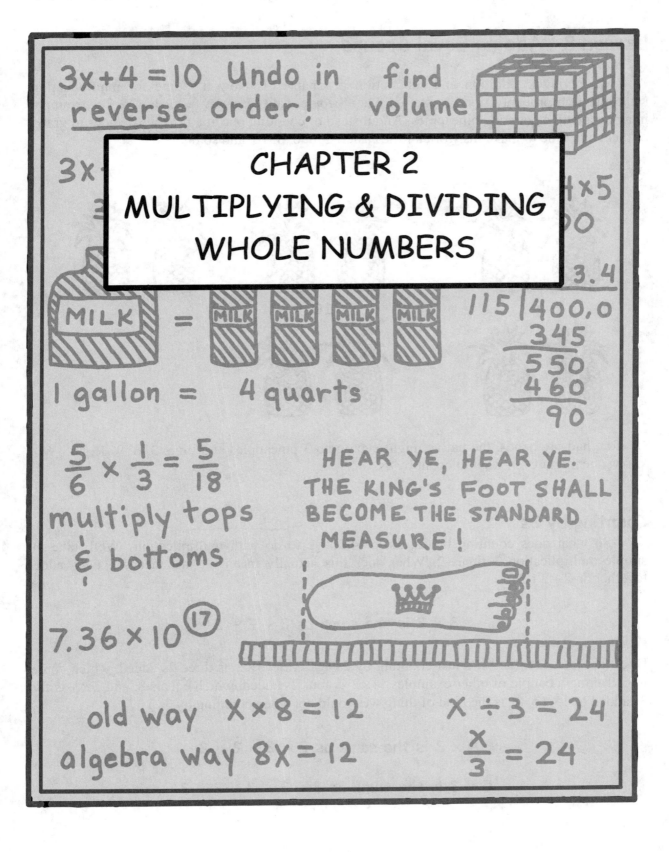

$3x+4=10$ Undo in reverse order!

find volume

CHAPTER 2
MULTIPLYING & DIVIDING
WHOLE NUMBERS

$3x$

4×5

3.4

$115\overline{)400,0}$
345
550
460
90

MILK = MILK MILK MILK MILK

1 gallon = 4 quarts

$\frac{5}{6} \times \frac{1}{3} = \frac{5}{18}$

multiply tops & bottoms

HEAR YE, HEAR YE.
THE KING'S FOOT SHALL
BECOME THE STANDARD
MEASURE!

7.36×10^{17}

old way $X \times 8 = 12$

algebra way $8X = 12$

$X \div 3 = 24$

$\frac{X}{3} = 24$

Lesson 8—Adding Equal Groups

We reviewed addition and subtraction in Chapter 1. Now it's time for multiplication. Multiplication probably first got started when people tried to count faster by 2s. For example, imagine a native counting pineapples. And instead of counting one at a time, he decides to grab 2 of them at a time to make his work a little easier: 2, 4, 6, 8, 10, and so on.

Or if he had big hands, the native might even grab 3 pineapples at a time: 3, 6, 9, 12, ... Who knows, he might even want to count by 4s.

Counting by 2s

So what does counting by 2s, 3s, or 4s have to do with multiplication? Well, take the simple multiplication 3 times 2. What does this actually mean? It just means 3 twos added together or $2 + 2 + 2$.

3 × 2 is the same as 2 + 2 + 2

Does this look familiar? It's just counting by 2s again. So 3×2 is three 2s added, which comes to 6. Taking a couple of other examples, 4×2 is four 2s added, which equals 8, and 5×3 is five 3s added or 15. (5×3 is the kind of thing we would get when counting by 3s.)

4 × 2 is the same as 2 + 2 + 2 + 2

5 × 3 is the same as 3 + 3 + 3 + 3 + 3

The Multiplication Table

After awhile, people realized that instead of counting by 2s or 3s, they'd be better off to just memorize all this stuff, so instead of taking the time to add $2+2+2$ each time, they memorized that 3 groups of 2 (or 3×2) is always equal to 6. And they memorized that 5 groups of 3 (or 5×3) is always equal to 15, and so on. This is where the **multiplication table** came from.

Obviously, it wasn't possible to memorize every multiplication in the world—that would take forever! So they just memorized the answers to the smaller multiplications, and used those facts to multiply larger numbers. We'll talk more about multiplying larger numbers in the next few lessons. But before we get to that, let's cover a few rules.

Basic Rules

The first basic rule for multiplying is that the order in which we multiply any two numbers won't change the answer. For example, 4×5 is the same as 5×4. Even though that's pretty obvious, there's an interesting diagram that shows why this works.

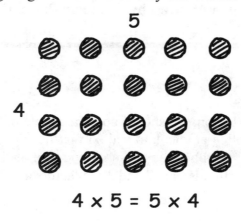

$$4 \times 5 = 5 \times 4$$

There are two ways to think about this diagram. We could think of it as 4 horizontal rows with 5 dots each. Then, the total number of dots would be four 5s. And that could be calculated like this: $4\times5=20$. Or we could think of the diagram as 5 vertical columns with 4 dots each. This way, the total number of dots is five 4s, which could be calculated as $5\times4=20$. So it doesn't matter whether we think in terms of columns or rows—we come up with the same number of dots either way, and that's why 4×5 is the same as 5×4. The technical name for the rule about multiplying two numbers in any order is the **commutative property of multiplication**. And the mathematicians write the rule as $a\times b=b\times a$ to show that it works for any two numbers.

The second rule is that any number multiplied by 1 equals the number itself. For example, $5\times1=5$. This makes perfect sense when you remember that multiplication by 1 is just taking the number 1 time, which just gives the original number. The mathematicians write this rule as $a\times1=a$.

The third rule is that any number multiplied by 0 is equal to 0. An example is $5 \times 0 = 0$. This makes sense too, because we can think of multiplying by 0 as taking the number 0 times, which is obviously zero. Here's the way this rule is written: $a \times 0 = 0$. Below is a summary of all three multiplication rules.

1.	According to the commutative property of multiplication, the order in which two numbers are multiplied won't affect the answer: a x b = b x a.
2.	Any number multiplied by 1 equals the number itself: a x 1 = a.
3.	Any number multiplied by 0 equals 0: a x 0 = 0.

Some Technical Names

Before wrapping up this lesson, we should cover a couple of technical names that are used a lot. Numbers that are multiplied are actually called **factors**. So in 4×5, the numbers 4 and 5 are factors. The answer to the multiplication, which in the case of 4×5 would be 20, is called the **product**. Another case is 7×3. In this one, 7 and 3 are factors and 21 is the product.

Practice 8

a. Write $7 + 7 + 7$ as a multiplication. 7×3

b. Write a multiplication problem to represent 6 groups of 2. 2×6

c. If you were counting objects by 2s and you ended up with 5 groups of 2, how many objects would you have counted? 10

d. Subtract
$$
\begin{array}{r}
733 \\
-465 \\
\hline
328
\end{array}
$$

e. Translate the word problem below into math, but don't solve the problem once it's written in math form.

The delivery man delivered 11 boxes of doohickeys. If each box contains 14 doohickeys, how many doohickeys are there in all?

$14 \times 11 =$

Problem Set 8

Tell whether each sentence below is True or False.

T 1. Multiplication probably began when people were trying to count by 2s, 3s, 4s, etc.

F 2. Multiplication is really just a shortcut for repeated subtraction.

F 3. Any number multiplied by 1 equals 0.

T 4. When multiplying numbers, the order doesn't affect the answer.

Complete the following.

5. 4,001 = __4__ thousands __0__ hundreds __0__ tens __1__ ones

6. 20,078,943 = __2__ ten millions __0__ millions __0__ hundred thousands __7__ ten thousands __8__ thousands __9__ hundreds __4__ tens __3__ ones

Write each number below (using modern numbers).

7. fifty thousand, three   5003

8. seven hundred million, four hundred thousand, three hundred two   700,400,302

9. two hundred eleven million, eighty-four   211,000,084

10. ten billion, one   10,000,000,001

Write each number below in words.

11. 99,875   12. 560,001

11. ninety-nine thousand, eight hundred seventy five

12. five thousand sixty and One

Answer each question below.

13. Write a number that is 1,000 greater than 200,065.   *1,000,200,065*

14. Write a number that is 1,000,000 less than 40,055,789.   *30,055,789*

(a) 15. Write $5 + 5 + 5 + 5$ as a multiplication.   *5 × 4*

(a) 16. Write $3 + 3 + 3 + 3 + 3 + 3 + 3$ as a multiplication.   *3 × 8*

(b) 17. Write a multiplication problem to represent 14 groups of 3.   *3 × 14*

(c) 18. If you were counting objects by 3s and you ended up with 9 groups of 3, how many objects would you have counted?   *27*

Add each group of numbers below.

19.
$$\begin{array}{r} {}^{2}{}^{1}{}^{1}347 \\ +853 \\ \hline 2100 \end{array}$$

20.
$$\begin{array}{r} {}^{1}{}^{2}{}^{3}5{,}045 \\ +4{,}994 \\ \hline 10009 \end{array}$$

21.
$$\begin{array}{r} {}^{1}{}^{1}{}^{1}{}^{1}48{,}786 \\ 123 \\ +5{,}348 \\ \hline 54357 \end{array}$$

Subtract each group of numbers below.

22.
$$\begin{array}{r} 75{,}595 \\ -310 \\ \hline 75285 \end{array}$$

23.
$$\begin{array}{r} {}^{8}94 \\ -65 \\ \hline 31 \end{array}$$

(d) 24.
$$\begin{array}{r} {}^{7}{}^{3}844 \\ -696 \\ \hline 198 \end{array}$$

44

Translate the word problem below into math, but don't solve the problem once it's written in math form.

(e) 25. Super entrepreneur Freddie Fandango shipped 12 cartons of his kitty cat breath freshener to several of the fanciest pet stores in America. If each carton contained 17 samples of breath freshener, how many samples (not cartons) did Freddie send out in total?

12c
17s

For the cat that deserves the best

12 × 17

Lesson 9—Multiplying with Zeros

The neat thing about multiplying with modern numbers is that you only need to know the simple multiplication table (which includes numbers under ten) to multiply numbers that are as big as you can imagine. Interestingly, this is another way in which modern numbers are better than the abacus. Multiplication was actually so difficult with the abacus that most people thought it wasn't worth the effort. Multiplying with numbers on paper is easy by comparison.

One Number Ending in 0

For starters, let's go over multiplication of numbers that end in zero. We'll try 50×3. The 50 is definitely way beyond what's covered in the multiplication table, but that doesn't mean we have to reach for a calculator. Forget about the 0 in the 50 for a minute and just multiply the 5 and 3 to get 15. Once this is done, bring the 0 back and tack it onto the end of the 15.

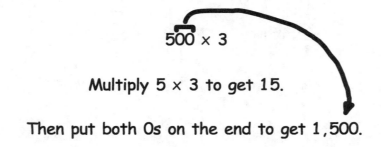

50 × 3

Multiply 5 × 3 to get 15.

Then put the 0 on the end to get 150.

That gives us an answer of 150, which is right.

The same technique will work no matter how many 0s are behind the 5. Let's try it on 500×3. We multiply the 5 and the 3 to get 15 (just as in the first example), but since 500 has two 0s, we have to remember to tack both of them on at the end.

500 × 3

Multiply 5 × 3 to get 15.

Then put both 0s on the end to get 1,500.

When we do this we get 1,500, which is also correct. We can continue all the way up: 500,000×3 equals 15 followed by five 0s, or 1,500,000.

The great thing about this method is that it's not limited to numbers starting with 5 and 3. We can multiply 200 and 7 in the same way. We know from the multiplication table that 2×7 is 14. If we tack the two 0s from the 200 onto 14, we get our answer, 1400. Let's try 5,000×9.

Again, we start with the fact that 5×9 equals 45 and then stick the three 0s from the 5000 on the end to get 45,000. So when one of the numbers has zeros, we put the same number of zeros in the answer.

Both Numbers Ending in Zero

But what happens when both numbers in the multiplication end in zero? Will the same method work? Lucky for us, the answer is yes. Let's take 400×300 as an example. First, we multiply 4 and 3 to get 12; then we tack all four zeros (two from 400 and two from 300) onto the end.

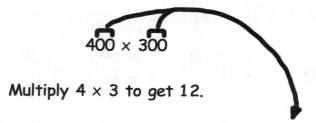

400 × 300

Multiply 4 × 3 to get 12.

Then put all four 0s on the end to get 120,000.

That gives an answer of 120,000. You can check it yourself; it's right.

This will work no matter how many zeros there are in each number. Take two big numbers like 9,000 and 70,000, for instance. We know 9×7 is 63, so 9,000×70,000 should be 63 followed by seven zeros, or 630,000,000. So the rule is that when both numbers have zeros, you put the number of zeros in both numbers into your answer.

Pop Up Zeros

There is one thing you need to watch out for when counting the 0s in your answer, though. Sometimes an extra 0 will pop up. For example, to do 400×500 we multiply 4 and 5 first to get 20; then we stick on four 0s. Our answer is 200,000, which has five 0s instead of four like we might have expected. Here's why. Since there was already one 0 in 20, the answer contains the four original 0s we stuck on, plus the extra one that appeared when we multiplied 4 and 5. That really isn't a violation of the rule, since we're still multiplying 4 and 5, then adding four 0s after it.

The main point of this lesson is that with nothing more than a knowledge of the multiplication table, we can multiply very large numbers that end in 0.

Practice 9

a. Write a multiplication problem to represent 100 groups of 5. 5×100

b. Multiply 4×300. 1200

c. Multiply $8 \times 7,000$. 56000

d. Multiply 600×300. 1800,00

e. Translate the word problem below into math; then solve.

If Howie's mom asked him to do 9 extra minutes of chores each day for the next 40 days, how many minutes is this? $9 \times 40 = 360$

Problem Set 9

Tell whether each sentence below is True or False.

1. To multiply a number by one hundred, just add 2 zeros to the number. tRuE

2. To multiply a number that ends in 5 zeros by another number that ends in 3 zeros, multiply the nonzero digits and add 2 zeros to the answer. false

Write each number below (using modern numbers).

3. eighteen thousand, four hundred twenty 18,420

4. six hundred thousand, one hundred thirty-four 600,134

Answer each question below.

5. Write a number that is 10,000 less than 312,019. 302,019

6. Write $19 + 19 + 19$ as a multiplication. 19×3

(a) 7. Write a multiplication problem to represent 100 groups of 17.

17×100

Add each group of numbers below.

8.
$$\begin{array}{r} \overset{1\,1\,1}{568} \\ +\,932 \\ \hline 1500 \end{array}$$

9.
$$\begin{array}{r} \overset{1\,1\,1\,1}{53{,}769} \\ +\,6{,}994 \\ \hline 60763 \end{array}$$

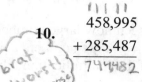

10.
$$\begin{array}{r} \overset{1\,1\,1\,1}{458{,}995} \\ +\,285{,}487 \\ \hline 744482 \end{array}$$

Subtract each group of numbers below.

11.
$$\begin{array}{r} 75{,}595 \\ -\,310 \\ \hline 75285 \end{array}$$

12.
$$\begin{array}{r} \overset{8}{9}4 \\ -\,65 \\ \hline 29 \end{array}$$

13.
$$\begin{array}{r} \overset{6}{8}74 \\ -\,646 \\ \hline 228 \end{array}$$

Multiply each group of numbers below.

14.   8×1   8

15.   5×9   45

16.   21×0   0

17.   42×10   420

(b) 18.   58×100   5800

(c) 19.   689×1,000   689,000

(d) 20.   400×500   200000

21.   300×20   6000

22.   3,000×100   300,000

Translate the word problem below into math; then solve.

(e) 23.   Bernie and Louise Samuelson have taken 20 days a year off for each of the last 30 years. How many days is this?

$$20 \times 30 = 600$$

Lesson 10—Multiplying Larger Numbers

We've seen how large numbers ending in 0 can be multiplied. Now let's go one step further and multiply two large numbers that don't end in zero. Once again, we can do the job with only a knowledge of the multiplication table. Let's start with an example.

Over a two-week period, Moose, the all-star defensive lineman, ate two cases of bratwurst (in honor of his having played 243 downs without a penalty). If each case had 243 bratwurst in it, how many bratwurst did Moose eat in total?

What we need to do here is multiply 243 by 2.

$$\begin{array}{r} 243 \\ \times 2 \\ \hline \end{array}$$

The procedure is to multiply the 2 on the bottom by each of the digits on top, moving right to left. Specifically, 2×3 is 6, 2×4 is 8, and 2×2 is 4.

$$\begin{array}{r} 243 \\ \times 2 \\ \hline \mathbf{486} \end{array}$$

That gives us 486 bratwurst!

Of course, you've been multiplying this way for years. It's nothing new. But let's try to figure out *why* the method works. It helps to remember that 243 is the same as $200 + 40 + 3$. So our multiplication could have been written like this.

$$
\begin{array}{r}
200 + 40 + 3 \\
\times 2 \\
\hline
\end{array}
$$

Now it's clear that when we multiplied 2 and 3 we were multiplying ones. The result was just 6, which we wrote down below in the ones column. But when we multiplied 2 by the 4 in the tens place we were actually multiplying 2 by 40. That equals 80. (Remember how to multiply numbers with zeros from the last lesson?) We wrote an 8 below, but notice where we wrote it: down in the tens spot, so it actually stands for 8 tens, or 80 (which is also right). Finally, we multiplied 2 and 2, but since the 2 on top was in the hundreds column we were really multiplying 2 by 200 to get 400. However, since we wrote the 4 in the hundreds place below, that worked out too.

Partial Product Method

Actually, there's a longer method that makes us write out the entire number (80 instead of 8 and 400 instead of 4) for each step. Even though it takes awhile, this method makes it even easier to see how the multiplication process really works. Let's go back to our original problem.

$$
\begin{array}{r}
243 \\
\times 2 \\
\hline
\end{array}
$$

We start off the same way we did the first time, multiplying the 2 and the 3 to get 6. But the next step works a little differently. Since we're actually multiplying 2 and 40 (since the 4 is in the tens place), instead of putting an 8 next to the 6, we write out 80 completely. But to give ourselves enough space we write the 80 below the 6 like this.

$$
\begin{array}{r}
243 \\
\times\ 2 \\
\hline
6 \\
80 \\
\end{array}
$$

Next, we do the same thing when multiplying 2 and 2. The 2 on top in the hundreds place is actually 200, so we're really multiplying 2×200 to get 400. To show that clearly, we write out the entire number 400 . Again, there's not enough space to write it out on the same line as the 80, so we put 400 on its own line below the 80 (below left). All that's left to do now is add everything up to get the answer (below right).

$$
\begin{array}{r}
243 \\
\times\ 2 \\
\hline
6 \\
80 \\
400
\end{array}
\quad\longrightarrow\quad
\begin{array}{r}
243 \\
\times\ 2 \\
\hline
6 \\
80 \\
400 \\
\hline
486
\end{array}
$$

With this longer method we get the same answer as before: 486.

The 6, the 80, and the 400 are all called **partial products.** And the important thing to notice is that even though it takes a little longer, the method of writing out all the partial products on separate lines helps us see what's really happening when we multiply two numbers.

Carrying

When doing addition, a column can sometimes add up to be greater than 10. When that happens, we have to carry into the next column. The same kind of thing can happen in multiplication. And using the partial product method is one of the best ways to figure out what's really going on when you have to carry while multiplying. To show you, let's multiply 1,852 by 3. We'll use the partial product method first.

$$
\begin{array}{r}
1{,}852 \\
\times\quad 3 \\
\hline
6 \\
150 \\
2400 \\
3000 \\
\hline
5556
\end{array}
$$

As you can see, we've shown each partial product on a separate line. And then to get the final answer, we added all those up.

Now let's go through the same problem using the normal method for multiplying (the one you learned in basic math). You're going to see that the normal method is really just a shortcut for doing it the long way (by showing the partial products).

$$
\begin{array}{r}
1{,}852 \\
\times\ 3 \\
\hline
\end{array}
$$

Step one is to multiply the 3 on bottom by the 2 on top. That gives 6 which goes in the ones column below.

$$\begin{array}{r} 1,852 \\ \times3 \\ \hline 6 \end{array}$$

Step two is to multiply the 3 by the 5 on top. That gives us 15. But since we don't have room for 15 below, we write only a 5 next to the 6 and carry the 1 into the next column like this.

$$\begin{array}{r} \overset{1}{} \\ 1,852 \\ \times3 \\ \hline 56 \end{array}$$

The 5 below is in the tens column, so it really stands for 50. And we carried the 1 into the hundreds column, so the 1 actually stands for 100. 100 and 50 make 150. That makes sense, because what we were really doing in this step was multiplying 3 by 50, which equals 150. And if you look back to where we worked the problem out the long way, you'll see that the second partial product is 150.

Step three is to multiply 3 by 8 to get 24. But we also need to add the 1 that was carried to get 25. Since we don't have room for 25 below, we write 5 and carry the 2 into the next column.

$$\begin{array}{r} \overset{2\,1}{} \\ 1,852 \\ \times3 \\ \hline 556 \end{array}$$

By multiplying 3 and 8, we're really multiplying 3 by 800 which equals 2,400. But there's an extra 100 that was carried, which boosts the result to 2,500. We put the 5 below in the hundreds column, so it stands for 500. And we carried the 2 into the thousands column, which means that it stands for 2,000. Everything works out perfectly.

The final step is to multiply 3 by the 1 to get 3. And then we need to add the 2 that was carried to get 5. The 5 is written down below like this.

$$\begin{array}{r} \overset{2\,1}{} \\ 1,852 \\ \times3 \\ \hline 5,556 \end{array}$$

We end up with 5,556, which is the same answer we got before.

Looking at the partial products shows you what's really going on when multiplying larger numbers. The process is actually quite complicated. But the mathematicians have worked out a short method that almost everybody can do (even though most don't fully understand all the steps). And amazingly, the method only requires a knowledge of the simple multiplication table.

Practice 10

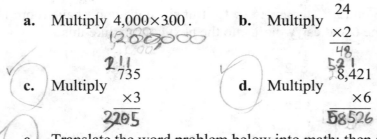

a. Multiply $4,000 \times 300$.

1,200,000

b. Multiply

24
×2
48

c. Multiply

2 1 1
735
×3
2205

d. Multiply

52 1
8,421
×6
58526

e. Translate the word problem below into math; then solve.

The director has sat through 27 auditions a day for each of the last 3 days. How many auditions is this altogether?

2
27
× 3
81

Problem Set 10

Tell whether each sentence below is True or False.

1. To multiply large numbers with Hindu-Arabic (modern) numbers, you absolutely must use a calculator.   False

2. It is easier to understand the process of multiplication if you show the partial products.
   true

Write each number below (using modern numbers).

3. two million, three thousand, nine   2,003,009

4. five billion, one hundred forty thousand   5,000,140,000

Answer each question below.

5. Write a number that is 1,000 greater than 9,000.   10,000

6. Write a number that is 100,000 less than 1,100,000.   1,000,000

Add each group of numbers below.

7. 1,000,001
    +101
    ‾‾‾‾‾‾‾
    1,000,102

8. ⁷⁴ (carries: 1 1)
    74
    32
    + 65
    ‾‾‾‾
    171

9. ¹ 125,000,000
    +5,000,000
    ‾‾‾‾‾‾‾‾
    130,000,000

Subtract each group of numbers below.

10. 655,999
     −342,587
     ‾‾‾‾‾‾‾
     313,412

11. ⁷8̶30
     −570
     ‾‾‾‾
     260

12. ⁸¹³9̶4̶3
     −796
     ‾‾‾‾
     147

Multiply each group of numbers below.

13. 35×10   350

14. 96×100   9,600

15. 799×1,000   799,000

16. 800×100   80,000

17. 400×20   8,000

(a) 18. 3,000×200   600,000

(b) 19.   43
         ×2
         ‾‾‾
         86

(c) 20. ¹¹¹ 657
         ×2
         ‾‾‾‾‾
         1,314

(d) 21. ¹¹¹ 9,563
         ×2
         ‾‾‾‾‾
         19,126

Translate the word problem below into math; then solve.

(e) 22. Joey can make 21 free throws in a single minute. How many free throws can he make in 5 minutes?

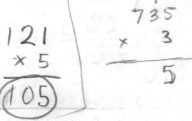

121
× 5
‾‾‾‾
(105)

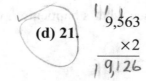

¹ 735
× 3
‾‾‾‾
5

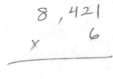

8,421
×   6
‾‾‾‾‾

Lesson 11—Multiplying with Two or More Digits

In the last lesson, we reviewed how to multiply larger numbers by a single-digit number. An example would be $2,386\times4$. In this case, the method is to multiply 4 by each of the digits of the big number, but what about multiplying by a two-digit number? Here's an example like that.

$$231$$
$$\times32$$

Notice that 32 has two digits. The method here is basically the same as multiplying with one digit. The only difference is that we have to multiply *each* of the digits on bottom (the 3 and the 2) by each of the digits of the number on top. Specifically, we multiply the 2 on bottom by the 1, the 3, and the 2 on top. Then we multiply the 3 on bottom by the 1, the 3, and the 2 on top. Here's what it looks like.

 Multiply each digit on bottom by each digit on top.

Just so you can see what's happening, we'll show all of the partial products.

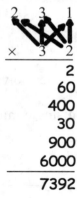

Let's go through each of these quickly. We always start with the ones digit on bottom and top. So 2 times 1 is just 2. Next, we multiply 2 times the 3 on top. But since the 3 is in the tens column, it's really a 30, and 2 times 30 is 60. So 60 is the next partial product. Moving on, 2 times 200 (since the 2 on top is in the hundreds column) is 400. Next, we multiply the 3 on bottom by each of the digits, starting with the 1 again. But since that 3 is actually a 30, we have 30 times 1 which is 30. Then 30 times 30 is 900 and 30 times 200 is 6,000.[1] The final step is to add up all the partial products. As you can see, the answer comes out to be 7,392.

---

[1] See how important it is to understand how to multiply numbers with zeros!

Of course, nobody actually multiplies this way, mainly because it takes up too much space and takes too long to write down every partial product. Most people use the shortcut method instead. We'll show you what the shortcut looks like. But we'll put the long version to the left of it, so we can compare the two.

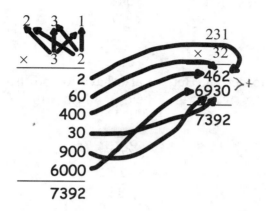

We end up with the same answer as before, naturally. But by following the arrows, you'll see that every one of our original partial products is included in the two partial products on the right. But instead of being listed separately, the partial products are scrunched together into two lines. That's the way the shortcut method works. When multiplying with a two-digit number on bottom, we end up with only two partial products.

Notice also that with the shortcut method we started with a 0 on the second line (6930). That's because when multiplying by 3, we were really multiplying by 30 (since 3 is in the tens place). And since 30 times 1 is 30, we put a 0 in to make sure that the 3 below goes in the tens place. Some people just leave that space blank. But it's probably better to write in a 0, since that shows what's going on. Notice too that we still add everything up to get our final answer.

Carrying Again

Now let's do another example involving multiplication with two digits. This one requires carrying.

$$548$$
$$\times 37$$

By the way, if you don't like carrying, you can always avoid it by showing every partial product. That's the one advantage of using the longer method. But we'll go with the shortcut method on this problem to show you how carrying works.

As always, we start with the ones: 7 times 8 is 56. Since 56 is too large to fit in the ones space below, we put the 6 below and carry the 5 above like this.

$$
\begin{array}{r}
^{5}\ \ \ \\
548 \\
\times\ 37 \\
\hline
6
\end{array}
$$

Next, we multiply 7 by 4 to get 28. But we also have to add the 5 that was carried to get 33. Since 33 is too big to fit below, we put the 3 below and carry the other 3 into the next column.

$$
\begin{array}{r}
^{3\,5}\ \ \\
548 \\
\times\ 37 \\
\hline
36
\end{array}
$$

We really multiplied 7 by 40 (since 4 is a ten) to get 280. Then we added 50 more (because the 5 from 56 was carried) to get 330. But notice how well the shortcut method worked. We put the 3 on bottom in the tens column, so that's 30. Then we carried the 3 into the hundreds column, which is 300. So everything turned out perfectly. The mathematicians have designed the shortcut method so that it's possible to multiply huge numbers with just a knowledge of the simple multiplication table. It's amazing.

Continuing the process, the next step is to multiply 7 by 5 to get 35. Then we add the 3 that was carried to get 38. Since 5 is the last digit on top, there's no need to carry.

$$
\begin{array}{r}
^{3\,5}\ \ \\
548 \\
\times\ 37 \\
\hline
3836
\end{array}
$$

Now we multiply the 3 on bottom by each of the digits on top. And we'll put our results on a separate line (below 3836). First, 3 times 8 is 24. Since 24 won't fit below, we put just a 4 down there and carry the 2.

$$
\begin{array}{r}
^{2}\ \ \ \\
548 \\
\times\ 37 \\
\hline
3836 \\
40
\end{array}
$$

Since 3 is in the tens column, we really multiplied 30 times 8, which is 240. That's why we put a 0 next to the 4 below. That puts the 4 in the tens column where it belongs.

Next, we multiply 3 by the 4 on top to get 12. Adding the 2 that was carried gives us 14. Since 14 is too big, we put the 4 below and carry the 1.

$$\begin{array}{r} \overset{1\ 2}{548} \\ \times\ 37 \\ \hline 3836 \\ 440 \end{array}$$

Finally, we multiply 3 by 5 which is 15. Adding the 1 that was carried gives 16. Since 5 is the last digit there's no need to carry. And we'll go ahead and add up the partial products in this step to get the answer, which comes out to 20,276.

$$\begin{array}{r} \overset{1\ 2}{548} \\ \times\ 37 \\ \hline 3836 \\ 16440 \\ \hline 20276 \end{array}$$

Just to make sure you understand what's really going on, let's compare this with the same problem done the long way.

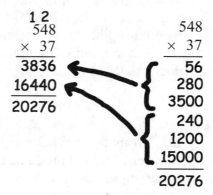

As you can see, with the shortcut method, the partial products are all scrunched together: 56, 280, and 3,500 add up to equal 3,836. And 240, 1,200 and 15,000 add up to equal 16,440, which is pretty neat.

Now for Three Digits

We'll do one last example. This time we'll multiply with a three-digit number on bottom. Since the process is basically the same, we'll go through this one a little faster.

$$3412$$
$$\times\,143$$

Believe-it-or-not, if we showed every partial product on this example it would take 12 separate lines! That's so long we won't even bother showing it. But with the shortcut method we can do the problem with just three partial products. The greater the number of digits, the more time (and space) the shortcut method saves you.

When the bottom number has three digits, all we have to do is multiply each of the digits on bottom by each of the digits on top, and carry wherever necessary. Here's the problem worked out in three steps, one for each partial product.

multiplying by 3	multiplying by 4	multiplying by 1
1	**1**	
3412	3412	3412
× 143	× 143	× 143
10236	10236	10236
	136480	136480
		341200
		487916

Notice that we have a zero on the far right of the second partial product. That's because when multiplying each digit on top by 4 we're actually multiplying by 40 (since the 4 is in the tens column). So when multiplying 4 by 2, we're multiplying 40 by 2, which is 80. But the third partial product actually has two zeros to the right. That's because when multiplying by 1 we're really multiplying by 100 (since the 1 is in the hundreds column). So when multiplying 1 by 2, we're really multiplying 100 by 2, which is 200. After adding all three partial products we get a final answer of 487,916.

The main point is that when multiplying two numbers, you always multiply each digit of one number by each digit of the other, no matter how many digits each has. Also, using the shortcut method, you can reduce the number of partial products to however many digits there are in the number on bottom. If there are two digits, there will be two partial products; if there are three digits, there will be three partial products, and so on.

Practice 11

a. Write a multiplication to represent 16 boxes with 429 whatchamacallits in each one.

b. Multiply
1,856
×2
3,712

c. Multiply
545
×35
2725
+16350
19,075

d. Multiply
872
×457
6104
40600
348800
395,504

e.   Translate the word problem below into math; then solve.

The consultant discovered that the company received an average of 211 complaints about soggy newspapers each week. How many complaints about soggy newspapers will the company receive in a year? (Remember, there are 52 weeks in a year.)

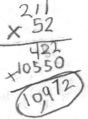

Problem Set 11

Tell whether each sentence below is True or False.

1.   When multiplying 12 and 23, you multiply each digit of 12 by each digit of 23. *also true*

2.   When multiplying any two numbers, no matter how many digits they have, you multiply each digit of the first number by each digit of the second. *true*

Answer each question below.

3.   Write 8 + 8 + 8 + 8 + 8 + 8 as a multiplication. 8×6

4.   Write a multiplication problem to represent 72 groups of 31.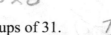

(a) 5.   Write a multiplication to represent 28 crates with 512 baseballs in each one.

6.   Multiply $2,000 \times 900$.

Add each group of numbers below.

7.
```
  2,142
+   637
```
1,987

8.
```
  54,801
+ 23,482
```
78,283

9.
```
    329
    214
+   875
```
1,418

10.
```
  3,656
+ 2,021
```
7,664

Subtract each pair of numbers below.

11.
$$578$$
$$-352$$
(226)

12.
$$7,561$$
$$-3,249$$
(4,312)

13.
$$5,863$$
$$-4,144$$
(1,719)

14.
$$8,901$$
$$-2,795$$
(6,106)

15.
$$45,006$$
$$-23,678$$
(21,328)

Multiply each pair of numbers below.

16.
$$311$$
$$\times 3$$
(933)

17.
$$572$$
$$\times 6$$
3,422

(b) 18.
$$2,678$$
$$\times 4$$
10,712

19.
$$43$$
$$\times 12$$
86
+430
(516)

20.
$$76$$
$$\times 32$$
(2,432)

(c) 21.
$$395$$
$$\times 65$$
1475
+22800
(24,275)

22.
$$234$$
$$\times 212$$
1468
2340
+46800
(49,608)

(d) 23.
$$931$$
$$\times 539$$

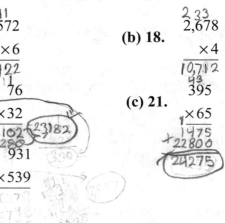

Translate the word problem below into math; then solve.

(e) 24. Upon further investigation (see practice e), the consultant discovered that the company's paperboys only hit the driveway an average of 138 times per week. How many times is that in a year? (Remember, there are 52 weeks in a year.)

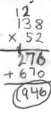
$$138$$
$$\times 52$$
276
+670
(946)

Lesson 12—Division

We've spent several lessons on multiplication. And you know that multiplication is just a fast way to add the same number to itself several times (4×7 is the same as $7+7+7+7$). So multiplying is adding up equal groups of things.

Breaking Down into Equal Groups

What's division then? It's breaking a total up into equal groups. It's the reverse of multiplication, just like subtraction is the reverse of addition. In the next several lessons, we're going to cover division. Let's start with a simple example of a division word problem.

Her Majesty's Official Seal

When the ruthless queen heard that there were only 18 white alligators in the world, she decided to buy them all and place them in the moats around her 3 ivory-colored castles. If each castle received the same number of alligators, how many alligators did each get?

To solve this, we need to break 18 into 3 equal groups. And we need to figure out how many are in each group. That's a classic division problem. To find the answer, all we have to do is divide 18 by 3, which, of course, is equal to 6.

This problem is so simple that there's no need to write anything down. But there are actually three ways to write a division problem. One is with the symbol ÷. The second is with a fraction bar, and the third is with the symbol $\overline{)}$. Here is 18 divided by 3 written in all three ways.

$$18 \div 3 \qquad\qquad \frac{18}{3} \qquad\qquad 3\overline{)18}$$

A Few Words and a Few Rules

There are some technical words and a few rules that you need to know as well. These are used a lot when working with division. First, the technical words. The number that you are dividing by is called the **divisor**. So in our example, the divisor is 3. The number you're dividing into is called the **dividend**. In our problem, the dividend is 18. And the answer to a division problem (6 in our example) is called the **quotient**.

Now for the rules. First, any number divided by 1 always equals the number itself. For example, 5 divided by 1 equals 5. Here are a few more cases.

$$8 \div 1 = 8 \qquad\qquad 14 \div 1 = 14 \qquad\qquad 31 \div 1 = 31$$

Of course, you already knew this rule. But you might not have known *why* it's true. The best way to answer a why question on division is to use multiplication. Since division is the reverse of multiplication, the multiplication tables (which you've memorized) can be used to understand division. For instance, what's 12 divided by 4? Well, think of a number that when you multiply it by 4 gives 12. That's 3. So 12 divided by 4 has to equal 3. Now apply that thinking to 5 divided by 1. Think of a number that when you multiply it by 1 equals 5. The number is 5. That's why 5 divided by 1 must equal 5. And it works the same way for any other number that's divided by 1. The answer is always the number itself.

Our second rule on division is that 0 divided by any number equals 0. To take some specific examples, 0 divided by 3 equals 0, and 0 divided by 7 equals 0, and 0 divided by 29 equals 0.

$$\frac{0}{3} \qquad\qquad \frac{0}{7} \qquad\qquad \frac{0}{29}$$

This rule is also pretty obvious, if we use multiplication. Think of a number that when multiplied by 3 equals 0. The only number that works is 0. That's why 0 divided by 3 must equal 0. That thinking works for 0 divided by any other number, of course.

A third important rule is that you can never divide by 0. So 11 divided by 0 ($11 \div 0$ or $\frac{11}{0}$) is said to be "undefined." That just means the problem doesn't have an answer. Here are several other examples.

$\frac{2}{0}$ is undefined $\frac{16}{0}$ is undefined $\frac{53}{0}$ is undefined

You may wonder why we can't divide by 0. Well, think about it in terms of multiplication again. What number multiplied by 0 equals 11? There is no such number! No matter what number you choose, after multiplying it by 0 the answer comes out 0. That's why division by 0 won't work.

Here are all three of our rules summarized.

1.	Any number divided by one equals the number itself.
2.	Zero divided by any number equals 0.
3.	You can never divide by 0.

Remainders

Another thing to keep in mind is that not all division problems work out evenly. You learned that a long time ago. Take 15 divided by 2 as an example. We can make 7 equal groups, but there's one left over.

$$15 \div 2 \text{ is 7 with a remainder of 1.}$$

The number left over in a division problem is called the **remainder**. You can write down the remainder next to the answer, and when people do this they usually use the capital letter R to stand for remainder.

$$15 \div 2 = 7 \text{ R1}$$

Another way to do it, though, is to use the remainder to turn the answer into a mixed number. Done that way, the answer to $15 \div 2$ is $7\frac{1}{2}$. We'll get more into mixed numbers and fractions later in the book.

Practice 12

a. Write a division problem to represent 56 moth balls divided into so many drawers, with 7 in each drawer.

$$7\overline{)56}$$

b. When dividing 70 by 8, what is the remainder?

6

c. Multiply $\begin{array}{r} 379 \\ \times 513 \end{array}$

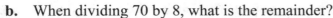

$$\begin{array}{r} 379 \\ \times 513 \\ \hline 1137 \\ 3790 \\ +189500 \\ \hline 194,427 \end{array}$$

d. Multiply $\begin{array}{r} 732 \\ \times 201 \end{array}$

$$\begin{array}{r} 732 \\ \times 201 \\ \hline 732 \\ 1000 \\ + \\ \hline 21196 \end{array}$$

e. Translate the word problem below into math; then solve.

Twila Glisten

Twila Glisten, the world's most famous game show host assistant, has always said that her favorite color is plaid. If Twila uses her wardrobe allowance to buy 15 plaid skirts each month, how many skirts will she purchase in 120 months (10 years)?

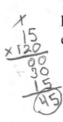

45 plaid skirts

Problem Set 12

Tell whether each sentence below is True or False.

True 1. Division is breaking a total down into equal groups.

2. Any number divided by 0 is equal to 0. _False_

3. Any number divided by 1 equals 1. _False_

Complete each sentence below with the best of the choices given.

4. The answer to a division problem is called the _quotient_ .

    A. divisor   (B) quotient   C. dividend
    D. sum   E. remainder

5. In a division problem, the number that you are dividing into is called the
_____C_____ .

    A. divisor   B. quotient   (C.) dividend
    D. sum   E. remainder

6. In a division problem, the number that you are dividing by is called the _____A_____ .

    (A.) divisor   B. quotient   C. dividend
    D. sum   E. remainder

7. In a division problem, a number that is "left over" after dividing into equal groups is called the _____E_____ .

    A. divisor   B. quotient   C. dividend
    D. sum   (E.) remainder

Answer each question below.

8. Write a division problem to represent 42 eggs divided equally into 7 baskets.

(a) 9. Write a division problem to represent 72 marbles divided into so many groups of 9.

(b) 10. When dividing 80 by 9, what is the remainder?

11. When dividing 41 by 8, what is the remainder?

Add each group of numbers below.

12. $\begin{array}{r} 168 \\ +426 \\ \hline 594 \end{array}$

13. $\begin{array}{r} 57 \\ 97 \\ +55 \\ \hline 209 \end{array}$

14. $\begin{array}{r} 3,685 \\ 4,997 \\ +4,085 \\ \hline 12,767 \end{array}$

Subtract each pair of numbers below.

15. $\begin{array}{r} 689 \\ -383 \\ \hline 306 \end{array}$

16. $\begin{array}{r} 3,075 \\ -2,969 \\ \hline 106 \end{array}$

17. $\begin{array}{r} 7,802 \\ -988 \\ \hline 6,814 \end{array}$

18. $\begin{array}{r} 59,146 \\ -43,899 \\ \hline 15,247 \end{array}$

Multiply each pair of numbers below.

19. $\begin{array}{r} 219 \\ \times 5 \\ \hline 1095 \end{array}$

20. $\begin{array}{r} 25 \\ \times 78 \\ \hline 200 \\ +1750 \\ \hline 1950 \end{array}$

21. $\begin{array}{r} 807 \\ \times 62 \\ \hline 1614 \\ +48420 \\ \hline 50,034 \end{array}$

(c) 22. $\begin{array}{r} 468 \\ \times 316 \\ \hline 2808 \\ 4680 \\ +140400 \\ \hline 147,888 \end{array}$

(d) 23. $\begin{array}{r} 925 \\ \times 304 \\ \hline 3700 \\ 00000 \\ +647500 \\ \hline 651,200 \end{array}$

Translate the word problem below into math; then solve.

24. On the next episode of *Treehouse Survivor*, contestants will be asked to live off of 145 acorns each day for 30 days. How many acorns is this?

$\begin{array}{r} 145 \\ \times 30 \\ \hline 000 \\ +4350 \\ \hline 4350 \end{array}$

Lesson 13—Dividing Numbers with Zeros

In the last lesson, we learned what division means. It's just taking a total and breaking it down into equal groups. We also did a division problem involving small numbers: $18 \div 3 = 6$. Simple divisions of this kind can be done in your head using the **division table**, which is just a list of divisions with smaller numbers. The great thing about the division table is that it's not necessary to memorize it. Once you have the multiplication table memorized, you can use those facts to find the answer to any division with small numbers. For example, to do 18 divided by 3, you just need to figure out what number must be multiplied by 3 to get 18. Since $3 \times 6 = 18$, the answer has to be 6.

But what about division with larger numbers? The division table won't help with those. Fortunately, our modern numbers are so good that they make division with larger numbers fairly easy. That's quite an accomplishment, because division is the toughest of the four basic operations (addition, subtraction, multiplication, and division). In fact, a thousand years ago, before modern numbers were widely used, only the smartest people in the world could divide!

Subtracting the Zeros

Do you remember when we did multiplication with large numbers a few lessons ago? We started off by learning how to multiply larger numbers that end with zeros (like $300 \times 4,000$). We were able to multiply those in our head by using only the multiplication table. Well, we're going to do the same thing with division. First, we'll learn how to divide numbers ending with zeros. Then, in the next lesson, we'll cover division of larger numbers that *don't* end with zeros. Here's our first example.

> Super entrepreneur Freddie Fandango vows that his new refrigerator backpacks will make the school lunchbox obsolete. In fact, he expects to sell 6,000 of them in the first 20 hours after they hit stores. How many is that (on average) an hour?

To figure this one out, we need to break down 6,000 into 20 equal groups. That means we should divide 6,000 by 20. Since both numbers end with zeros, we can do this one in our head. The first step is to divide the nonzero parts of the numbers, using the division table: 6 divided by 2 is 3. The next step is to *subtract* the number of zeros in the two numbers: 3 zeros minus 1 zero is 2 zeros. That's the basic difference between multiplying numbers ending in zero and dividing them. When multiplying, you add the zeros in both numbers; when dividing, you subtract the zeros. The last step—after subtracting the zeros—is to stick that many zeros (2 of them) at the end of our answer: 6 divided by 2 was 3, so putting two zeros after 3 gives us 300.

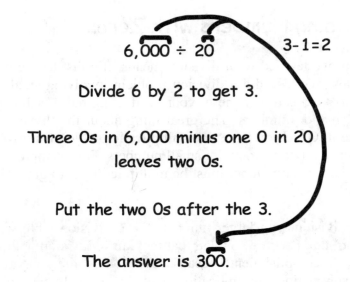

Divide 6 by 2 to get 3.

Three 0s in 6,000 minus one 0 in 20 leaves two 0s.

Put the two 0s after the 3.

The answer is 300.

Freddie Fandango must be expecting to sell 300 refrigerator backpacks per hour.[2]

A Couple More Examples

Let's do another example to make sure you're getting the concept. This one has just numbers (with no word problem).

$$80,000 \div 400$$

We start by dividing the nonzero parts of each number: 8 divided by 4 equals 2. Then we subtract the zeros: four zeros minus two zeros is two zeros. The last step is to stick those 2 zeros after the 2 to get 200. So $80,000 \div 400$ equals 200.

Let's do one more. This time we'll use really huge numbers.

$$72,000,000,000 \div 90,000$$

With our method, we can even do this problem in our head. First, we divide 72 by 9 to get 8. Next, we take the 9 zeros from 72 billion and subtract the 4 zeros from 90 thousand to get 5 zeros. Finally, we stick those 5 zeros after 8 to get 800,000. So $72,000,000,000 \div 90,000$ equals 800,000.

The main point of the lesson is that two large numbers ending with zeros can be divided in our head. First we divide the nonzero digits, and then instead of adding the number of zeros at the end of the two numbers, we subtract them. The last step is to stick that number of zeros after the answer.

---

[2] Seems unrealistic.

Practice 13

a. Multiply $\begin{array}{r} 2{,}203 \\ \times 303 \end{array}$ 667,509

b. Multiply $\begin{array}{r} 1{,}063 \\ \times 3{,}007 \end{array}$ 3,196,241

c. Divide $1{,}800 \div 60$. 30

d. Divide $3{,}600{,}000 \div 4{,}000$. 600

$$\begin{array}{r} 2{,}203 \\ \times \ \ 303 \\ \hline 6{,}609 \\ 00\ 000 \\ +\ 660\ 900 \\ \hline 667509 \end{array}$$

$$\begin{array}{r} 1{,}063 \\ \times 3{,}007 \\ \hline 7{,}241 \\ 000\ 0 \\ 000\ 00 \\ +\ 3189\ 000 \\ \hline 3196241 \end{array}$$

e. Translate the word problem below into math; then solve.

The ancient Romans are known to have fielded as many as 300,000 men in a single battle. This giant army would have been divided into *legions*, each consisting of 5,000 men. Each legion, in turn, was made up of *centuries*, each of which contained 100 men. How many centuries, therefore, would an army of 300,000 men have?

$$300{,}000 \div 100 = 3{,}000$$

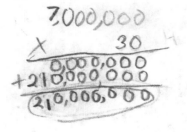

Problem Set 13

Tell whether each sentence below is True or False.

1. It is possible to divide large numbers that end with zeros, using only a knowledge of the division table. *true*

2. When dividing large numbers ending with zeros, you subtract the zeros in each number. *true*

Answer each question below.

3. When dividing 32 by 5, what is the remainder?

4. When dividing 50 by 7, what is the remainder?

5. Multiply $30 \times 7{,}000{,}000$.

$$\begin{array}{r} 7{,}000{,}000 \\ \times \quad 30 \\ \hline 0{,}000{,}000 \\ +210{,}000{,}000 \\ \hline 210{,}000{,}000 \end{array}$$

Add each group of numbers below.

6.
$$829$$
$$+365$$
$$1194$$

7.
$$278$$
$$5,650$$
$$+6,208$$
$$12136$$

8.
$$3,620$$
$$6,100$$
$$2,005$$
$$+4,073$$
$$15798$$

Subtract each pair of numbers below.

9.
$$807$$
$$-125$$
$$982$$

10.
$$4,752$$
$$-3,523$$
$$1,229$$

11.
$$72,844$$
$$-6,895$$
$$65,949$$

12.
$$53,969$$
$$-39,170$$
$$14,799$$

Multiply each pair of numbers below.

13.
$$372$$
$$\times 54$$
$$1488$$
$$+17500$$
$$18988$$
$$1,304$$

14.
$$648$$
$$\times 725$$
$$3240$$
$$3240$$
$$+129600$$
$$1,052$$

15.
$$586$$
$$\times 957$$

(a) 16.
$$\times 202$$
$$2608$$
$$00000$$
$$+260800$$
$$263,408$$

(b) 17.
$$\times 4,009$$
$$19468$$
$$+208000$$
$$4208800$$
$$4217468$$

Divide each pair of numbers below. Use your knowledge of the division table.

(c) 18. $2,700 \div 90$ 30

19. $15,000 \div 300$ 50

20. $250,000 \div 50$ 5000

(d) 21. $4,200,000 \div 6,000$ 700

Translate the word problem below into math; then solve.

(e) 22. After El Capitan's ship sank, he and 199 of his fellow pirates managed to swim to a nearby deserted isle. Once they arrived, the only thing they had to eat was 400 kumquats. Assuming each of the pirates (there are 200 including El Capitan) got his fair share, how many kumquats did each receive?

$$400 \div 200 = \boxed{2}$$

Lesson 14—Division with Large Numbers

In this lesson we're going to cover division with larger numbers that don't end in zero. These kinds of problems can't be done in our head. We have to use a method called **long division,** as you know. And even though modern numbers make division far easier than it used to be with an abacus (or with Roman numerals), the process is still fairly tough.

The Usual Method

Let's go through an example.

Millicent Fenwick's pet parrot, Major Beauregard, whistled *Twinkle, Twinkle Little Star* a total of 639 times over a 3 month period. How many times is that (on average) each month?

The problem itself is pretty easy. We just need to break down 639 into 3 equal groups, which means we should divide 639 by 3. But since 639 is large and doesn't end with zeros, we can't come up with the answer in our head. We'll have to use long division. To set up the problem, we use the $\overline{)}$ symbol. The number being divided (the dividend) goes inside, and the other number (the divisor) goes on the outside.

$$3\overline{)639}$$

The first step of the process is to divide 3 into the far left digit of 639, which is 6. Since 3 goes into 6 two times, we put a 2 up on top, directly over the 6 (below left). Next, we multiply 2 and 3 to get 6 and put the 6 below, directly underneath the 6 in 639 (below middle). After that, we just subtract the 6s to get 0 (below right).

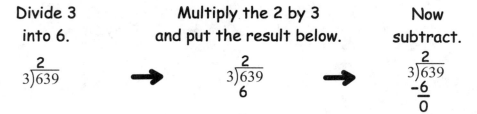

At this point, we bring down the 3, by writing it next to the 0 (below left). And then we divide the 3 outside into the 3 below to get 1, which goes on top (below right).

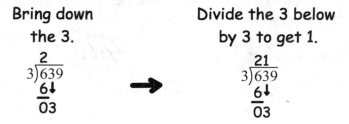

Notice that the 1 goes directly over the 3 in 639.

The next step is to multiply the 1 on top by the 3 on the outside to get 3, which goes down below (below left). Now we can subtract again to get 0 (below right).

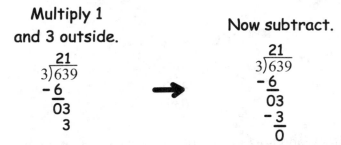

From here, we bring down the 9 (below left). Then we divide the 3 outside into the 9 to get 3, which goes on top (below right).

Bring down the 9.

21
3)639
−6
‾‾
03
−3
‾‾
09

Divide 9 by the 3 outside.

213
3)639
−6
‾‾
03
−3
‾‾
09

Now multiplying 3 and 3 we get 9 and subtracting 9 from 9 leaves 0. So the final answer is 213.

Remainder 0

```
      213
  3)639
   -6
    03
    -3
     09
     -9
      0
```

How Does it Work?

That's the way we do long division. You learned the method a long time ago, so it's nothing new. But you may have never learned *why* long division works. Long division is actually just a shortcut for a longer method. To help you understand what's really going on, let's go through the example again—the long way. Here's the original problem.

```
3)639
```

The first step of the longer method is to divide 3 into "6." But since 6 is in the hundreds place (in 639), we're really dividing 3 into 600. And 600 divided by 3 equals 200. That's why when using the shortcut method we had to be careful to write the 2 directly above the 6 in the hundreds column (because it was really a 200). But since we're using the long method this time, we'll write out 200 completely.

600 divided by 3

equals 200.

```
    200
 3)639
```

The next step is to multiply 200 by 3 to get 600. With the shortcut method, as you remember, we multiplied 2 by 3 to get 6. But we were really multiplying 200 by 3. Since we're showing everything, instead of writing just 6 below, we'll write 600 (below left). From here we subtract. But this time it's not 6 minus 6. It's 639 minus 600.

Now subtract.

```
    200
 3)639
 - 600
   39
```

That gives us 39, which makes perfect sense, because 3 goes into 639 two hundred times with 39 left over.

Now we divide the 3 outside into the 3 below (in 39). But the 3 in 39 is really a 30. And 3 goes into 30 exactly 10 times. That's why when using the shortcut method we had to make sure to put the 1 directly above the 3 in the tens column. This time, we'll write out the 10 completely, on another line above the 200 (below left). Next, we multiply 10 by the 3 on the outside to get 30. And 30 is written on the bottom (below middle). Then, we subtract the 39 and 30 to get 9 (below right).

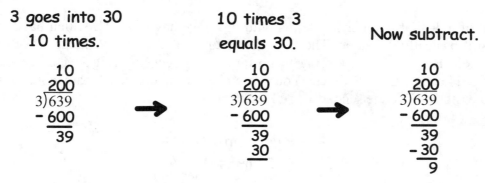

The next step is to divide the 3 outside into the 9 to get 3. Since 9 just represents ones, the answer is 3 and we'll write that above the 200 and the 10 (below left). Now we multiply the 3 on top by the 3 on the outside to get 9, which is written underneath (below middle). Since 9 minus 9 is 0, we get a remainder of 0 (below right).

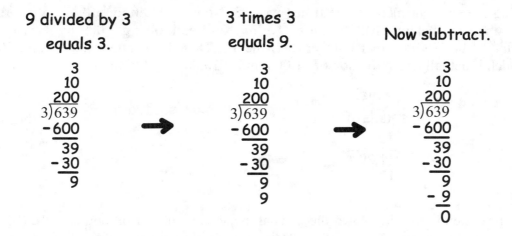

Notice that this long method gives us three partial answers on top. The last step is to add those up: $200 + 10 + 3 = 213$. The final answer comes out to 213, which is what we got before.

The method of long division that everybody learns in arithmetic is actually a shortcut for this longer method. With the shortcut, everything is squeezed into fewer lines, which saves space and time. But the shortcut also makes it harder to understand what's really going on. That's because the shortcut for long division is a lot like the shortcut for long multiplication. It's designed so that you can get the answer without having to know anything other than your basic division facts.

An Even Bigger Number

In our next example, let's divide an even bigger number. And on this one, we'll go back to using the shortcut method. But you should understand the steps better, now that you've done long division the really long way!

$$2\overline{)11,294}$$

See, instead of a 3-digit number inside (as with 639), we have 11,294, which has 5 digits. Our method is still basically the same. The first step is to try and divide 2 into 1, which is the first digit on the left. But since 2 is too big to go into 1, we need to bring in the second digit and divide 2 into 11. That goes 5 times. You remember from previous math courses that we're supposed to write 5 above the second 1 in 11, like this.

2 goes into 11
5 times.

$$2\overline{)11,294}^{5}$$

But do you know why the 5 goes there? It's because we've really just divided 2 into 11,000 to get 5,000. (6 is too big, because $2\times6,000$ equals 12,000). Since 5 represents 5,000 it has to go in the thousands column of the answer. We could even write out the 5,000 completely. But since we're using the shortcut method, we'll just write 5. Now we multiply 5 by 2 to get 10, which goes below the 11 (below left). Of course, we're really multiplying 5,000 by 2 to get 10,000. That's why 10 has to go directly underneath the 11. Then we subtract the 11 and 10 (below right), which is actually a subtraction of 11,000 minus 10,000, by the way.

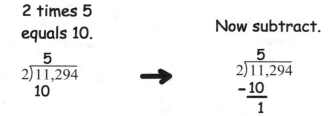

2 times 5
equals 10.

Now subtract.

The next step is to bring down the 2. That makes the number on bottom a 12 (below left). Now we can divide 2 into 12 to get 6, with the 6 going directly over the 2 (below right). What we're actually doing here is dividing 2 into 1,200 to get 600. That's why 6 needs to go in the hundreds column (over the 2).

Bring down
the 2.

$$2\overline{)11,294}^{5}$$
$$\underline{10}\downarrow$$
$$12$$

2 into 12 is 6.

$$2\overline{)11,294}^{56}$$
$$-\underline{10}$$
$$12$$

From here, we multiply 6 by 2 to get 12 and put that below (below left). Then we can subtract (below middle). The next step is to bring down the 9 (below right).

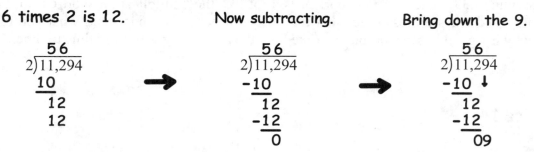

6 times 2 is 12.	Now subtracting.	Bring down the 9.
56 2)11,294 10 ―― 12 12	56 2)11,294 −10 ―― 12 −12 ―― 0	56 2)11,294 −10 ↓ ―― 12 −12 ―― 09

Now we can divide 2 into 9 to get 4, which goes on top directly over the 9 in the tens column (below left). That's because we're really dividing 2 into 90 to get 40. Multiplying 4 times 2 gives us 8, and that goes below the 9 on bottom (below middle). Now we can subtract to get 1 (below right).

2 divided into 9 is 4.	4 times 2 is 8.	Now subtracting.
564 2)11,294 −10 ―― 12 −12 ―― 09	564 2)11,294 −10 ―― 12 −12 ―― 09 8	564 2)11,294 −10 ―― 12 −12 ―― 09 −8 ―― 1

The next step is to bring down the 4. That gives us 14 on bottom (below left). And what we do is divide 2 into 14 to get 7 (below middle). The 7 goes above the 4, in the ones column, because it just represents a plain 7. Finally, we multiply 7 and 2 to get 14 and put that on the bottom and subtract (below right). We end up with an answer of 5,647 and a remainder of 0.

Bring down the 4.	2 divided into 14 equals 7.	Now subtracting for a remainder of 0.
564 2)11,294 −10 ↓ ―― 12 −12 ―― 09 −8 ―― 14	5647 2)11,294 −10 ―― 12 −12 ―― 09 −8 ―― 14	5647 2)11,294 −10 ―― 12 −12 ―― 09 −8 ―― 14 −14 ―― 0

So the shortcut for dividing large numbers just leaves out all the zeros in each step and squeezes the answer into one line on top (rather than having several partial answers, as we did when dividing 639). The division shortcut is a lot like the multiplication short cut in this way. It's shorter and takes up less space, but that makes it harder to understand what you're doing. That's why it's good to see a problem worked out the really long way from time to time.

Practice 14

a. Multiply $1,000 \times 4,700$.

4,700,000

b. Multiply
$$\begin{array}{r} 6,057 \\ \times 2,840 \\ \hline \end{array}$$

c. Divide $3\overline{)1,767}$. Write any remainders next to your answer.

d. Divide $4\overline{)3,157}$. Write any remainders next to your answer.

R1

e. Translate the word problem below into math; then solve.

In a rare kind-hearted moment, the ruthless queen decided to give away 234 of her silk shawls—all the ones with out-of-date colors or not enough purple—to 3 people: her breakfast carrier, her head flower arranger, and her chief pillow fluffer. Assuming each person received the same number of shawls, how many did each get?

Problem Set 14

Tell whether each sentence below is True or False.

1. The method for dividing larger numbers is called radical division.

false

2. There is a short method and a long method for dividing larger numbers.

false

Answer each question below.

(a) 3. Multiply $1,000 \times 3,800$.

3,800,000

4. Divide $54,000 \div 90$.

600

5. When dividing 63 by 8, what is the remainder?

7

Add each group of numbers below.   *Margaret ♡ — use the graph paper notebook for these)*

6.
```
  79
  45
+ 78
```

7.
```
  273
  780
+ 429
```

8.
```
  7,626
  7,250
+ 5,478
```

Subtract each pair of numbers below.

9.
```
  859
- 365
```

10.
```
  3,581
- 2,611
```

11.
```
  38,275
- 15,287
```

Multiply each pair of numbers below.

12.
```
9,739
  × 4
```

13.
```
  662
× 500
```

14.
```
1,021
× 900
```

15.
```
  325
× 248
```

(b) 16.
```
 8,093
× 4,570
```

17.
```
 7,462
× 5,361
```

Divide each pair of numbers below. Write any remainders next to your answer.

18. 3)‾288‾

19. 4)‾276‾ R2

(c) 20. 5)‾2,260‾

21. 8)‾258‾ R2

(d) 22. 9)‾4,073‾ R5

Translate the word problem below into math; then solve.

(e) 23. On last week's episode of *Designer Closets*, the contractor created 4 identical, "sweater spaces" for a total cost of $580. How much did it cost to create each sweater space?

145

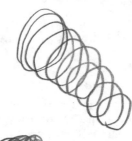

Lesson 15—Division with Two or More Digits

In the last lesson, we learned to do long division, where the number that we're dividing by (the divisor) had one digit, which means it's less than 10. The two examples we did were $3\overline{)639}$ and $2\overline{)11,294}$ (both 3 and 2 are less than 10).

Two Digits on the Outside

But what about dividing by a two-digit number that's greater than 10? Here's an example like that.

$$14\overline{)3,850}$$

As you can see, this one has a 14 on the outside. The steps for doing the division are basically the same, though. First, we try to divide 14 into 3. But since 14 is too big, we need to bring in the next number and divide 14 into 38. How many times does 14 go into 38? Everybody has smaller divisions, like $24 \div 8 = 3$ and $36 \div 9 = 4$, memorized. But almost nobody memorizes their 14s!

That's what makes dividing by a larger number kind of tough. It's not like multiplication. With multiplication, no matter how big the numbers are we can do the calculation with just the basic multiplication facts for numbers less than 10. It's the same way with addition and subtraction. We can do calculations with even huge numbers with just basic addition and subtraction facts. But with division, when the numbers get large, basic division facts aren't enough.

Getting back to our example (since we don't have our 14s memorized), to figure out how many times 14 goes into 38, we need to do a few calculations on a scratch sheet. We could just divide 14 into 38 formally to get 2 plus a remainder. That means 14 goes 2 times with some left over. Or we could guess and check. Fourteen times 1 is 14, and 14 times 2 is 28. Those are both below 38. But 14 times 3 is 42, which is too big. That tells us 14 goes 2 times. Whatever method we use, a 2 needs to go on top, directly over the 8 (below left).[3] The next step is to multiply 2 by 14 to get 28, and that goes directly underneath the 38 (below middle). Then we can subtract 38 minus 28 to get 10 (below right).

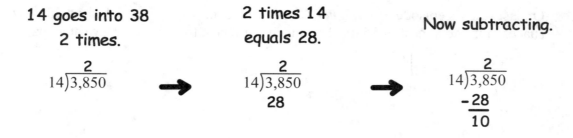

14 goes into 38 2 times. $\rightarrow$ 2 times 14 equals 28. $\rightarrow$ Now subtracting.

---

[3] Keep in mind that we're really dividing 14 into 3,800 to get 200. That's why the 2 goes above the 8 (in the hundreds column). If we put a 3 on top that would be too big, because 14 times 300 is 4,200 (which is greater then 3,800).

Continuing the process, we bring down the 5 (below left). And now we divide 14 into 105. This is kind of tough again, because the numbers are large. Dividing 14 into 105 on a scratch sheet (using long division), we get 7 plus a remainder. That means we need to put a 7 directly above the 5 (below middle). Next, we multiply 7 and 14 to get 98, which goes on the bottom (below right).

**Bring down
the 5.**

$$\begin{array}{r} 2 \\ 14\overline{)3{,}850} \\ -28\downarrow \\ \hline 105 \end{array}$$

➡

**14 goes into 105
7 times.**

$$\begin{array}{r} 27 \\ 14\overline{)3{,}850} \\ -28 \\ \hline 105 \end{array}$$

➡

**7 times 14
equals 98.**

$$\begin{array}{r} 27 \\ 14\overline{)3{,}850} \\ -28 \\ \hline 105 \\ 98 \end{array}$$

Now we subtract: 105 minus 98 is 7 (below left). The last number to bring down is the 0 (below middle). That gives us a 70 on the bottom, which means we need to divide 14 into 70. If you do long division on a scratch sheet again, you'll get exactly 5. So 5 goes on top, directly above 0 in the ones place (below right).

**105 minus 98
equals 7.**

$$\begin{array}{r} 27 \\ 14\overline{)3{,}850} \\ -28 \\ \hline 105 \\ -98 \\ \hline 7 \end{array}$$

➡

**Bring down
the 0.**

$$\begin{array}{r} 27 \\ 14\overline{)3{,}850} \\ -28\downarrow \\ \hline 105 \\ -98 \\ \hline 70 \end{array}$$

➡

**14 goes into 70
5 times.**

$$\begin{array}{r} 275 \\ 14\overline{)3{,}850} \\ -28 \\ \hline 105 \\ -98 \\ \hline 70 \end{array}$$

Finally, we multiply 5 and 14 to get 70. That goes on bottom (below left), where we subtract for a 0 remainder (below right). So 14 goes into 3,850 exactly 275 times.

**5 times 14
equals 70.**

$$\begin{array}{r} 275 \\ 14\overline{)3{,}850} \\ -28 \\ \hline 105 \\ -98 \\ \hline 70 \\ 70 \end{array}$$

➡

**Subtracting for
a remainder of 0.**

$$\begin{array}{r} 275 \\ 14\overline{)3{,}850} \\ -28 \\ \hline 105 \\ -98 \\ \hline 70 \\ -70 \\ \hline 0 \end{array}$$

So that's how we divide by a two-digit number that's greater than 10. The process is basically the same one we always use. Only it's a little harder, since the numbers that need to be divided in each step are bigger.

More than Two Digits

Sometimes a division problem will require us to divide by a three-digit number. Here's an example like that.

$$125 \overline{)79,250}$$

This one is tough, because the numbers we have to deal with are so large. But the method is still basically the same. The first step is to try and divide 125 into 7. Since 7 is too small, we bring in the 9 and try to divide 125 into 79. But even 79 is too small, so we bring in the 2. It turns out that 125 will go into 792. Actually, it goes 6 times, which means we need to put a 6 directly over the 2.

125 goes into 792
6 times.

$$125 \overline{)79,250}^{6}$$

Since this is a long problem, we won't go through all the rest of the steps. If you continue the process, 125 divides into 79,250 exactly 634 times, with no remainder.

The main point is that the long division process is the same even when the number you're dividing by (the divisor) has 3 digits. It's just tougher because the numbers are so big. You have to do a lot more scratch sheet work on these.

Checking Your Answers

Finally, what about checking an answer to a division problem? Since division is the "reverse" (actually, it's called inverse) of multiplication, we can always check a division by using multiplication. It's a lot like checking subtraction by using addition. To show you how it works, let's go back to the last example.

To check, multiply
634 by 125.

$$125 \overline{)79,250}^{634}$$

All we have to do is multiply the answer, 634 in this case, by the divisor, which is 125. If that comes out to equal the number underneath the division symbol (79,250), then the answer is correct. If it comes out to some different number, then you've made a mistake somewhere and you need to go back and check your work. So the method for checking is to multiply the answer by the divisor (the number you're dividing by) to get the dividend (the number that's being divided).

Practice 15

a. Multiply $10,000 \times 23,800$.

238,000,000

b. Multiply
$$\begin{array}{r} 2,587 \\ \times\, 4,839 \end{array}$$

c. Divide $16\overline{)6,256}$. Write any remainders next to your answer.

R8

d. Divide $19\overline{)8,592}$. Write any remainders next to your answer.

R.0

e. Translate the word problem below into math; then solve.

Pauline bought each of her 11 students a special graduation gift. If she spent a combined total of $935 for the gifts, how much did she spend (on average) on each?

85

Problem Set 15

Tell whether each sentence below is True or False.

1. Division with a two-digit divisor requires dividing numbers larger than those in the division table. True

2. It is not possible to do division with a divisor of more than two digits. FALSE

3. You check division by adding the quotient to the divisor. F

Answer each question below.

(a) 4. Multiply $10,000 \times 42,500$.

425,000,000

5. Divide $490,000 \div 700$. Write any remainders next to your answer.

6. Divide $16,000,000 \div 40$. Write any remainders next to your answer.

400,000

Add each group of numbers below.

7.
$$\begin{array}{r} 476 \\ 293 \\ +\,232 \\ \hline 1001 \end{array}$$

8.
$$\begin{array}{r} 894 \\ 222 \\ 314 \\ +262 \\ \hline 1,692 \end{array}$$

9.
$$\begin{array}{r} 6,431 \\ 1,212 \\ 4,321 \\ +1,056 \\ \hline 13,020 \end{array}$$

Subtract each pair of numbers below.

10.
$$\begin{array}{r} 574 \\ -\,281 \\ \hline 293 \end{array}$$

11.
$$\begin{array}{r} 1,243 \\ -\,265 \\ \hline 978 \end{array}$$

12.
$$\begin{array}{r} 47,323 \\ -\,12,594 \\ \hline 34,729 \end{array}$$

Multiply each pair of numbers below.

13.
$$\begin{array}{r} 1,839 \\ \times 13 \end{array}$$

14.
$$\begin{array}{r} 857 \\ \times 325 \end{array}$$

15.
$$\begin{array}{r} 786 \\ \times 902 \end{array}$$

16.
$$\begin{array}{r} 9,740 \\ \times 3,674 \end{array}$$

(b) 17.
$$\begin{array}{r} 1,256 \\ \times 8,967 \end{array}$$

Divide each pair of numbers below. Write any remainders next to your answer.

18. $7\overline{)917}$ 131

19. $4\overline{)2,720}$ 680

20. $3\overline{)2,384}$ 794 R2

21. $13\overline{)3,146}$ 242

(c) 22. $25\overline{)7,950}$ 318

(d) 23. $22\overline{)9,750}$ 44 R16

Translate the word problem below into math; then solve.

(e) 24. At the age of ninety-two, Mr. Howard finally decided that he was too old to keep collecting comic books. If Mr. Howard has a total of 29,108 comics, and he plans to distribute his collection evenly amongst his 19 grandchildren, how many will each of his grandchildren get?

Lesson 16—Divisibility

We've been learning about division. And so far we've found the answer to every one of our problems. But sometimes, we don't need to know the actual answer to a division problem. We just need to know whether one number will divide into another evenly. That means whether it will divide with a remainder of 0. For instance, 12 can be divided evenly by 3 because we get an answer of 4 with a remainder of 0. There are a lot of situations where you might just want to know whether a number divides evenly into another. Here's a not-so-realistic example.

Madame Pompadour

The ruthless queen's younger sister, Madame Pompadour, is so crazy about poodles that she treats them as if they were real people. For example, next week she's holding a tea party for her poodle and his five best friends. At the party, Madame P. is planning to serve a tray of doggie biscuits, but she wants to make sure that each poodle receives the same number. If she serves 80 biscuits in total, can each of the poodles be given an equal amount or will one of them (sadly) get shortchanged?

In this problem, Madame Pompadour doesn't really care how many biscuits each poodle is going to get. She just wants to make sure that they all get the same number. That means she just needs to know whether 80 can be divided evenly by 6. If there's no remainder, then every poodle has to

87

get the same number of doggie biscuits. If there is a remainder, then some poodles will get more doggie biscuits than others.

You might think that the only way to figure this out is to go through the entire division problem of 80 divided by 6. But actually we don't have to work out the whole problem. There are rules that will tell us very quickly whether one number can be divided evenly by another. These are called the **divisibility rules**.

The number 80 is small enough that the divisibility rules wouldn't be that much of a time saver. It just takes a few seconds, after all, to figure out that 80 divided by 6 gives you 13 plus a remainder of 2, so some poodle is going to get shortchanged. But what if the problem were 85,254 divided by 6? Then it would take a long time to do the division. That's where the divisibility rules are really helpful.

Divisibility Rules for 2, 5, and 10

We'll go through all of the major divisibility rules, starting with the simplest. One rule that almost everybody knows about is the divisibility rule for dividing evenly by 2. To see how that one works, look at the list of numbers below.

They all divide evenly by 2.

0, 2, 4, 6, 8, 10, 12, 14, 16, 18, 20, 22, 24, 26, 28, 30, 32….

Every one of these numbers can be divided evenly by 2. Can you see the pattern in the numbers? The last digit is always 0, 2, 4, 6, or 8. As you probably know, numbers ending in 0, 2, 4, 6, or 8 are called **even numbers**. And the rule is that every even number can be divided evenly by 2 (with no remainder). All other numbers are called **odd numbers**, by the way, and they can't be divided evenly by 2. So, for example, the number 324 ends with the digit 4. That makes it an even number, which tells us immediately that 324 can be divided evenly by 2. However, the number 1,407 ends in 7, so it has to be odd. From that we know it won't divide evenly by 2. Sometimes people will say that 1,407 is not "divisible" by 2. It means the same thing.

What about dividing evenly by 5? That rule is easy too. Look at this list.

They all divide evenly by 5.

0, 5, 10, 15, 20, 25, 30, 35, 40, 45, 50, 55….

Every one of these numbers can be divided evenly by 5. And if you look closely, you'll see that they all end in either 5 or 0. The general rule is that no matter how big or small a number is, as long as it ends in 5 or 0, the number can be divided evenly by 5. And, once again, divisibility rules are most helpful when working with really big numbers. What if we had a number like 237,815? Does that divide evenly by 5? Yes it does, because the last digit (the number in the ones place) is 5.

The rule for divisibility by 10 is even easier than the one for 5. You've known this rule for years. Any number that can be divided evenly by 10 has to end in 0. Here are some examples.

They all divide evenly by 10.

0, 10, 20, 30, 40, 50, 60, 70, 80, 90, 100, 110, 120, ...

The pattern continues all the way up. As long as the last digit is 0, then it has to work.[4]

Divisibility Rules for 4 and 8

The rules for 2, 5, and 10 are simple, because we only have to look at the last digit. The rule for dividing by 4 is a little tougher. To tell whether a number can be divided by 4 evenly, we have to look at the last *two* digits. If those two digits are divisible by 4, then so is the entire number. An example is 7,324. Focus on the last two digits of 7,324, which are 2 and 4. Since the number 24 divides evenly by 4 (to get 6), we know that the entire number 7,324 must divide evenly by 4 as well.

**7,324 divides evenly by 4, since
the last two digits (24) divide evenly by 4.**

That's the way the divisibility rule for 4 works.

What about dividing by 8? There we have to look at the last *three* digits. If they can be divided by 8 evenly, then so can the entire number. For example, 10,888 can be divided evenly by 8 because 888 divided by 8 equals 111 (with no remainder).

**10,888 divides evenly by 8, since
the last three digits (888) divide evenly by 8.**

Divisibility Rules for 3, 9, and 6

For some divisibility rules, we have to look at all of the digits. Take dividing by 3, for instance. To figure out whether a number can be divided evenly by 3, we have to add up all the digits of the number. If that sum can be divided evenly by 3, then so can the entire number. We'll show you how it works on an example. Let's figure out whether 414 can be divided by 3. The first step is to add the digits: $4+1+4=9$. Next, we take that sum, which is 9, and divide it by 3. Since 9 divided by 3 equals 3, with no remainder, we know automatically that 414 divides evenly by 3 too. That's the way it works.

---

[4] Notice that every list starts with 0. That's because 0 can be divided evenly by *any* number. That's because 0 divided by any number always equals 0!

**414 divides evenly by 3, since 4 + 1 + 4
equals 9 and 9 divides evenly by 3.**

You can check it for yourself by carrying out the division: 414 divided by 3 actually equals 138 and the remainder is 0.

Let's do one more example to see if a number is divisible by 3. This time we'll use the large number 7,234,209. It would take quite awhile to divide this by 3 using long division. But with our divisibility rule, we just add up the digits: $7 + 2 + 3 + 4 + 2 + 0 + 9 = 27$. Then, since 27 divides evenly by 3 (for an answer of 9, with no remainder), we know that 7,234,209 must divide evenly by 3 as well.

**7,234,209 divides evenly by 3, since
7 + 2 + 3 + 4 + 2 + 0 + 9
equals 27, and 27 divides evenly by 3.**

What about dividing evenly by 9? This rule works just like the divisibility rule for 3. We just add up all the digits and see whether the sum can be divided by 9. If it can, then so can the entire number. To go through an example, we'll use a big number again: 9,273,618. Adding all of the digits gives us $9 + 2 + 7 + 3 + 6 + 1 + 8$ which equals 36. And since 36 divides evenly by 9 (for an answer of 4 with no remainder), we know that 9,273,618 must divide evenly by 9 as well.

**9,273,618 divides evenly by 9, since
9 + 2 + 7 + 3 + 6 + 1 + 8
equals 36, which divides evenly by 9.**

It turns out that 9,273,618 divided by 9 equals 1,030,402 with no remainder.

The divisibility rule for 9 even comes up in the multiplication table. Some people learn their 9s by memorizing that any number in the table times 9 has to equal a number whose digits add up to 9. For instance, $9 \times 2 = 18$ and $1 + 8$ equals 9, $9 \times 3 = 27$ and $2 + 7$ equals 9, $9 \times 4 = 36$ and $3 + 6$ equals 9, etc. That's consistent with our rule, because 9 can obviously be divided evenly by itself.

There is also a rule for dividing by 6. This one is pretty complicated. The easiest way to explain it is to go through an actual example first. We'll use the number 1,356. First, we need to add up all the digits: $1 + 3 + 5 + 6 = 15$. Now we see if that sum, 15, can be divided evenly by 3 (not 6). Since 15 divided by 3 equals 5 with no remainder, that works. But we're not done yet. The next step is to see if 1,356 is an even number. Since the last digit of 1,356 is 6, it is even. That means 1,356 is divisible by 6. You can also check this one for yourself. ($1,356 \div 6 = 226$ with no remainder) The interesting thing about this rule is that if the number had been odd, no matter what the sum of the digits turned out to be, then it would not have been divisible by 6. So the number has to be even and the sum of the digits has to divide evenly by 3, not 6. It's a tricky rule.

1,356 divides evenly by 6, since
it is even and 1 + 3 + 5 + 6
equals 15, which divides evenly by 3.

What about figuring out whether a number can divide evenly by 7? Well, there's really not a good rule for 7. There aren't any good rules for numbers greater than 10 either, because they're a lot more complicated. So the rules that we've covered are the main ones that you need to remember.

Practice 16

a. Divide $145,000,000 \div 100,000$.

1450

b. Tell whether 262 can be divided evenly by 2.

yes

c. Tell whether 184,824 can be divided evenly by 9.

yes

d. Divide $16\overline{)5,235}$. Write any remainders next to your answer.

e. Translate the word problem below into math; then solve.

Claude Ebair, the legendary French fashion designer, expects his rattlesnake high-tops to be a huge hit, so last week he shipped out 120 crates of them. If each crate contained 1,500 pairs, how many pairs did Monsieur Ebair make in all?

Problem Set 16

Tell whether each sentence below is True or False.

1. Any number that ends in 0, 2, 4, 6, or 8 is called an even number and can be divided evenly by 2.

True

2. Any number whose digits add to 3 can be divided evenly by 3.

False

3. Any number whose digits add to 9 can be divided evenly by 9.

false

Answer each question below.

4. Multiply $100,000 \times 237,000$.

237,000

(a) 5. Divide $238,000,000 \div 100,000$.

2,380

(b) 6. Tell whether 382 can be divided evenly by 2.

yes

(c) 7. Tell whether 198,936 can be divided evenly by 9.

1+9+8+9+3+6   36   yes

8. Tell whether 2,000,005 can be divided evenly by 10.

no

Add each group of numbers below.

9.
$$6,545$$
$$6,636$$
$$+ 25$$

10.
$$8,000$$
$$3,768$$
$$4,469$$
$$+903$$

11.
$$5,269$$
$$874$$
$$7,210$$
$$+7,025$$

Subtract each pair of numbers below.

12.
$$636$$
$$-257$$

13.
$$9,098$$
$$-689$$

14.
$$47,368$$
$$-14,379$$

Multiply each pair of numbers below.

Remember to stagger the products!

15.
$$372$$
$$\times 165$$

16.
$$563$$
$$\times 472$$

17.
$$6,532$$
$$\times 1,003$$

Divide each pair of numbers below. Write any remainders next to your answer.

18. $8\overline{)275}$

19. $6\overline{)2,334}$

20. $8\overline{)3,771}$

21. $25\overline{)8,075}$

(d) 22. $19\overline{)7,306}$

Translate the word problem below into math; then solve.

(e) 23. Madame Pompadour recently ordered her servants to dig 158 tunnels underneath her winter hideaway (all so her pet poodle could avoid the frigid weather while stretching his little legs). If each tunnel took 75 days to create, how many days did it take to complete the entire project?

Come along FiFi.

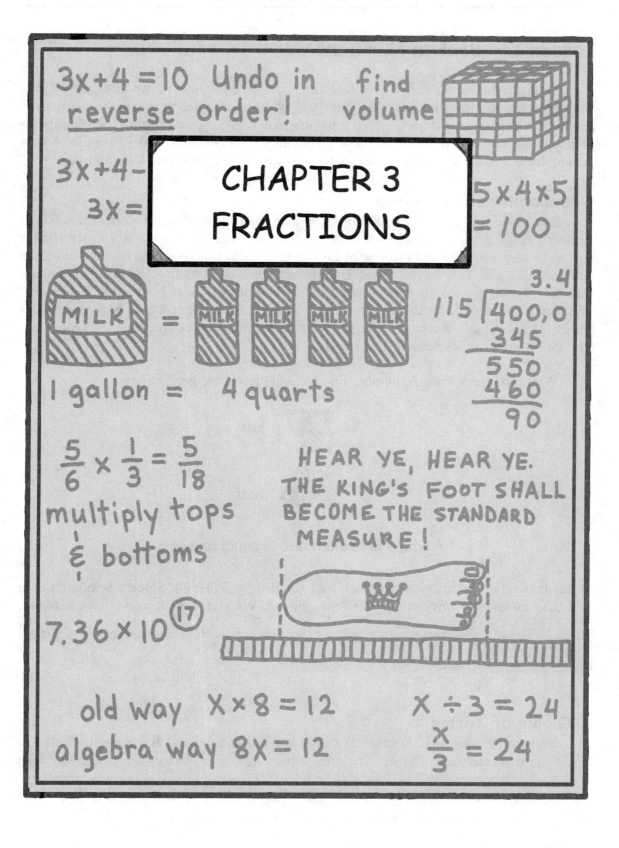

CHAPTER 3 FRACTIONS

Lesson 17—Broken Numbers

So far in this book, we've been learning about whole numbers. And whole numbers work really well when we need to count things. For example, to count the number of people at a party, we just need whole numbers like 1, 2, 3, 4, and so on. There might be 18 people at the party or 19 people, but there can't be between 18 and 19 people. A half person doesn't make any sense. That's why whole numbers work fine for counting.

One Becomes Two Halves

But sometimes instead of counting, we need to measure. The problem is that whole numbers don't work very well for measurement. For example, what if Farmer Brown needed to measure the length of one of his fields? Would it be possible for his field to be between 172 and 173 yards? Sure. But if that were the length, then whole numbers wouldn't work. We would need a new kind of number that was between 172 and 173. The way it's done is to "break up" the whole numbers into pieces. These broken numbers are called **fractions**, of course. And you've been learning about fractions for years,[1] but let's go through a quick review of the basics.

When we break a whole number into 2 equal pieces, we get 2 halves.

half

half

A whole is broken into 2 equal halves.

Mathematically, we can view each half as 1 divided by 2 ($1 \div 2$). Since 1 is smaller than 2, there's no need to carry out the division, though. We just leave it alone. And, actually, instead of using the division symbol, we write $1 \div 2$ with a fraction bar: $\frac{1}{2}$. So $\frac{1}{2}$ represents one half of a whole.

A Couple of Terms

The top number of a fraction is called the **numerator** and the bottom number is called the **denominator**. The denominator tells us how many pieces the whole has been broken into. The numerator tells us how many of those pieces we have. So $\frac{1}{2}$ means the whole has been divided into 2 equal pieces and we have 1 of them.

---

[1] The word fraction actually comes from a Latin word meaning "broken."

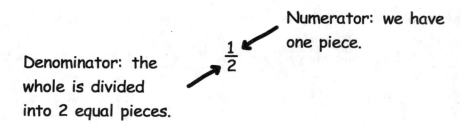

Thirds Too

Of course, a whole doesn't have to be broken into 2 equal pieces. It could be broken into 3 equal pieces. If we sawed a board into three equal pieces, each of those pieces would be "a third."

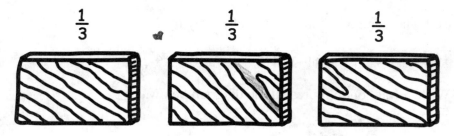

A board sawed into thirds (3 equal pieces.)

Mathematically a third is written as $\frac{1}{3}$. The denominator is 3 because the whole is broken (or sawed as in the last case) into 3 equal pieces. And the numerator is 1 because $\frac{1}{3}$ represents 1 of those pieces.

Now let's finish measuring Farmer Brown's field. The field was between 172 and 173 yards, which means that whole numbers won't allow us to get a precise measurement. But with fractions, we can do the measurement easily. What if the field turns out to be 172 yards plus an extra half of a yard?

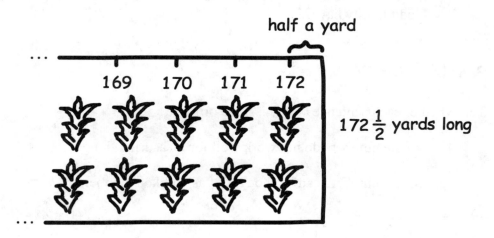

All we have to do is use the number $\frac{1}{2}$ to measure the extra. That would make the field 172 and $\frac{1}{2}$ yards long, which is written as $172\frac{1}{2}$ yards. But what if the extra length was a third of a yard more than 172? Then we could use $\frac{1}{3}$ to measure the extra. In that case, the field would be $172\frac{1}{3}$ yards long.

Practice 17

a. Tell whether 2,334 can be divided evenly by 3.   *yes*   *2+3+3+4=12*

b. Tell whether 6,084 can be divided evenly by 4.   *yes*

c. Write a fraction to represent the diagram below.

¼

d. Divide $42\overline{)6,538}$. Write any remainders next to your answer.

e. Translate the word problem below into math; then solve.

Santa put 13 candy canes in each of the Dodd family's Christmas stockings. If the family received a total of 195 candy canes, how many members does the Dodd family have?   *1*   *✗*

Problem Set 17

Tell whether each sentence below is True or False.

1. Whole numbers do not work well for measuring things.   *true*

2. Whole numbers can be thought of as "broken numbers."   *false*

3. The denominator tells you how many pieces into which the whole has been broken. *true*

4. The numerator tells you how many pieces you have of a whole that's been divided into equal groups. *true*

Answer each question below.

5. Divide $42,000,000 \div 6,000$.

700

(a) 6. Tell whether 3,246 can be divided evenly by 3.

+ = 15 *yes*

(b) 7. Tell whether 5,724 can be divided evenly by 4.

yes

(c) 8. Write a fraction to represent the diagram below.

$\frac{1}{3}$

Add each group of numbers below.

	9.		10.		11.
	6,000		8,953		8,753
	307		939		2,104
	+995		+39		3,962
					+5,623

Subtract each group of numbers below.

	12.		13.		14.
	679		4,758		59,289
	−164		−2,986		−42,658

Multiply each group of numbers below.

	15.		16.		17.
	942		732		5,409
	×39		×809		×2,305

Divide each group of numbers below. Write any remainders next to your answer.

18. $6\overline{)324}$ **19.** $2\overline{)1,064}$ **20.** $3\overline{)2,564}$

21. $28\overline{)9,604}$ **(d) 22.** $58\overline{)7,975}$

Translate the word problem below into math; then solve.

(e) 23. Mrs. Gargantua made each of her in-laws 3 vats of tangy alligator stew for the holidays. If she made a total of 84 vats, how many in-laws does she have?

Lesson 18—More on Fractions

In the last lesson, we learned that whole numbers can be broken up into pieces called fractions. Well, as you probably already know, it's possible to break a whole number into as many pieces as you need in order to do a proper measurement. In other words, we're not limited to halves or third.

Fourths, Fifths, and on Up

For example, what if we need to break a whole into 4 equal pieces? Then we end up with fourths. And that's written $\frac{1}{4}$, as you know. Here's a board sawed into fourths.

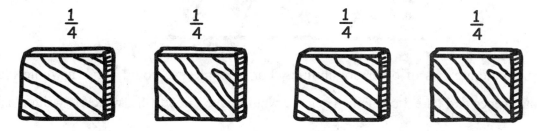

A board sawed into fourths (4 equal pieces.)

Each of these pieces represents $\frac{1}{4}$ of the whole. The 4 in the denominator tells how many pieces the board was sawed into, and the 1 in the numerator says that we have just one of those pieces.

Of course, we could have just as easily sawed the board into five equal pieces. That would have given us fifths ($\frac{1}{5}$). Or we could have sawed it into six equal pieces to get sixths ($\frac{1}{6}$). There's really no end to the process. The point is that we can saw the board into as many pieces as we want and there will be a fraction to represent the pieces, no matter how small they are.

More than One Piece

The other interesting thing is that we don't always have to focus on just one of the pieces. For instance, if a whole is broken up into three equal pieces (thirds), we might need two of those to make a measurement. Remember the example of measuring the field from the last lesson? What if the extra amount of the field was equal to exactly two of those thirds? In that case, we would need "two thirds." That's written as $\frac{2}{3}$. The 3 in the denominator shows that we've still broken up the whole into three equal pieces. And the 2 in the numerator shows that we're taking 2 of those pieces instead of just 1.

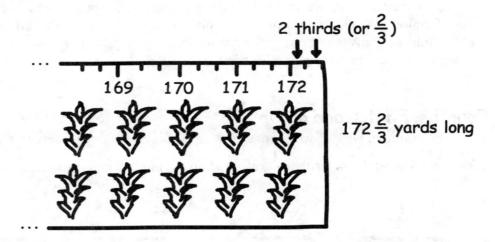

There are lots of other possibilities. For example, we could break a whole into 5 equal pieces and take 3 of them. Then we would have three fifths, which is written as $\frac{3}{5}$. Here's $\frac{3}{5}$ of a stick.

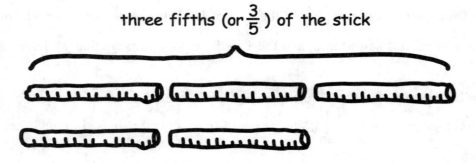

Some other possibilities are $\frac{2}{7}$ (where the whole is broken into 7 equal pieces and we have 2 of them), and $\frac{5}{9}$ (where the whole is broken into 9 equal pieces and we have 5 of them). We can have any number we want in the top or bottom of a fraction. The bottom always tells the number of pieces the whole has been broken into, and the top tells the number of pieces that we have.

Practice 18

a. Tell whether 1,152 can be divided evenly by 6.

no

b. A whole has been divided into 8 equal parts. Write a fraction to show that you have 5 of those parts.

$\frac{5}{8}$

c. Write a fraction to represent the diagram below.

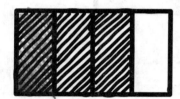

$\frac{3}{4}$

d. Divide $34\overline{)9,020}$. Write any remainders next to your answer.

e. Translate the word problem below into math; then solve.

The former teen idol has to lose a lot of weight in a big hurry if he is to have any hope of getting the bit part in the Broadway production. If he has to lose a total of 38 pounds, and he sticks to his goal of losing 2 pounds per week, how many weeks will he need to diet?

$38 \div 2$

Problem Set 18

Tell whether each sentence below is True or False.

1. It is possible to break a whole number into as many pieces as you need in order to properly measure something.

true

2. It is not possible for a fraction to have a numerator greater than 10.

False

Answer each question below.

3. Tell whether 24,681 can be divided evenly by 2.

no

4. Tell whether 75,231 can be divided evenly by 3.

$+ = 18$ yes

(a) 5. Tell whether 2,412 can be divided evenly by 6.

$+ = 9$ no

(b) 6. A whole has been divided into 4 equal parts. Write a fraction to show that you have 2 of those parts.

$\frac{2}{4}$

(b) 7. A whole has been divided into 11 equal parts. Write a fraction to show that you have 6 of those parts.

$$\frac{6}{11}$$

(c) 8. Write a fraction to represent the diagram below.

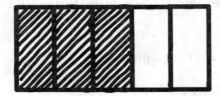

$$\frac{3}{5}$$

Add each group of numbers below.

9.
$$\begin{array}{r} 6,751 \\ +1,579 \\ \hline \end{array}$$

10.
$$\begin{array}{r} 321 \\ 504 \\ +723 \\ \hline \end{array}$$

11.
$$\begin{array}{r} 6,421 \\ 311 \\ 4,216 \\ +18 \\ \hline \end{array}$$

Subtract each pair of numbers below.

12.
$$\begin{array}{r} 578 \\ -199 \\ \hline \end{array}$$

13.
$$\begin{array}{r} 2,879 \\ -545 \\ \hline \end{array}$$

14.
$$\begin{array}{r} 45,135 \\ -14,665 \\ \hline \end{array}$$

Multiply each pair of numbers below.

15.
$$\begin{array}{r} 2,034 \\ \times 34 \\ \hline \end{array}$$

16.
$$\begin{array}{r} 9,876 \\ \times 67 \\ \hline \end{array}$$

17.
$$\begin{array}{r} 1,839 \\ \times 214 \\ \hline \end{array}$$

Divide each pair of numbers below. Write any remainders next to your answer.

18. $7\overline{)268}$

19. $2\overline{)1,348}$

20. $9\overline{)3,309}$

21. $36\overline{)9,828}$

(d) 22. $77\overline{)9,550}$

Translate the word problem below into math; then solve.

(e) 23. If the parasite hunter only covers about 3 inches per day, how many days will it take him to cover 1,932 inches?

Lesson 19—Improper Fractions

In the last lesson, we said that it was possible to have any number in the top or bottom of a fraction. But what about the fraction $\frac{3}{3}$? This one has the same number in the top (numerator) and bottom (denominator). Or what about the fraction $\frac{4}{3}$? It has a bigger number in the numerator than in the denominator. Are these fractions legal?

Same on Top and Bottom

Absolutely. The fraction $\frac{3}{3}$ just means that the whole has been divided into 3 equal pieces and we have 3 of them. Here's a picture of a pie (don't ask what kind) that's divided into three pieces.

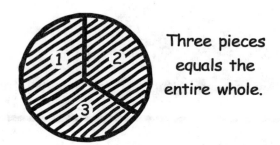

cherry!

Three pieces equals the entire whole.

Since all three pieces are shaded, the entire pie is shaded. That just means we have the entire whole. So $\frac{3}{3} = 1$.

It works the same way for any fraction where the numbers in the top and bottom are the same: $\frac{2}{2}, \frac{4}{4}, \frac{7}{7}$. In every case, we have all the pieces that the whole has been divided into, so we must have the entire whole.

Bigger on Top than Bottom

What about $\frac{4}{3}$? This means that the whole has been divided into 3 equal pieces again, but we have 4 of them! Let's draw a picture of this one.

$$\frac{4}{3} \text{ is greater than 1.}$$

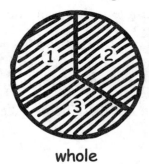 

whole   plus 1 piece

We have one more than the 3 pieces of the pie, which means we have more than the whole. The fraction $\frac{4}{3}$ must be greater than 1. In fact, any time the top of a fraction is bigger than its bottom, the fraction has to be greater than 1. Here are a few more examples.

$$\frac{3}{2} \qquad\qquad \frac{7}{6} \qquad\qquad \frac{5}{3}$$

So we've covered two basic rules for fractions. Here they are summarized.

1.	A fraction with the same top and bottom is always equal to 1.
2.	A fraction where the top is bigger than the bottom is always greater than 1.

A lot of people think fractions which have the same number on top and bottom or that have a bigger number on top than on bottom are kind of weird or abnormal. That's one reason why such fractions have been given the name **improper fractions**. The "normal" fractions—the ones with bottoms bigger than their tops—are called **proper fractions**.

But there's actually nothing wrong with improper fractions. They're as normal and acceptable as any other fractions mathematically. It's just that proper fractions are used more often than improper fractions, so people have gotten more comfortable with them.

Practice 19

93%

a. Tell whether 74,235 can be divided evenly by 5.

yes

b. A whole has been divided into 4 equal parts. Write a fraction to show that you have 5 of those parts.

$\frac{5}{4}$

c. Multiply $\begin{array}{r} 6,050 \\ \times 739 \\ \hline \end{array}$

d. Divide $63\overline{)9,545}$. Write any remainders next to your answer.

e. Translate the word problem below into math; then solve.

The noble savage decided to share his coconuts equally with his two best friends. If he had 105 coconuts in all, how many did each of the 3 get?

Problem Set 19

Tell whether each sentence below is True or False.

1. A proper fraction is a fraction whose numerator is less than its denominator.

yes

2. An improper fraction is a fraction whose numerator is greater than its denominator.

yes

3. Any fraction whose numerator and denominator are the same is equal to 0.

no

Answer each question below.

(a) 4. Tell whether 99,395 can be divided evenly by 5.

yes

5. A whole has been divided into 17 equal parts. Write a fraction to show that you have 3 of those parts.

$\frac{3}{17}$

(b) 6. A whole has been divided into 2 equal parts. Write a fraction to show that you have 3 of those parts.

$\frac{3}{2}$

7. Write a fraction to represent the diagram below.

Add each group of numbers below.

8.
    976
    43
  + 88

9.
    2,931
  + 3,452

10.
    7,364
    2,581
    2,479
  + 6,846

Subtract each pair of numbers below.

11.
    877
  − 248

12.
    3,005
  − 2,346

13.
    68,444
  − 24,468

Multiply each pair of numbers below.

14.
    937
   × 7

15.
    497
   × 76

(c) 16.
    4,030
   × 946

Divide each pair of numbers below. Write any remainders next to your answer.

17. 7)339

18. 5)419

19. 56)8,176

20. 84)9,492

(d) 21. 63)9,835

Translate the word problem below into math; then solve.

(e) 22. Lawrence of Siberia has 68 ounces of frozen water in his canteen. If he and his three companions agree to share this amount equally, how many ounces will each of the 4 get?

Lesson 20—Equivalent Fractions

We'll start this lesson with an improper fraction $\frac{10}{5}$. It's improper because the number on top is bigger than the number on bottom. Since a fraction bar is a symbol for division, we could actually divide 10 by 5 to get 2. That tells us that $\frac{10}{5}$ is equal to 2.

Multiplying Top and Bottom by the Same Number

Now let's do something which may seem kind of strange. Let's multiply the top and bottom of $\frac{10}{5}$ by 2.

$$\frac{10 \times 2}{5 \times 2} = \frac{20}{10} \qquad \textbf{Multiplying top} \\ \textbf{and bottom by 2}$$

We end up with another fraction, $\frac{20}{10}$. We can divide this fraction too: 20 divided by 10 also equals 2. Notice what's happened. We multiplied the top and bottom of $\frac{10}{5}$ by 2, and the value of the fraction didn't change a bit. It was still equal to 2.

Let's try that again, only this time we'll multiply the top and bottom of $\frac{10}{5}$ by 3.

$$\frac{10 \times 3}{5 \times 3} = \frac{30}{15} \qquad \textbf{Multiplying top} \\ \textbf{and bottom by 3}$$

We end up with the fraction $\frac{30}{15}$. If we divide 30 by 15, the answer still comes out to 2. So again, the fraction's value didn't change.

How about multiplying the top and bottom of $\frac{10}{5}$ by 4?

$$\frac{10 \times 4}{5 \times 4} = \frac{40}{20} \qquad \textbf{Multiplying top} \\ \textbf{and bottom by 4}$$

That gives us $\frac{40}{20}$. And if we divide 40 by 20, we end up with 2 as well.

What about multiplying $\dfrac{10}{5}$ by 10?

$$\dfrac{10 \times 10 = 100}{5 \times 10 = 50}$$

Multiplying top and bottom by 10

This time, we get $\dfrac{100}{50}$. And if we divide 100 by 50, the answer comes out to 2. The value is still the same.

Do you see what's happening? No matter what number we use, when we multiply the top and bottom of the fraction by the same number, the value of the fraction never changes.[2] That means that there are a lot of different fractions that have the same value: $\dfrac{10}{5}, \dfrac{20}{10}, \dfrac{30}{15}, \dfrac{40}{20}$, and $\dfrac{100}{50}$ are all equal, just to name a few.

The really interesting thing about multiplying the top and bottom by the same number is that it works even when the fraction isn't improper. For instance, let's take the proper fraction $\dfrac{1}{3}$. (It's proper, remember, because its bottom is bigger than its top.)

Watch what happens when we multiply the top and bottom of $\dfrac{1}{3}$ by 2.

$$\dfrac{1 \times 2 = 2}{3 \times 2 = 6}$$

Multiplying top and bottom by 2

We get $\dfrac{2}{6}$, which is supposed to equal $\dfrac{1}{3}$, if our rule really works. The two fractions do turn out to be equal. The easiest way to see is to look at a couple of pictures.

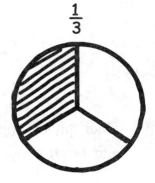

---

[2] There is one exception to this rule. We can't multiply top and bottom by 0. That would cause the denominator to become 0, and division by 0 isn't allowed.

The drawing on the left represents $\frac{1}{3}$, because the pie has been cut into 3 equal pieces and 1 of those is shaded. The drawing on the right represents $\frac{2}{6}$, because the pie has been cut into 6 equal pieces and 2 of those are shaded. But look at the shaded parts of each pie. They're exactly the same size in each. That shows that $\frac{1}{3}$ and $\frac{2}{6}$ are actually equal. So even when the fraction is proper (with bottom bigger than top), multiplying the top and bottom by the same number won't change its value.

Dividing Top and Bottom by the Same Number

What would happen if, instead of multiplying by the same number, we divided the top and bottom of a fraction by the same number? Let's try that on the fraction $\frac{50}{10}$. We know that $\frac{50}{10}$ is equal to 5, because if we divide 50 by 10 we get 5. But now let's *divide* the top and bottom by 2.

$$\frac{50 \div 2}{10 \div 2} = \frac{25}{5} \qquad \text{Dividing top and bottom by 2}$$

We end up with $\frac{25}{5}$. But 25 divided by 5 is still equal to 5. So look what happened. Dividing the top and bottom by the same number didn't change the value of the fraction either.

Let's try again. This time we'll take the same fraction, $\frac{50}{10}$, and divide the top and bottom by a different number, 5.

$$\frac{50 \div 5}{10 \div 5} = \frac{10}{2} \qquad \text{Dividing top and bottom by 5}$$

We get $\frac{10}{2}$, which is still equal to 5. It worked here too. Rather than keep doing examples, we'll just go ahead and tell you that dividing the top and bottom of a fraction by the same number will never change the fraction's value.[3]

---

[3] Zero is the one number that won't work here, because division by 0 isn't allowed.

Just as with multiplication, the division rule also works on proper fractions (where the bottom is bigger than the top). To show you, let's divide the top and bottom of $\frac{2}{6}$ by the number 2.

$$\frac{2 \div 2}{6 \div 2} = \frac{1}{3}$$

Dividing top and bottom by 2

We get $\frac{1}{3}$, which we already know is equal to $\frac{2}{6}$. In fact, this is the same situation we had earlier with our pie pictures. Here are the pictures again.

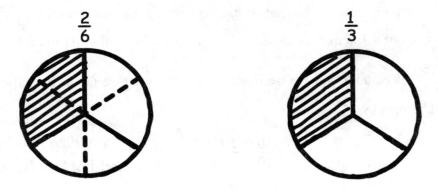

See, dividing the top and bottom of $\frac{2}{6}$ by 2 is like making the pieces of the pie bigger but taking fewer of them. We still end up with the same amount of pie that we had before.

We can actually combine the multiplication and division rules into one big rule: The top and bottom of a fraction can be multiplied or divided by the same number (except 0) without changing the fraction's value.

Naming the Rule

We said that because of this rule, there are lots of fractions that have the same value (like $\frac{2}{6}$ and $\frac{1}{3}$). Fractions with the same value are technically called **equivalent fractions**. So $\frac{2}{6}$ and $\frac{1}{3}$ are equivalent fractions and so are $\frac{50}{10}$ and $\frac{25}{5}$. Our rule about multiplying or dividing the top and bottom of a fraction by the same number also has a technical name. It's called the **Law of Equivalent Fractions**. Here are the names and definitions written formally.

1.	Fractions that have the same value are called *equivalent fractions.*
2.	The Law of Equivalent Fractions says that you can multiply or divide the top and bottom of any fraction by the same number (except 0) without changing the fraction's value.

Comparing Fractions

One important use of the Law of Equivalent Fractions is in figuring out which of two fractions is greater. Of course, it's easy to tell if one fraction is greater than another when the fractions have the same denominator. For example, we know that $\frac{5}{6}$ is greater than $\frac{1}{6}$, because having five sixths of something is more than having just one sixth of something (like a pie).

$$\frac{5}{6} \text{ is obviously greater than } \frac{1}{6}$$

And $\frac{3}{4}$ is obviously greater than $\frac{1}{4}$, because both fractions are fourths and the top number in $\frac{3}{4}$ is greater than the top number in $\frac{1}{4}$. You may also remember from arithmetic that $\frac{3}{4}$ is greater than $\frac{1}{4}$ is actually written like this: $\frac{3}{4} > \frac{1}{4}$. Notice that the > symbol is opening up toward the greater number. If the $\frac{1}{4}$ had been written on the left instead of the right, we would have needed to use the < symbol, so be sure your symbol always opens toward the greater number.

But when two fractions have different denominators, it's a lot tougher to do a comparison. For example, what if we have $\frac{3}{5}$ and $\frac{2}{3}$?

$$\text{But which is greater } \frac{3}{5} \text{ or } \frac{2}{3} \text{?}$$

Since we're comparing fifths with thirds, there's no easy way to tell which is bigger.

This is where the Law of Equivalent Fractions comes in. The best way to figure out which fraction is greater is to make the denominators the same. We can do that with $\frac{3}{5}$ and $\frac{2}{3}$ by multiplying the top and bottom of the first fraction by 3 and multiplying the top and bottom of the second fraction by 5.

$$\frac{3 \times 3}{5 \times 3} = \frac{9}{15} \qquad \frac{2 \times 5}{3 \times 5} = \frac{10}{15}$$

Now it's easy to see which one is greater.

Because of the Law of Equivalent Fractions, we know we haven't changed the value of the fractions at all. But now both have the same denominator (15). And that makes it easy to see that $\frac{10}{15}$ is greater than $\frac{9}{15}$, because we're comparing fifteenths with fifteenths.

$$\frac{10}{15} > \frac{9}{15}$$

And since $\frac{10}{15}$ is equal to $\frac{2}{3}$ and $\frac{9}{15}$ is equal to $\frac{3}{5}$, we know that $\frac{2}{3}$ must be greater than $\frac{3}{5}$.

$$\frac{2}{3} > \frac{3}{5}$$

Practice 20

a. Tell whether a <, >, or = sign should go between these fractions $\frac{4}{7} \;\underline{<}\; \frac{9}{7}$.

b. Tell whether a <, >, or = sign should go between these fractions $\frac{3}{8} \;\underline{<}\; \frac{1}{2}$.

c. Tell whether a <, >, or = sign should go between these fractions $\frac{2}{7} \;\underline{<}\; \frac{3}{7}$.

d. Write a fraction to represent the diagram below.

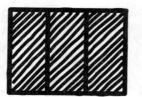 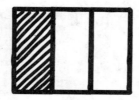

e. Translate the word problem below into math; then solve.

Podunk University is offering a new course called Baby Gibberish. If 12 people have signed up and the course costs $399, how much money did the university take in?

$$\begin{array}{r} 399 \\ \times\ 12 \\ \hline \end{array} =$$

Problem Set 20

Tell whether each sentence below is True or False.

1. Multiplying the top and bottom of a fraction by the same number will change the fraction's value.

NO!

2. Dividing the top and bottom of a fraction by the same number will change the fraction's value.

NO!

Tell whether a <, >, or = sign should go between these fractions.

(a) 3. $\dfrac{3}{4}$ $\le$ $\dfrac{5}{4}$

(b) 4. $\dfrac{3}{10}$ $>$ $\dfrac{1}{5}$

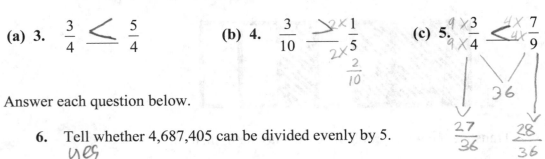

(c) 5. $\dfrac{3}{4}$ $<$ $\dfrac{7}{9}$

Answer each question below.

6. Tell whether 4,687,405 can be divided evenly by 5.

yes

7. Tell whether 3,286 can be divided evenly by 3.

NO

(d) 8. Write a fraction to represent the diagram below.

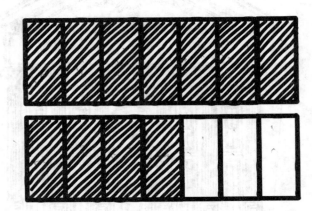

Add each group of numbers below.

9. 322
   416
   + 789

10. 837
    116
    209
    + 663

11. 5,885
    2,526
    1,928
    + 6,447

Subtract each pair of numbers below.

12. 468
    − 426

13. 6,102
    − 5,574

14. 70,035
    − 56,279

Multiply each pair of numbers below.

15. 947
    ×27

16. 142
    ×104

17. 931
    ×603

Divide each pair of numbers below. Write any remainders next to your answer.

18. $4\overline{)307}$ **19.** $9\overline{)1{,}856}$ **20.** $43\overline{)2{,}150}$

21. $20\overline{)1{,}386}$ **22.** $37\overline{)2{,}621}$

Translate the word problem below into math; then solve.

(e) 23. Encouraged by the success of its Baby Gibberish course, Podunk U. decided to offer three new classes: Scientific Mumbo Jumbo, Surfer Slang, and Office Lingo. How much money did the university take in from their Surfer Slang course, if the course costs $450 and 28 people signed up?

Lesson 21—Reducing Fractions

In the last lesson, we learned about the **Law of Equivalent Fractions**. Remember, this law allows us to multiply or divide the top and bottom of a fraction by the same number without changing the fraction's value.

Making a Fraction Simpler

We already covered one use of the Law of Equivalent Fractions: We learned how it can help us figure out which of two fractions is greater. But there's another use of the law which is even more important. It can be used to make fractions simpler. Let's go through an example.

$$\frac{25}{75}$$

This fraction has some pretty big numbers, and that can make a fraction hard to deal with. It would be better if we could make the top and bottom numbers smaller without changing the fraction's value. Can we do that? Yes. We just need to divide the top and bottom by 5.

$$\frac{25 \div 5}{75 \div 5} = \frac{5}{15} \qquad \textbf{Dividing top and bottom by 5}$$

That leaves us with $\frac{5}{15}$. And we know from the Law of Equivalent Fractions that this new fraction must be equal to $\frac{25}{75}$. But is there any way to make $\frac{5}{15}$ simpler? In other words, can we make the numbers even smaller? Yes. We can actually divide the top and bottom by 5 again.

$$\frac{5 \div 5}{15 \div 5} = \frac{1}{3} \qquad \textbf{Dividing top and bottom by 5 again}$$

We end up with $\frac{1}{3}$. And since we followed the Law of Equivalent Fractions, we know that $\frac{1}{3}$ must also equal $\frac{25}{75}$.

$$\frac{25}{75} = \frac{1}{3}$$

So we simplified $\frac{25}{75}$ all the way down to $\frac{1}{3}$. Obviously, $\frac{1}{3}$ is a lot easier to work with, since the numbers are smaller. After all, if you wanted to tell somebody how much of a pie was left in the refrigerator, you would rather say $\frac{1}{3}$ than $\frac{25}{75}$, even though they mean the same thing.

Of course, what we just did was to **reduce** the fraction $\frac{25}{75}$. That just means to write it so that the numerator and denominator are as small as possible. You've been reducing fractions for years in arithmetic. But we just wanted to show you that when reducing a fraction, we're actually using the Law of Equivalent Fractions. That's one of the main uses of the law.

Getting a Fraction Fully Reduced

There's one other point, though. How do we know when a fraction can't be reduced any further? Remember, at first we reduced $\frac{25}{75}$ to $\frac{5}{15}$, but then we were able to reduce that on down to $\frac{1}{3}$. Well, here's the test. When there's no whole number that will divide the top and the bottom evenly (without a remainder), the fraction has been made as simple as possible. At that point, we say that the fraction is **fully reduced**.

So $\frac{4}{8}$ isn't fully reduced because we can divide 2 into the top and bottom.

$$\frac{4 \div 2}{8 \div 2} = \frac{2}{4}$$ **Top and bottom can both be divided by 2 evenly.**

But $\frac{2}{4}$ isn't fully reduced either, since its top and bottom can both be divided evenly by 2 as well.

$$\frac{2 \div 2}{4 \div 2} = \frac{1}{2}$$ **Top and bottom can both be divided by 2 evenly.**

However, $\frac{1}{2}$ is fully reduced. That's because there's no whole number that will divide both 1 and 2 evenly (with no remainder).

119

Reducing All at Once

We should also mention that $\frac{4}{8}$ could have been reduced directly to $\frac{1}{2}$. All we would have had to do is divide the top and bottom of $\frac{4}{8}$ by 4.

$$\frac{4 \div 4}{8 \div 4} = \frac{1}{2}$$

Dividing top and bottom by 4 evenly.

This is faster than reducing the fraction in two steps. If you want to reduce a fraction all the way in one step, just think of the biggest number that will divide the top and bottom evenly. Divide by that one first and then you're done.

Practice 21

a. Tell whether a <, >, or = sign should go between these fractions $\frac{9}{7}$ _____ $\frac{13}{9}$.

b. Tell whether 335,439 can be divided evenly by 9.

$$\neq = 27 \quad yes$$

c. Fully reduce the fraction $\frac{3}{21}$. $\div \frac{3}{3} = \left(\frac{1}{7}\right)$

d. Fully reduce the fraction $\frac{27}{135}$. $= \frac{3 \cdot 3 \cdot 3}{3 \cdot 3 \cdot 3 \cdot 5} = \frac{1}{5}$

e. Translate the word problem below into math; then solve.

In an effort to speed up service, the drive-in restaurant chain decided to make all of its waitresses wear roller skates. If 3,330 pairs of roller skates were sent out, and if every restaurant has 18 waitresses, how many restaurants are in the chain?

$18 + 18 \cup 18 = 3,330$

$18r = 3,330$

$r = \frac{3330}{18} = \frac{3330}{18}$

Roller $\boxed{3330}$ $3,330 RS$ $18 \, wts$

R

Problem Set 21

Tell whether each sentence below is True or False.

1. The Law of Equivalent Fractions can be used to reduce fractions.

    False

2. There is no way to tell whether a fraction is fully reduced.

    False

Tell whether a <, >, or = sign should go between these fractions.

3. $\dfrac{3}{9}$ $=$ $\dfrac{1}{3} \times 3$

(a) 4. $\dfrac{8}{5} \times 6 < \dfrac{11}{6} \times 5$

Answer each question below.

5.   Tell whether 2,750 can be divided evenly by 10.

   yes

(b) 6.   Tell whether 229,617 can be divided evenly by 9.

   $+ = 27$ yes

7.   Write a fraction to represent the diagram below.

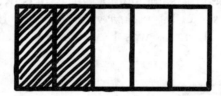

$\dfrac{2}{5}$

Add each group of numbers below.

8.   7,221
     4,374
    +9,519

9.   5,948
     9,256
     4,594
    +4,003

Subtract each pair of numbers below.

10.   803
     −253

11.   8,720
     −6,892

12.   80,947
     −38,388

Multiply each pair of numbers below.

13.   875
     ×64

14.   903
     ×98

15.   129
     ×286

121

Divide each pair of numbers below. Write any remainders next to your answer.

16. $6\overline{)328}$

17. $7\overline{)6,545}$

18. $32\overline{)2,400}$

Fully reduce each fraction below.

(c) 19. $\dfrac{2}{10}$

(d) 20. $\dfrac{8}{24}$

21. $\dfrac{10}{12}$

Translate the word problem below into math; then solve.

(e) 22. The plane dropped the same number of leaflets over 12 different areas, and each leaflet said the same thing: *Surrender or else!* If the total number of leaflets dropped over all 12 areas was 185,760, how many leaflets were dropped over each area?

Lesson 22—Factoring and Canceling

In the previous lesson we learned to reduce fractions by dividing the top and bottom by the same number. Well, it turns out that there's another method for reducing fractions. Take a look at this example.

THE GREAT EL MAGNIFICO
PRESENTS
A MARRIAGE OF
ART & TECHNOLOGY
UNDER THE STARS

El Magnifico, the great artist/composer, plans to produce 21 spectacular laser light shows at various points on the equator. Five minutes after he announced the shows, 14 of them sold out. What fraction sold out? Make sure your answer is fully reduced.

All we have to do is take the number of shows produced (21) and make that the denominator of the fraction. And the number of shows that sold out (14) should be the numerator of the fraction. That gives us $\frac{14}{21}$, which is the fraction of shows that sold out.

But the problem says that the answer should be fully reduced. So we need to reduce $\frac{14}{21}$.

123

Factoring: Writing a Number as a Multiplication

We could reduce the fraction by dividing the top and bottom by 7. We know that's legal according to the Law of Equivalent Fractions. But instead of dividing top and bottom by 7, let's do something different. Let's first write the 14 and 21 as multiplications. We'll change 14 to 2×7 and 21 to 3×7. This may seem odd, but hold on a minute.

$$\frac{2\times7}{3\times7}$$

Rewriting a number as a multiplication is called **factoring**. So we say the number 14 was "factored" as 2×7, and 21 was factored as 3×7. The numbers 2 and 7 are also called **factors** of 14, and 3 and 7 are factors of 21.

Canceling: Marking Out Common Factors

Next, to reduce, all we have to do is mark out the numbers on the top and bottom that are the same. That means we mark out the 7s, like this.

$$\frac{2 \times \cancel{7}}{3 \times \cancel{7}} = \frac{2}{3}$$

Canceling the 7s

Marking out factors is called **canceling**, by the way. Canceling the 7s leaves us with a 2 on top and a 3 on bottom for the fraction $\frac{2}{3}$. And that's fully reduced. So another method for reducing fractions is by **factoring and canceling.** The procedure is to write the top and bottom as multiplications (factor), and then mark out the factors that are the same on top and bottom (cancel). Whatever is left becomes the numerator and denominator of the reduced fraction. Here's a summary.

Reducing a Fraction by Factoring and Canceling

1.	Factor the top and bottom of the fraction, which just means to write each as a multiplication.
2.	Cancel (mark out) the factors that are the same on the top and bottom.
3.	The factors that are left become the numerator and denominator of the reduced fraction.

How Does Factoring and Canceling Work?

Factoring and canceling is a nice method for reducing fractions. But you may be wondering how the method works. Is it legal to mark out numbers? Actually, it is. That's because canceling is really just a shortcut for dividing the top and bottom by the same number. Think about it. When we divide the top of the fraction $\frac{14}{21}$ by 7, we get $14 \div 7$ or 2. If we have the top factored (as 2×7), why not just mark out the 7? That will leave a 2 by itself on top, which is right. And when we divide the bottom of $\frac{14}{21}$ by 7, we get $21 \div 7$ or 3. So why not mark out the 7 in 3×7 so that a 3 is left by itself on bottom?

$$\frac{2 \times \cancel{7}}{3 \times \cancel{7}} = \frac{2}{3} \text{ is just a shortcut for } \frac{14 \div 7}{21 \div 7} = \frac{2}{3}$$

It always works this way. When we divide by one of the factors (dividing 2×7 by 7, for instance), we always get the other factor as the answer. So we can just mark out the factor that we're dividing by. That's why factoring and canceling really is just another way to divide the top and bottom of a fraction by the same number. And according to the Law of Equivalent Fractions that's perfectly legal.

Why Bother?

If both methods (dividing and factoring/canceling) are the same is there any reason to use one rather than another? Well, the advantage of factoring and canceling is that with everything factored, it's easy to see what numbers will go evenly into the top and bottom. For instance, with $\frac{14}{21}$ written as $\frac{2 \times 7}{3 \times 7}$, it's obvious that both 14 and 21 can be divided evenly by 7, because those 7s are staring right at us. Basically, any time the same number is a factor of both the top and bottom of a fraction, we know automatically that that number will divide evenly into both. And to do the division, we can just mark those out.

Of course, not every fraction can be reduced. What happens when we factor a non-reducible fraction? Check out this example.

$$\frac{14}{15}$$

We can factor the top as 2×7 and the bottom as 3×5 to get this.

$$\frac{2 \times 7}{3 \times 5}$$

But notice that the numbers on top are all different from the numbers on bottom, which doesn't leave us anything to cancel. That's how we know that $\frac{14}{15}$ is already fully reduced. It always works that way when we factor a fully-reduced fraction. All the factors in the top will be different from those in the bottom.

Practice 22

a. Tell whether a <, >, or = sign should go between these fractions $\dfrac{4 \times 11}{9 \times 11} < \dfrac{5 \times 9}{11 \times 9}$.

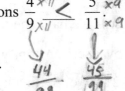

$$\frac{44}{99} \qquad \frac{45}{99}$$

b. Divide $18\overline{)2{,}228}$. Write any remainders next to your answer.

c. Fully reduce the fraction $\dfrac{6}{14}$ by factoring and canceling.

d. Fully reduce the fraction $\dfrac{15}{10}$ by factoring and canceling.

e. Translate the word problem below into math; then solve.

The Do-Nothing Duo never forgets to fulfill their quota of 5 pea knuckle matches each day. If the Duo has had 900 matches this year, how many days have there been so far in the year?

$$400 \qquad \underset{5\overline{)900}}{\overset{180}{}}$$
$$\begin{array}{r} -5 \\ \hline 40 \\ -40 \\ \hline 0 \end{array}$$

Problem Set 22

Tell whether each sentence below is True or False.

1. Rewriting a number as a multiplication is called factoring.   *true*

2. Canceling is just a shortcut for dividing the top and bottom of a fraction by the same number.   *true*

Tell whether a <, >, or = sign should go between these fractions.

3. $\dfrac{5}{7} \leq \dfrac{12}{14}$ $\dfrac{6 \times 2}{7 \times 2}$ $\dfrac{6}{7}$ (a) 4. $\dfrac{3 \times 7}{8 \times 7} \geq \dfrac{2 \times 8}{7 \times 8}$ $\dfrac{21}{56}$ $\dfrac{16}{56}$

Answer each question below.

5. Tell whether 2,121,121 can be divided evenly by 2.   *no*

6. Tell whether 2,781 can be divided evenly by 9. $+ = 18$ *yes*

126

Add each group of numbers below.

7.
$$\begin{array}{r} 2,346 \\ 8,532 \\ +\,6,291 \\ \hline \end{array}$$

8.
$$\begin{array}{r} 4,957 \\ 9,578 \\ 3,373 \\ +\,8,733 \\ \hline \end{array}$$

Subtract each pair of numbers below.

9.
$$\begin{array}{r} 8,592 \\ -\,3,657 \\ \hline \end{array}$$

10.
$$\begin{array}{r} 6,173 \\ -\,1,846 \\ \hline \end{array}$$

11.
$$\begin{array}{r} 71,943 \\ -\,24,086 \\ \hline \end{array}$$

Multiply each pair of numbers below.

12.
$$\begin{array}{r} 380 \\ \times\,55 \\ \hline \end{array}$$

13.
$$\begin{array}{r} 209 \\ \times\,38 \\ \hline \end{array}$$

14.
$$\begin{array}{r} 406 \\ \times\,951 \\ \hline \end{array}$$

Divide each pair of numbers below. Write any remainders next to your answer.

15. $8\overline{)395}$

16. $6\overline{)2,740}$

(b) 17. $23\overline{)1,162}$

Fully reduce each fraction below by factoring and canceling.

(c) 18. $\dfrac{6}{10}$

(c) 19. $\dfrac{10}{22}$

(d) 20. $\dfrac{21}{15}$

Translate the word problem below into math; then solve.

(e) 21. Every day since his accounting class started, Dylan has read 7 pages out of his accounting textbook (because he knows that at this rate he will finish the book by the last day of class). If Dylan has read 504 pages out of the text, how many days ago did class start?

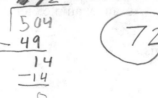

Lesson 23—Prime Numbers

We've been learning to reduce fractions by factoring and canceling. Let's try to reduce the fraction $\frac{18}{30}$ with that method. We can factor the 18 on top as 2 times 9 and the 30 on bottom as 3 times 10 to get this.

$$\frac{2\times9}{3\times10}$$

The factors on top are all different from the factors on bottom. In the last lesson, we learned that fractions where all the factors on top are different from those on bottom are already fully reduced. So apparently, $\frac{18}{30}$ is fully reduced.

But 2 and 9 aren't the only pair of numbers that multiply to equal 18. And 3 and 10 aren't the only pair of numbers that multiply to equal 30. What if we factored $\frac{18}{30}$ like this?

$$\frac{3\times6}{5\times6}$$

This works, because $3\times6=18$ and $5\times6=30$. But look at the factors now. The top and bottom have a pair of 6s in common, and those can be canceled.

$$\frac{3\times\cancel{6}}{5\times\cancel{6}}=\frac{3}{5}$$

Canceling the 6s reduces the fraction.

Factoring this way, the fraction reduces to $\frac{3}{5}$. So $\frac{18}{30}$ wasn't fully reduced after all.

Factoring the Right Way

This example raises a really important question. How can we be sure we've factored a fraction in the right way, so the factors that can be canceled will show up? Simple. We just factor the top and bottom into as many numbers as possible; then we can see *all* the factors. As an example, let's go back to the fraction $\frac{18}{30}$. Originally, we factored $\frac{18}{30}$ like this.

$$\frac{2\times9}{3\times10}$$

128

But instead of giving up here, we could have taken one more step and factored the 9 as 3×3 and the 10 as 2×5. That would have given us

$$\frac{2\times3\times3}{3\times2\times5}.$$

Now we can see that the top and bottom actually have two factors in common (a 2 and a 3). Let's cancel both of these.

$$\frac{\cancel{2}\times\cancel{3}\times3}{\cancel{3}\times\cancel{2}\times5}=\frac{3}{5}$$

Canceling 2s and 3s reduces the fraction.

As you can see, we end up with $\frac{3}{5}$, which is fully reduced.

Of course, canceling is just a shortcut for dividing the top and bottom by the number being marked out. So what we really just did was divide the top and bottom of $\frac{18}{30}$ by 2 (when canceling the 2s). Then we also divided the top and bottom by 3 (when canceling the 3s). That's the same thing as dividing by 2×3 or 6, if you think about it.

The main point is that factoring the numerator and denominator as far as possible will always show every factor. Then if you cancel *all* the factors that are the same in the top and bottom, you'll know for sure that the fraction is fully reduced.

Factoring into Prime Numbers

In our example, once we got down to just 2s, 3s, and 5s there was no way to factor further. Numbers like 2, 3, and 5, which can't be broken down any more as multiplications of smaller whole numbers, are called **prime numbers** ("primes" for short).[4] So when reducing fractions by factoring and canceling, we should really factor the numerator and denominator into prime numbers; then cancel everything possible.

Let's do another example that's kind of interesting. Let's reduce the fraction below by factoring and canceling.

$$\frac{9}{27}$$

The first step is to factor the top and bottom into prime numbers. On top, 9 can be broken down to 3×3. Since 3 is a prime number, that's as far as we can go up there. As for the

---

[4] We could write 2 as 2×1 and 3 as 3×1. That doesn't count, though, because it really doesn't break the number down any further. Technically, a number is prime if it cannot be written as a multiplication of whole numbers any way other than the number itself times 1.

bottom, 27 can be broken down as 3×9. But then 9 can be factored further as 3×3. So that gives us $3 \times 3 \times 3$ on bottom.

$$\frac{3 \times 3}{3 \times 3 \times 3}$$ **Factoring the top and bottom into primes.**

The next step is to cancel. We have to make sure to cancel *every* possible factor, though. There are two pairs of 3s that can be canceled here.

$$\frac{\cancel{3} \times \cancel{3}}{\cancel{3} \times \cancel{3} \times 3}$$ **Canceling the factors in top and bottom.**

After canceling, look what happened. There's nothing left on top. What should go in the numerator of the answer then? Should the numerator be 0? No. Think about what canceling really means. It's just a shortcut for division. By canceling the 3s, we were really dividing the top and bottom of the fraction by 3 twice, which is the same as dividing by 9. The original numerator was 9. So what's 9 divided by 9? It's 1. That means the numerator of the answer has to be 1.

$$\frac{1}{3}$$ **Fully reduced answer**

The rule is that anytime everything cancels, we have to put a 1 in place of the canceled factors. And once again, that's because canceling is really just a shortcut for dividing. So by canceling the 3s, we were really dividing the top by 9.

It's possible for everything to cancel on the bottom too. Let's quickly look at an example like that.

$$\frac{14}{7}$$

Step one is to factor the top and bottom into prime numbers or prime factors, as they're also called. On top, 14 factors as 2×7. On bottom, 7 is a prime number, so it can't be broken down any further.

$$\frac{2 \times 7}{7}$$ **Factoring the top and bottom into primes.**

Step two is to cancel every factor possible. There's just one pair of 7s that will cancel.

$$\frac{2 \times \cancel{7}}{\cancel{7}} = \frac{2}{1} = 2$$ **Canceling the 7s leaves a 1 on bottom.**

Notice that everything on the bottom canceled this time. By canceling, all we really did was divide the top and bottom of the fraction by 7. And on bottom 7 divided by 7 is 1. So we just put a 1 in the bottom. The answer, then, is $\frac{2}{1}$, which equals 2 (since any number over 1 is just equal to itself).

The main point of the lesson is that to make sure a fraction is fully reduced you should factor the top and bottom into prime numbers and then cancel every possible factor.

Practice 23

a. Tell whether 3,540 can be divided evenly by 3.

b. Tell whether 7,264 can be divided evenly by 4.

c. Fully reduce the fraction $\frac{81}{243}$ by factoring and canceling.

d. Fully reduce the fraction $\frac{28}{32}$ by factoring and canceling.

e. Translate the word problem below into math; then solve.

Mrs. Ritter put 4 smiley faces on each of her student's penmanship papers. If Mrs. Ritter gave out 76 smiley face stickers in all, how many penmanship papers did she grade?

Problem Set 23

Tell whether each sentence below is True or False.

1. A prime number cannot be factored into smaller whole numbers (other than itself and 1).

2. When reducing a fraction, it's best to factor the numerator and denominator into prime numbers.

3. If all the factors on top or bottom cancel, then a 1 should go in their place.

Tell whether a <, >, or = sign should go between these fractions.

4. $\dfrac{5 \times 22}{11 \times 22}$ $\dfrac{9 \times 11}{22 \times 11}$

$\dfrac{110}{242}$ $\dfrac{99}{242}$

5. $\dfrac{5 \times 5}{8 \times 5}$ $\dfrac{3 \times 8}{5 \times 8}$

$\dfrac{25}{40}$ $\dfrac{24}{40}$

Answer each question below.

(a) 6. Tell whether 5,331 can be divided evenly by 3.

12   yes

(b) 7. Tell whether 9,932 can be divided evenly by 4.

8   yes

8. Write a fraction to represent the diagram below.

$\dfrac{1}{2}$

Add each group of numbers below.

9.
$$\begin{array}{r} 1,321 \\ 6,053 \\ +\,9,672 \\ \hline \end{array}$$

10.
$$\begin{array}{r} 6,826 \\ 1,335 \\ 2,476 \\ +\,1,637 \\ \hline \end{array}$$

Subtract each pair of numbers below.

11.
$$\begin{array}{r} 6,014 \\ -\,3,549 \\ \hline \end{array}$$

12.
$$\begin{array}{r} 3,624 \\ -\,2,336 \\ \hline \end{array}$$

13.
$$\begin{array}{r} 12,365 \\ -\,8,975 \\ \hline \end{array}$$

Multiply each pair of numbers below.

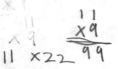

14.
$$\begin{array}{r} 129 \\ \times\,37 \\ \hline \end{array}$$

15.
$$\begin{array}{r} 406 \\ \times\,58 \\ \hline \end{array}$$

16.
$$\begin{array}{r} 780 \\ \times\,490 \\ \hline \end{array}$$

Divide each pair of numbers below. Write any remainders next to your answer.

17. $9\overline{)388}$ **18.** $5\overline{)1,974}$ **19.** $24\overline{)1,996}$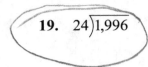

Fully reduce each fraction below by factoring and canceling.

20. $\dfrac{14}{12}$ **(c) 21.** $\dfrac{16}{32}$ **(d) 22.** $\dfrac{20}{32}$

Translate the word problem below into math; then solve.

(e) 23. Millicent Fenwick gives Major Beauregard, her pet parrot, 3 pellets of food every time he makes a negative comment about a bad guy on TV. If Major Beauregard has received 894 pellets of food this way, how many negative comments has he made about bad guy characters?

298 comments on bad guy characters

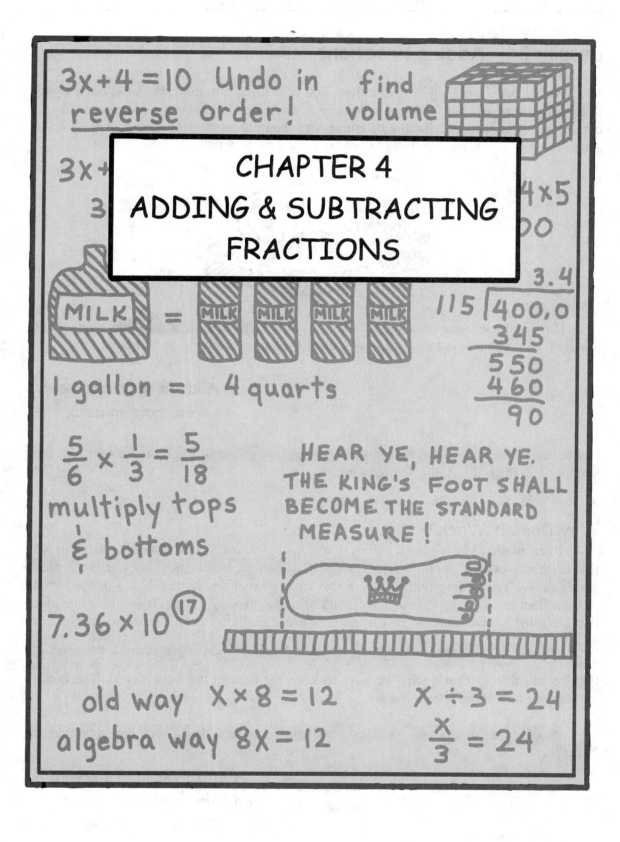

CHAPTER 4
ADDING & SUBTRACTING
FRACTIONS

Lesson 24—Adding Fractions

We've been working with fractions one at a time, but sometimes we need to add fractions just as we add whole numbers. For example, let's say we ate one third of a cinnamon-sugar loaf on Monday morning, and then ate another one third of the loaf on Tuesday morning. What fraction of the loaf did we eat in total?

If we just use common sense, it's simple. A third plus another third has to equal two thirds. That's all there is to it. But now look at the same statement in numbers.

$$\frac{1}{3} + \frac{1}{3} = \frac{2}{3}$$

Add the tops and keep the bottom as 3.

Notice that we can get the right answer by adding the tops (the numerators) and then keeping 3 in the bottom (the denominator).

Why Does it Work?

Even though you've been adding fractions for years, you may not be clear on why that method works. Remember, the bottom of a fraction tells us how big our piece of the whole is. We're working with thirds in this case, so that's why there's a 3 in the bottom of each fraction. The top tells us how many of those pieces we have. If we have one piece that's a third in size and add that to another piece that's a third in size, we end up with two thirds, or $\frac{2}{3}$. The pieces don't change their size just because we added them together: they're still thirds. That's why we have to keep the bottom the same (as 3). The bottom just tells us how large our pieces are.

A lot of beginners get confused about this, and they try to add the tops and the bottoms.

$$\frac{1}{3} + \frac{1}{3} \implies \frac{2}{6}$$

A lot of beginners try to add the tops and bottoms. But this is wrong.

But if you really understand fractions, it's obvious that this has to be wrong. A third added to another third must be two thirds not two sixths. The size of the pieces don't change when we add them together, remember.

Fourths, Fifths, and Up

The method of adding the tops and keeping the bottoms the same will work on not just thirds, but also on fourths, fifths, sixths, and all the way up. Here's an example involving fifths.

$$\frac{1}{5} + \frac{1}{5} = \frac{2}{5}$$ **Add the tops and keep the bottom as 5.**

See, we have one fifth added to one fifth, and the answer has to be two fifths. Adding one piece to another piece gives us two pieces, but their size stays the same. Here's another one.

$$\frac{2}{7} + \frac{3}{7} = \frac{5}{7}$$ **Add the tops and keep the bottom as 7.**

This time we start with two pieces but then add three more pieces. That gives us a total of five pieces. But since all the original pieces were sevenths, we end up with five sevenths. The bottom of the answer stays the same.

Also, it doesn't matter whether the fractions are proper or improper.[1] Here's a problem with improper fractions.

$$\frac{3}{2} + \frac{8}{2} = \frac{11}{2}$$ **Add the tops and keep the bottom as 2.**

We start with three halves, which is greater than 1. Then we add eight more halves, and that's a lot greater than 1. The result is a total of eleven halves. Even though the fractions are big, the method for adding them stays the same: add the tops and keep the bottom the same.

Practice 24

a. Fully reduce the fraction $\frac{18}{4}$ by factoring and canceling.

b. Fully reduce the fraction $\frac{54}{6}$ by factoring and canceling.

---

[1] Remember, an improper fraction has a bigger number on top than on bottom.

c. Add $\dfrac{2}{9}+\dfrac{5}{9}$.

d. Add $\dfrac{1}{5}+\dfrac{4}{5}$.

e. Translate the word problem below into math; then solve.

The grumpy boss spent $\dfrac{1}{3}$ of his day posting new deadlines and another $\dfrac{1}{3}$ telling people to get back to work. What fraction of the boss's day was spent on these two activities?

$\dfrac{2}{3}$

Problem Set 24

Tell whether each sentence below is True or False.

1. To add two fractions, you should add their tops and bottoms.

   false

2. Only proper fractions can be added.

   false

Tell whether a <, >, or = sign should go between these fractions.

3. $\dfrac{2}{9}$ ___ $\dfrac{4}{18}$

4. $\dfrac{12}{8}$ ___ $\dfrac{6}{4}$

Answer each question below.

5. Tell whether 7,235 can be divided evenly by 5.

   yes

6. Write a fraction to represent the diagram below.

$\dfrac{2}{2}$ $\dfrac{2}{1}\ \dfrac{1}{1} = 2$

Add each group of numbers below.

7.   4,504
       6,052
    + 7,129
    _____

8.   67,072
     17,000
      6,893
    + 5,211
    _____

Subtract each pair of numbers below.

9. $\begin{array}{r} 746 \\ -578 \\ \hline \end{array}$

10. $\begin{array}{r} 72{,}600 \\ -50{,}490 \\ \hline \end{array}$

Multiply each pair of numbers below.

11. $\begin{array}{r} 470 \\ \times 29 \\ \hline \end{array}$

12. $\begin{array}{r} 802 \\ \times 56 \\ \hline \end{array}$

13. $\begin{array}{r} 869 \\ \times 505 \\ \hline \end{array}$

Divide each pair of numbers below. Write any remainders next to your answer.

14. $5\overline{)228}$

15. $6\overline{)1{,}206}$

16. $79\overline{)5{,}228}$

Fully reduce each fraction below by factoring and canceling.

(a) 17. $\dfrac{12}{9}$

18. $\dfrac{14}{21}$

(b) 19. $\dfrac{24}{6}$

Add each pair of fractions below. Make sure your answers are fully reduced.

20. $\dfrac{1}{5} + \dfrac{3}{5}$

(c) 21. $\dfrac{2}{7} + \dfrac{4}{7}$

(d) 22. $\dfrac{1}{4} + \dfrac{3}{4}$

Translate the word problem below into math; then solve. Make sure your answer is fully reduced.

(e) 23. The world's smallest guitar is called a nanoguitar. It is so small that its length is less than the width of a human hair. If one nanoguitar is $\dfrac{1}{10{,}000{,}000}$ meters long, how long (in meters) are 2 nanoguitars? Make sure your answer is fully reduced.

Lesson 25—Subtracting Fractions

We reviewed how to add fractions in the last lesson. What about subtracting fractions? Food examples always work really well for fractions, especially pie. So let's do a quick subtraction problem involving pie.

Mom served three eighths of her hot steaming apple pie to the kids. But after just five minutes, two eighths had already been eaten. How much of Mom's pie was left?

Common sense tells us that if we started with three eighths and then took away two eighths, that leaves us with one eighth.

Just Subtract the Tops

Now look at the problem in numbers.

$$\frac{3}{8} - \frac{2}{8} = \frac{1}{8}$$

Notice that we can get the answer by just subtracting the tops and leaving the bottom the same. So the rule for subtracting fractions is pretty much the same as the rule for adding fractions. Only instead of adding the numbers on top, we subtract them. But the important thing is that the number on bottom stays the same. And that's because the bottom number is just telling us the size of the pieces that are being subtracted. Don't try to subtract the bottom numbers too. That's wrong.

It Always Works

This rule will work on fractions of any size. Let's look at an example involving sixths.

$$\frac{5}{6} - \frac{1}{6} = \frac{4}{6}$$

We're starting with five sixths and taking away one sixth. To do the calculation, we just subtract the tops: $5-1$ equals 4. Then we keep the bottom the same. The answer is $\frac{4}{6}$.

One thing to keep in mind, though, is that answers should always be fully reduced. Why should an answer be any more complicated than it needs to be? So we need to reduce $\frac{4}{6}$ by factoring and canceling. The first step is to break down the top and bottom into prime numbers. On top, 4 can be factored as 2×2, and on bottom, 6 becomes 2×3.

$$\frac{2\times2}{2\times3}$$

Now we just cancel the factors that are the same on top and bottom. There's just one pair of 2s that can be canceled, and that leaves us with $\frac{2}{3}$ as our fully reduced answer.

$$\frac{\cancel{2}\times2}{\cancel{2}\times3} = \frac{2}{3}$$ **Cancel the 2s.**

Just as when we add fractions, the method for subtracting fractions will work on improper fractions too. Here's a quick example.

$$\frac{17}{5} - \frac{13}{5} = \frac{4}{5}$$

Both fractions are improper because their tops are bigger than their bottoms. But we still just subtract the numbers on top and keep the bottoms the same. Seventeen fifths minus thirteen fifths leaves just four fifths. And since $\frac{4}{5}$ can't be reduced, that's our final answer.

The main point of this fairly simple lesson is that the rule for subtracting fractions is to subtract the tops and keep the bottom the same.

Practice 25

a. Fully reduce the fraction $\frac{16}{50}$ by factoring and canceling.

b. Add $\frac{4}{3}+\frac{5}{3}$.   **c.** Add $\frac{1}{18}+\frac{5}{18}$.   **d.** Subtract $\frac{7}{12}-\frac{5}{12}$.

e. Translate the word problem below into math; then solve.

A lot of the rhubarb pie, $\frac{8}{9}$ to be exact, was left. That is, until Moose, the all-star defensive lineman, discovered it. Now, only $\frac{1}{9}$ of the pie is left. What fraction of the pie did Moose eat?

Problem Set 25

Tell whether each sentence below is True or False.

1. To subtract two fractions, subtract their numerator and put the answer over the common denominator.   *true*

2. The rule for subtracting fractions will work on both proper and improper fractions.   *true*

Tell whether a <, >, or = sign should go between these fractions.

3. $\frac{9}{45}$ —— $\frac{3}{15}$

4. $\frac{7}{2}$ —— $\frac{11}{3}$

Add each group of numbers below.

5.
$$\begin{array}{r} 2,314 \\ 8,731 \\ +\,2,193 \\ \hline \end{array}$$

6.
$$\begin{array}{r} 21,406 \\ 13,270 \\ 5,821 \\ +\,39,746 \\ \hline \end{array}$$

Subtract each pair of numbers below.

7.
$$\begin{array}{r} 14,207 \\ -\,9,153 \\ \hline \end{array}$$

8.
$$\begin{array}{r} 99,173 \\ -\,25,469 \\ \hline \end{array}$$

Multiply each pair of numbers below.

9.
$$906 \\ \times 58$$

10.
$$987 \\ \times 348$$

Divide each pair of numbers below. Write any remainders next to your answer.

11. $3\overline{)2,255}$

12. $31\overline{)2,586}$

Fully reduce each fraction below by factoring and canceling.

13. $\dfrac{3}{27}$

14. $\dfrac{11}{22}$

(a) 15. $\dfrac{32}{36}$

Add each pair of fractions below. Make sure your answers are fully reduced.

16. $\dfrac{5}{9} + \dfrac{2}{9}$

(b) 17. $\dfrac{1}{2} + \dfrac{3}{2}$

(c) 18. $\dfrac{1}{8} + \dfrac{3}{8}$

Subtract each pair of fractions below. Make sure your answers are fully reduced.

19. $\dfrac{4}{5} - \dfrac{1}{5}$

20. $\dfrac{10}{11} - \dfrac{8}{11}$

(d) 21. $\dfrac{7}{9} - \dfrac{4}{9}$

Translate the word problem below into math; then solve.

(e) 22. The beaker was $\dfrac{12}{13}$ full; then Igor, the lab assistant, mistakenly poured out some of its contents. Now the beaker is only $\dfrac{3}{13}$ full. What fraction of the beaker was poured out?

Lesson 26—Different Denominators

We've learned how to add and subtract fractions with the same denominator. All we do is add the tops (numerators) and keep the bottom (denominators) the same, remember. Or if the fractions are subtracted, we subtract the tops and keep the bottom the same. An example is $\frac{1}{5} + \frac{2}{5} = \frac{3}{5}$.

Making the Pieces the Same Size

But what do we do when the denominators of the fractions are different, as in this problem?

$$\frac{1}{2} + \frac{1}{4}$$

We can't just add the tops like before. That's because we're adding different-sized pieces. The first fraction is one *half* and the second fraction is one *fourth*. The only way to add in a situation like this is to make the denominators the same first. In other words, we have to make the pieces the same size. Then we can add normally.

Let's change the denominator of $\frac{1}{2}$ from 2 to 4. We can do that by multiplying the bottom by 2. But don't forget the Law of Equivalent Fractions. Remember, according to that law, in order to keep from changing the value of the fraction, we have to multiply the bottom *and* the top by the same number. So what we really need to do is multiply both bottom and top by 2.

$$\frac{1 \times 2}{2 \times 2} + \frac{1}{4}$$

Multiplying top and bottom by 2

That changes $\frac{1}{2}$ to $\frac{2}{4}$. That makes sense, because those two are equivalent (they represent the same share of the whole).

$$\frac{2}{4} + \frac{1}{4}$$

Now the denominators are the same: we're adding fourths to fourths. That means we can add by the usual method. We add the tops and keep the bottom the same to get $\frac{3}{4}$, which is fully reduced.

$$\frac{2}{4} + \frac{1}{4} = \frac{3}{4}$$

Add the tops and the bottom stays the same

Subtraction Too

Here's a subtraction example with different denominators.

$$\frac{3}{4}-\frac{1}{3}$$

We can't just subtract the tops, because we're subtracting fourths and thirds. The pieces aren't the same size. So the first step is to make the denominators the same. But this problem is tougher than the last example, because here we have to multiply the top and bottom of *both* fractions. And it has to be tops and bottoms, because we don't want to change the value of the fractions in the process. That would blow the whole problem. Let's multiply the top and bottom of the first fraction by 3 and the top and bottom of the second fraction by 4.

$$\frac{3 \times 3}{4 \times 3}-\frac{1 \times 4}{3 \times 4}$$ **Making the bottoms the same.**

That leaves us with this.

$$\frac{9}{12}-\frac{4}{12}$$

Now we're subtracting pieces that are the same size. It's nine twelfths minus four twelfths. All we have to do is subtract the tops and keep the bottom the same.

$$\frac{9}{12}-\frac{4}{12}=\frac{5}{12}$$ **Subtract the tops and the bottom stays the same**

We end up with $\frac{5}{12}$. That's fully reduced. You can check for yourself by factoring it. The top and bottom don't have anything in common that can be canceled.

Practice 26

a. Add $\frac{1}{6}+\frac{1}{12}$.

b. Add $\frac{3}{4}+\frac{1}{3}$.

c. Subtract $\frac{7}{9}-\frac{1}{3}$.

d. Subtract $\frac{5}{7}-\frac{1}{3}$.

e. Translate the word problem below into math; then solve.

If Suzy combined a ketchup bottle that was $\frac{1}{3}$ full with a ketchup bottle that was $\frac{1}{6}$ full, what fraction of a bottle does she have now?

Problem Set 26

Tell whether each sentence below is True or False.

1. When adding fractions with different denominators, the denominators have to be made the same before adding. _true_

2. The law of equivalent fractions is not used when adding fractions with different denominators. _false_

Tell whether a <, >, or = sign should go between these fractions.

3. $\dfrac{3}{4}$ _____ $\dfrac{36}{48}$ 4. $\dfrac{4}{7}$ _____ $\dfrac{7}{12}$

Add or subtract each group of numbers below.

5.
$$
\begin{array}{r}
660 \\
5,910 \\
2,364 \\
+1,119 \\
\hline
\end{array}
$$

6.
$$
\begin{array}{r}
4,667 \\
-859 \\
\hline
\end{array}
$$

7.
$$
\begin{array}{r}
34,478 \\
8,509 \\
56,091 \\
+18,403 \\
\hline
\end{array}
$$

8.
$$
\begin{array}{r}
83,500 \\
-3,672 \\
\hline
\end{array}
$$

9.
$$
\begin{array}{r}
20,890 \\
23,476 \\
10,070 \\
+8,479 \\
\hline
\end{array}
$$

Multiply each pair of numbers below.

10.
$$
\begin{array}{r}
926 \\
\times 46 \\
\hline
\end{array}
$$

11.
$$
\begin{array}{r}
805 \\
\times 319 \\
\hline
\end{array}
$$

146

Divide each pair of numbers below. Write any remainders next to your answer.

12. $8\overline{)4,664}$ **13.** $21\overline{)7,255}$

Fully reduce each fraction below by factoring and canceling.

14. $\dfrac{4}{18}$ **15.** $\dfrac{7}{49}$ **16.** $\dfrac{10}{8}$

Add each pair of fractions below. Make sure your answers are fully reduced.

17. $\dfrac{1}{7}+\dfrac{3}{7}$ **(a) 18.** $\dfrac{2}{5}+\dfrac{1}{10}$ **(b) 19.** $\dfrac{1}{2}+\dfrac{2}{3}$

Subtract each pair of fractions below. Make sure your answers are fully reduced.

20. $\dfrac{4}{9}-\dfrac{2}{9}$ **(c) 21.** $\dfrac{5}{8}-\dfrac{1}{4}$ **(d) 22.** $\dfrac{4}{5}-\dfrac{1}{3}$

Translate the word problem below into math; then solve.

(e) 23. In a move to lower prices even further, Super Duper Saver Grocery has decided to offer partially-consumed boxes of chocolates. If Vicki bought $\dfrac{1}{4}$ of a box of cherry chocolates and $\dfrac{1}{8}$ of a box of assorted chocolates, what fraction of a whole box did she buy?

Lesson 27—Finding the Lowest Common Denominator

We just finished learning how to add and subtract fractions that have different denominators. We have to make the denominators the same before doing the addition or subtraction, remember. That means we have to find a **common denominator**, which is just a number that we can change both denominators to.

Multiplying the Denominators Together

But sometimes it's pretty hard to find a common denominator. Take a look at this example.

$$\frac{11}{30} - \frac{1}{20}$$

We need to make both denominators the same, but what should we do? We can't multiply just one of the denominators. That won't work. But it's not easy to see how we can make the denominators the same even if we multiply both of them.

One method that will always give us a common denominator is to multiply the two denominators together. We can take 30×20 to get 600. That's a common denominator. And the great thing about this method is that it's easy to make both denominators equal 600. All we have to do is multiply the 30 by 20 and the 20 by 30.

$$\frac{11 \times 20}{30 \times 20} - \frac{1 \times 30}{20 \times 30} \qquad \textbf{Making the bottoms the same.}$$

Notice we've multiplied the tops of each fraction by the same number to avoid violating the Law of Equivalent Fractions. But here's what we get.

$$\frac{220}{600} - \frac{30}{600}$$

Now we can subtract the numerators and put that result over 600.

$$\frac{190}{600}$$

This is the answer, but look at how huge the numbers are. This is the big drawback of finding a common denominator by just multiplying the bottoms together. If the original fractions have big numbers in them, the common denominator will be really big. And then it could take a long time to reduce the answer.[2]

The Lowest Common Denominator

Instead of just multiplying the denominators together, a better approach is to find the **lowest common denominator** (or LCD for short). That's the smallest number that both denominators will divide into evenly. By using the lowest common denominator, we can keep the numbers in our fraction as small as possible.

But how do we find the LCD? Do we just come up with a bunch of common denominators and pick the lowest one? No. There's actually a method for finding the LCD which will work every time.

We'll show you how the method works on $\frac{11}{30} - \frac{1}{20}$. Step one is to factor each denominator into prime numbers. The 30 factors as $2 \times 3 \times 5$, and the 20 factors as $2 \times 2 \times 5$.

$$\frac{11}{2 \times 3 \times 5} - \frac{1}{2 \times 2 \times 5}$$ **Factor the bottoms into prime numbers.**

Now here's an important fact. An LCD has to include all of the factors from each denominator, with no extras. So step two is to list all of the factors in the two denominators. Starting with the first denominator, 30 contains one 2, one 3, and one 5. That means our LCD needs to have one 2, one 3, and one 5. We'll list those and show them multiplied together.

$$LCD = 2 \times 3 \times 5 \text{ ...}$$

The second denominator, 20, contains two 2s and one 5. We already have one 2, but since the second denominator has two 2s, our LCD needs another one. So we include it in the list.

$$LCD = 2 \times 3 \times 5 \times 2$$ **Include another 2**

The second denominator also has a 5. But since our LCD already has one 5, there's no need to add another one. That's what it means to say that the LCD can't have any extra factors.

Step three of the process is just to multiply all those factors together.

$$LCD = 2 \times 3 \times 5 \times 2 = 60$$ **Multiply the factors**

---

[2] Actually, the fraction $\frac{190}{600}$ isn't all that hard to reduce. It reduces to $\frac{19}{60}$.

We end up with a lowest common denominator (LCD) of 60. That's a lot smaller than 600. (Remember, that's the common denominator we got by multiplying 30 and 20.) So 60 is going to be a lot easier to work with.

From here, subtracting the fractions is easy. We need to make both denominators equal 60. Here are the fractions again.

$$\frac{11}{30} - \frac{1}{20}$$

To change 30 to 60, we just need to multiply by 2. Of course, we have to multiply the bottom and the top by 2. To make 20 equal to 60, we need to multiply the top and bottom by 3.

$$\frac{11 \times 2}{30 \times 2} - \frac{1 \times 3}{20 \times 3}$$ **Making the bottoms equal 60 (the LCD).**

Calculating everything gives us this.

$$\frac{22}{60} - \frac{3}{60}$$

Finally, the denominators are the same. We're subtracting sixtieths from sixtieths. The last step is to subtract the tops.

$$\frac{22}{60} - \frac{3}{60} = \frac{19}{60}$$

We get $\frac{19}{60}$, which is fully reduced.

There's one last point we should make. From time to time, you may hear people refer to the lowest common denominator as **the lowest common multiple**. That's the lowest number that a group of numbers will divide into evenly. If that sounds familiar, it's because it's just our definition of lowest common denominator. But when adding or subtracting fractions, instead of saying they're finding the lowest common denominator, some people will say they're finding the lowest common multiple of the denominators. But the two terms mean pretty much the same thing.

Practice 27

a. Find the lowest common denominator of $\frac{2}{3}$, $\frac{1}{4}$, and $\frac{3}{8}$.

b. Find the lowest common denominator of $\frac{1}{4}$, $\frac{2}{7}$, and $\frac{1}{8}$. **56**

c. Add $\frac{6 \times 9}{7 \times 9} + \frac{6 \times 7}{9 \times 7} = \frac{54}{63} + \frac{42}{63} = \frac{96}{63} = \frac{32}{21}$ d. Subtract $\frac{1 \times 10}{3 \times 10} - \frac{3 \times 3}{10 \times 3} = \frac{10}{30} - \frac{9}{30} = \frac{1}{30}$

e. Translate the word problem below into math; then solve.

Michael drank $\frac{1}{9}$ of the can of pop during his first gulp and $\frac{1}{12}$ during his second. What fraction of the can has Michael drunk?

$\frac{1 \times 4}{9 \times 4} + \frac{1 \times 3}{12 \times 3} = \frac{4}{36} + \frac{3}{36} = \frac{7}{36}$

$36 \qquad 36$

Problem Set 27

Tell whether each sentence below is True or False.

1. The lowest common denominator (LCD) is the smallest number that the denominators will divide into evenly.   true

2. The lowest common denominator must include all of the factors in each of the denominators and no extras.   true

Add or subtract each group of numbers below.

3.
2 1 2
1,902
2,355
4,874
+ 5,009
14,140

4.
65,563
− 9,924

5.
43,573
23,497
17,943
+ 3,759

6.
38,225
− 27,870

$\begin{array}{r} 54 \\ + 42 \\ \hline 96 \end{array}$

Multiply each pair of numbers below.

7.
$$\begin{array}{r} 574 \\ \times 28 \\ \hline \end{array}$$

8.
$$\begin{array}{r} 412 \\ \times 532 \\ \hline \end{array}$$

Divide each pair of numbers below. Write any remainders next to your answer.

9. $4\overline{)7{,}929}$

10. $25\overline{)5{,}075}$

Fully reduce each fraction below by factoring and canceling.

11. $\dfrac{15}{25}$

12. $\dfrac{20}{24}$

Find the lowest common denominator for each group of fractions below.

13. $\dfrac{2}{3}, \dfrac{1}{6}$

(a) 14. $\dfrac{3}{4}, \dfrac{1}{2}, \dfrac{5}{6}$

(b) 15. $\dfrac{1}{8}, \dfrac{7}{9}, \dfrac{1}{6}$

Add each pair of fractions below. Make sure your answers are fully reduced.

16. $\dfrac{3}{4} + \dfrac{1}{4}$

17. $\dfrac{1}{3} + \dfrac{2}{9}$

(c) 18. $\dfrac{5}{6} + \dfrac{3}{8}$

Subtract each pair of fractions below. Make sure your answers are fully reduced.

19. $\dfrac{5}{11} - \dfrac{2}{11}$

20. $\dfrac{9}{10} - \dfrac{3}{5}$

(d) 21. $\dfrac{5}{8} - \dfrac{7}{12}$

Translate the word problem below into math; then solve.

(e) 22.   The Do-Nothing Duo spent $\dfrac{1}{3}$ of last weekend whistling their favorite tunes and $\dfrac{1}{2}$ blowing bubbles. What fraction of the weekend did the Duo spend doing these activities?

Lesson 28—Mixed Numbers

We've been adding and subtracting fractions, but what about adding or subtracting a whole number and a fraction? Here's an example.

$$5 + \frac{1}{3}$$

See, we have the whole number 5 added to the fraction $\frac{1}{3}$.

Put the Whole Number Over 1

Although this may seem tricky, it's actually pretty easy. The first step is to turn 5 into a fraction. Remember, any whole number can be turned into a fraction by putting it over 1. So putting 5 over 1 gives us this.

$$\frac{5}{1} + \frac{1}{3}$$

That changes the problem into an addition of two fractions, which is something we know how to do. Since these fractions have different denominators, we need to find the lowest common denominator (LCD). Our two denominators are really small, so we can find the LCD in our head: it's 3.

Now we need to make both denominators equal to 3. The second fraction, $\frac{1}{3}$, already has a denominator of 3. To make the first denominator equal to 3, we just multiply the bottom and the top (as always) by 3.

$$\frac{5 \times 3}{1 \times 3} + \frac{1}{3} \qquad \textsf{Multiplying top and bottom by 3}$$

$$\frac{15}{3} + \frac{1}{3}$$

Next, we add the fractions by adding their tops and putting the result over 3 to get $\frac{16}{3}$.

$$\frac{15}{3} + \frac{1}{3} = \frac{16}{3} \qquad \textsf{Add the tops and keep the bottom the same.}$$

Since $\frac{16}{3}$ is fully reduced, that's our final answer. So $5 + \frac{1}{3}$ is equal to $\frac{16}{3}$. Of course, if we were subtracting a fraction from a whole number we'd follow the same process.

Being Lazy with Mixed Numbers

People tend to be a little lazy when it comes to adding a whole number and a fraction. A lot of times they won't even bother doing the addition. For instance, they might just leave $5 + \frac{1}{3}$ as $5 + \frac{1}{3}$. In fact, this happens so often that people no longer even bother writing the + sign (which is really lazy). They just squeeze the numbers together like this.

$$5 + \frac{1}{3} \text{ is often written as } 5\frac{1}{3}$$

So $5\frac{1}{3}$ and $5 + \frac{1}{3}$ mean the same thing. As you probably remember from arithmetic, $5\frac{1}{3}$ is called a mixed number. A **mixed number** is just a whole number plus a fraction with the plus sign left out. None of this is new to you, because mixed numbers are used a lot in arithmetic. But one thing you might not know is that mixed numbers aren't used as much in higher math. In more advanced courses, improper fractions (like $\frac{16}{3}$) are used a lot more often.

Converting a Mixed Number to an Improper Fraction

Now that we've mentioned mixed numbers, let's talk about how to change or "convert" (that's the technical term) a mixed number to a single fraction.[3] Take $4\frac{1}{2}$ for example. Since a mixed number is just a whole number plus a fraction, $4\frac{1}{2}$ really means $4 + \frac{1}{2}$. So all we have to do is add these two.

$$4 + \frac{1}{2} \qquad \textbf{Just add them.}$$

The first step is to just change 4 to $\frac{4}{1}$.

$$\frac{4}{1} + \frac{1}{2}$$

Now we add the fractions normally. The LCD is 2. And all we have to do to make the denominators the same is multiply the top and bottom of $\frac{4}{1}$ by 2.

$$\frac{4 \times 2}{1 \times 2} + \frac{1}{2} \qquad \textbf{Multiplying top and bottom by 2}$$

---

[3] When you change a mixed number to a fraction, the fraction will be an improper fraction because the numerator (top) will be bigger than the denominator (bottom).

$$\frac{8}{2}+\frac{1}{2}$$

With the denominators the same, we can just add the tops to get $\frac{9}{2}$, which is fully reduced. So the mixed number $4\frac{1}{2}$ converts into the improper fraction $\frac{9}{2}$.

A Neat Shortcut

There is also a shortcut for converting a mixed number to an improper fraction. Almost everybody learns it in arithmetic. To refresh your memory, we'll show you how it works on $4\frac{1}{2}$.

The first step is to take the denominator of the fraction part of the mixed number and multiply it by the whole number part. So we take 2 (the denominator of $\frac{1}{2}$) and multiply it by 4 (the whole number part) to get 8. The next step is to add the numerator (1) to that result: $8+1$ equals 9. Then we put 9 on top of 2 (the denominator of $\frac{1}{2}$ again) to get our improper fraction.

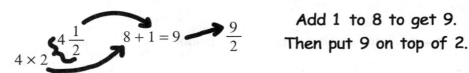

**Add 1 to 8 to get 9.
Then put 9 on top of 2.**

We end up with $\frac{9}{2}$, which is the same answer we got before. Here are the steps for the shortcut summarized.

Shortcut for Converting Mixed Number to Improper Fraction

1.	Multiply the denominator of the fraction part by the whole number and add the numerator.
2.	Put the result over the denominator.

The interesting thing about the shortcut is that it's actually the same thing as adding 4 and $\frac{1}{2}$ normally. Remember, when we added $\frac{4}{1}$ and $\frac{1}{2}$, we had to multiply 2 by the 4 on top to change $\frac{4}{1}$ to $\frac{8}{2}$. Then we added 8 and 1 to add the numerators ($\frac{8}{2}+\frac{1}{2}$). So the shortcut is just a fast way of adding the whole number to the fraction.

Converting the other Way

What about converting the other way by changing an improper fraction into a mixed number? That's easy. We just divide the denominator into the numerator and put the remainder over the denominator. For example, to convert $\frac{9}{2}$ back to a mixed number, we divide 2 into 9.

$$\begin{array}{r} 4 \\ 2\overline{)9} \\ -\,8 \\ \hline 1 \end{array}$$

That gives us 4 with a remainder of 1. So 4 is the whole number part. And to get the fraction part, we put the remainder 1 over 2 (the divisor) to get $4\frac{1}{2}$. That's all there is to it.

Practice 28

a. Find the lowest common denominator of $\frac{1}{6}$, $\frac{7}{12}$, and $\frac{11}{18}$.

b. Add $3+\frac{4}{7}$ to get an improper fraction.

c. Change $\frac{17}{6}$ to a mixed number.

d. Add $1\frac{1}{4}+\frac{1}{12}$.

e. Translate the word problem below into math; then solve.

Farmer Brown has an artistic streak. He likes to paint the spots on his cows different shades of blue. If he painted $\frac{1}{4}$ of his cows with navy spots, $\frac{1}{3}$ of his cows with indigo spots, and $\frac{1}{6}$ of his cows with cobalt spots, what fraction of his cows were painted one of these three colors? Be sure to reduce your answer fully.

Problem Set 28

Tell whether each sentence below is True or False.

1. A mixed number is just a whole number plus a fraction with the plus sign left out. *true*

2. It's better to change improper fractions to mixed numbers before adding or subtracting. *false*

Add or subtract each group of numbers below.

3.
$$\begin{array}{r} 7,342 \\ 240 \\ 3,398 \\ +1,432 \\ \hline \end{array}$$

4.
$$\begin{array}{r} 12,886 \\ -4,592 \\ \hline \end{array}$$

5.
$$\begin{array}{r} 983 \\ 5,002 \\ 14,280 \\ +6,793 \\ \hline \end{array}$$

Multiply or divide each pair of numbers below.

6.
$$\begin{array}{r} 721 \\ \times 85 \\ \hline \end{array}$$

7. $27\overline{)83,421}$

8.
$$\begin{array}{r} 504 \\ \times 433 \\ \hline \end{array}$$

Fully reduce each fraction below by factoring and canceling.

9. $\dfrac{8}{30}$

10. $\dfrac{28}{21}$

Find the lowest common denominator for each group of fractions below.

(a) 11. $\dfrac{1}{12}, \dfrac{5}{4}, \dfrac{3}{7}$

(a) 12. $\dfrac{2}{7}, \dfrac{5}{21}, \dfrac{9}{14}$

Add each pair of numbers below to get an improper fraction.

13. $4 + \dfrac{1}{3}$

(b) 14. $7 + \dfrac{2}{9}$

Change each improper fraction below into a mixed number.

15. $\dfrac{22}{7}$

(c) 16. $\dfrac{11}{4}$

Add or subtract each pair of numbers below. Make sure your answers are fully reduced.

17. $\dfrac{3}{5}+\dfrac{4}{15}$

18. $\dfrac{5}{7}-\dfrac{1}{8}$

(d) 19. $1\dfrac{1}{2}+\dfrac{1}{6}$

Translate the word problem below into math; then solve.

(e) 20. When Farmer Jones found it hard to keep some of his cows from getting onto the highway after dark, Farmer Brown (see practice problem e) suggested that he paint their spots bright colors. Now $\dfrac{1}{6}$ of Farmer Jones' cows have neon pink spots, $\dfrac{1}{8}$ have glow-in-the-dark yellow spots, and $\dfrac{1}{12}$ have spots that are safety orange. What fraction of his cows did Farmer Jones protect with paint? Be sure to reduce your answer fully.

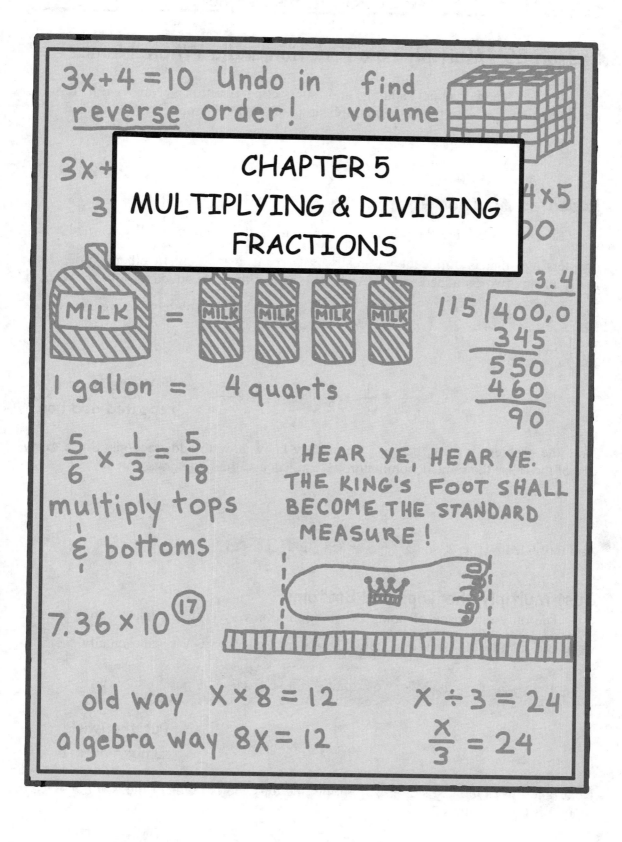

Lesson 29—Multiplying a Fraction and a Whole Number

We've learned about adding and subtracting fractions. Now we'll turn to multiplication. Let's start with the multiplication of a whole number and a fraction.

$$6 \times \frac{1}{2}$$

Repeated Addition Again

See, here we have the whole number 6 times the fraction $\frac{1}{2}$. We learned a few chapters ago that multiplication is really just repeated addition. In other words, 2×5 really means two 5s added: $5+5$. And 3×4 means three 4s added: $4+4+4$. Well, if that's true, shouldn't $6 \times \frac{1}{2}$ be the same as six $\frac{1}{2}$s added? Absolutely. So we can change $6 \times \frac{1}{2}$ to this.

$$\frac{1}{2} + \frac{1}{2} + \frac{1}{2} + \frac{1}{2} + \frac{1}{2} + \frac{1}{2}$$

Write it as a repeated addition.

Now the problem is easy, because we already know how to add fractions. Since every one of these has the same denominator, we can just add their numerators to get

$$\frac{6}{2}.$$

And 6 divided by 2 is 3, so our answer actually reduces to 3.

Just Multiply the Tops and Bottoms

The only drawback of doing the problem this way is that it takes a long time to write out all those $\frac{1}{2}$s. Fortunately, there's an easier way. We can actually multiply $6 \times \frac{1}{2}$ in two quick steps. First, we turn the 6 into a fraction by putting it over 1.

$$\frac{6}{1} \times \frac{1}{2}$$

Put the whole number over 1

Next (and this is the key step), we multiply the tops and bottoms of the two fractions: 6 times 1 is 6 and 1 times 2 is 2.

$$\frac{6}{1} \times \frac{1}{2} = \frac{6}{2} = 3$$

Multiply the tops and bottoms.

That gives us $\dfrac{6}{2}$ or 3, which is the same answer as before. Here are the steps for multiplying a fraction and a whole number summarized.

Multiplying a Whole Number and Fraction

1.	Turn the whole number into a fraction by putting it over 1.
2.	Multiply the tops and bottoms of the two fractions.

It Always Works

The great thing about this method is that it will work even when the answer doesn't reduce to a whole number (like 3). Here's an example like that.

$$2 \times \dfrac{1}{5}$$

To multiply the whole number 2 by the fraction $\dfrac{1}{5}$, we just follow the steps. First, we turn 2 into a fraction by putting it over 1.

$$\dfrac{2}{1} \times \dfrac{1}{5}$$

Next, we multiply the tops and bottoms.

$$\dfrac{2}{1} \times \dfrac{1}{5} = \dfrac{2}{5}$$

We end up with an answer of $\dfrac{2}{5}$, which won't reduce to a whole number. We know this has to be right, though, because $2 \times \dfrac{1}{5}$ is the same as $\dfrac{1}{5} + \dfrac{1}{5}$, and that adds to equal $\dfrac{2}{5}$.

Here's another case.

$$3 \times \dfrac{4}{7}$$

As always, we just turn the whole number 3 into a fraction and then multiply the tops and bottoms.

$$\frac{3}{1} \times \frac{4}{7} = \frac{12}{7}$$

We end up with $\frac{12}{7}$. That's an improper fraction, and it's already fully reduced. We can check to make sure that $\frac{12}{7}$ is right. Since $3 \times \frac{4}{7}$ is the same as $\frac{4}{7} + \frac{4}{7} + \frac{4}{7}$, we add the three fractions to get $\frac{12}{7}$. So it works.

Practice 29

a. Change $\frac{36}{8}$ to a mixed number.

b. Add $\frac{1}{3} + \frac{1}{4} + \frac{5}{8}$.   **c.** Multiply $5 \times \frac{3}{4}$.   **d.** Multiply $\frac{5}{8} \times 16$.

e. Translate the word problem below into math; then solve.

Slow-roasted Turkey

(Hold the stuffing)

Buckaroo Bob's Golden Brown Buffet usually serves up 14 slow-roasted turkeys (one at a time, not simultaneously) on the weekends. But if Moose, the all-star defensive lineman, happens to show up, this is barely enough. Assuming that Moose takes $\frac{1}{3}$ of a turkey on each of his 12 trips to the buffet bar, how many turkeys will he eat? Be sure to reduce your answer fully.

Problem Set 29

Tell whether each sentence below is True or False.

1. Any whole number can be turned into a fraction by putting it over 1.

   true

2. To multiply a whole number and fraction, turn the whole number into a fraction first, then multiply the two fractions normally.

   true

Add or subtract each group of numbers below.

3.
$$
\begin{array}{r}
756 \\
9,348 \\
845 \\
+\ 6,432 \\
\hline
\end{array}
$$

4.
$$
\begin{array}{r}
64,914 \\
-\ 42,856 \\
\hline
\end{array}
$$

5.
$$
\begin{array}{r}
2,902 \\
1,853 \\
4,269 \\
+\ 3,005 \\
\hline
\end{array}
$$

Multiply or divide each pair of numbers below.

6.
$$
\begin{array}{r}
638 \\
\times\ 72 \\
\hline
\end{array}
$$

7. $9\overline{)2,837}$

8.
$$
\begin{array}{r}
279 \\
\times\ 822 \\
\hline
\end{array}
$$

Fully reduce each fraction below by factoring and canceling.

9. $\dfrac{13}{26}$

10. $\dfrac{25}{35}$

Find the lowest common denominator for each group of fractions below.

11. $\dfrac{9}{8}, \dfrac{5}{6}, \dfrac{1}{10}$

12. $\dfrac{2}{9}, \dfrac{4}{15}, \dfrac{9}{10}$

Add each pair of numbers below to get an improper fraction.

13. $9 + \dfrac{2}{5}$

14. $11 + \dfrac{3}{10}$

Change each improper fraction below into a mixed number. Make sure your answers are fully reduced.

15. $\dfrac{29}{7}$ **(a) 16.** $\dfrac{38}{6}$

Add or subtract each group of numbers below. Make sure your answers are fully reduced.

17. $\dfrac{5}{3}+\dfrac{1}{9}$ **18.** $6\dfrac{1}{2}-\dfrac{2}{3}$ **(b) 19.** $\dfrac{1}{5}+\dfrac{3}{4}+\dfrac{1}{2}$

Multiply each pair of numbers below.

20. $30\times\dfrac{1}{5}$ **(c) 21.** $8\times\dfrac{2}{3}$ **(d) 22.** $\dfrac{3}{7}\times14$

Translate the word problem below into math; then solve.

Pan-fried Chicken with Potatoes
(Moose's favorite)

(e) 23. Moose loves slow-roasted turkey (see practice problem e), but if there's one thing he likes even better, it's Buckaroo Bob's famous pan-fried chicken and potatoes. If Moose takes $\dfrac{3}{4}$ of the pan-fried chicken tray on each of his 12 trips to the buffet bar, how many trays will he eat? Be sure to reduce your answer fully.

Lesson 30—Finding the Fraction of a Number

We just finished learning how to multiply a fraction and a whole number. In this lesson, we're going to see how that calculation is actually used in the real world. Take a look at this example.

A florist has 450 bouquets set out for Valentine's Day, but $\frac{1}{5}$ of them are wilting. How many bouquets are wilting?

Either Divide or Multiply

There are actually two ways to solve this problem. One way is to divide 5 into 450.

$$\begin{array}{r} 90 \\ 5\overline{)450} \\ -45 \\ \hline 00 \\ 0 \end{array}$$

That leaves us with 90. So there must be 90 bouquets wilting.

But the other way to solve the problem is to multiply 450 by $\frac{1}{5}$. And we already know how to multiply a whole number by a fraction. We learned it in the last lesson. We just turn the whole number 450 into a fraction by putting it over 1.

$$\frac{450}{1} \times \frac{1}{5}$$

Then we multiply the tops and bottoms of the fractions to get $\frac{450}{5}$. But that's just 450 divided by 5, which is the first way we used to solve the problem. So see, the two ways are exactly the same. We can find $\frac{1}{5}$ of 450 either by dividing by 5 or multiplying by $\frac{1}{5}$.

The second method actually confuses a lot of people because they think whenever a number is multiplied by something the number should get bigger. But actually multiplying a number by a fraction makes the number smaller (as long as the top of the fraction is smaller than the bottom, so that the fraction is less than 1).

A Numerator Greater than 1

If the multiplication method is confusing, why not just always divide to find the fraction of a number? Well, it turns out that multiplying works better on cases where the numerator of the fraction is greater than 1. For instance, what if $\frac{3}{5}$ of the bouquets were wilting? Then it would definitely be easier to multiply the fraction by the number.

$$\frac{450}{1} \times \frac{3}{5} \qquad\qquad \textbf{Multiply when the numer-}$$
$$\textbf{ator is greater than 1.}$$

We would just put the 450 over 1 and multiply the tops and bottoms.

$$\frac{450}{1} \times \frac{3}{5} = \frac{1,350}{5}$$

That gives us 1,350 over 5. We won't go through the division, but the answer comes out to 270 wilting bouquets. But the point is that multiplying is easier when the fraction is more complicated. Some people like to multiply every time when they're finding the fraction of a number. That's because multiplication will always work—no matter how simple or complicated the fraction is.

Practice 30

a. Subtract $2\frac{3}{8} - 1\frac{1}{12}$.

b. Add $2\frac{1}{2} + \frac{9}{10} + \frac{3}{5}$.

c. What is $\frac{5}{6}$ of 78?

d. What is $\frac{3}{8}$ of 136?

e. Translate the word problem below into math; then solve.

Sheila only owns $\frac{2}{5}$ as many vintage tablecloths as Monique. If Monique owns 130 vintage tablecloths, how many does Sheila own?

Problem Set 30

Tell whether each sentence below is True or False.

1. To find a fraction of a whole number, just multiply the fraction and the number. *true*

2. Multiplying a whole number by a proper fraction will always make the whole number larger. *true*

Add or subtract each group of numbers below.

3.
$$
\begin{array}{r}
8,106 \\
5,230 \\
984 \\
+ 235 \\
\hline
\end{array}
$$

4.
$$
\begin{array}{r}
67,032 \\
- 35,579 \\
\hline
\end{array}
$$

Multiply or divide each pair of numbers below.

5.
$$
\begin{array}{r}
589 \\
\times 64 \\
\hline
\end{array}
$$

6. $43\overline{)9,279}$

Fully reduce each fraction below by factoring and canceling.

7. $\dfrac{18}{48}$
8. $\dfrac{20}{45}$

Find the lowest common denominator for each group of fractions below.

9. $\dfrac{1}{16}, \dfrac{3}{4}, \dfrac{7}{8}$
10. $\dfrac{9}{26}, \dfrac{1}{13}, \dfrac{5}{4}$

Add each pair of numbers below to get an improper fraction.

11. $8 + \dfrac{5}{6}$
12. $12 + \dfrac{3}{5}$

Change each improper fraction below into a mixed number. Make sure your answers are fully reduced.

13. $\dfrac{30}{4}$
14. $\dfrac{46}{8}$

Add or subtract each group of numbers below. Make sure your answers are fully reduced.

15. $\dfrac{3}{4} + \dfrac{3}{5}$
(a) 16. $8\dfrac{1}{6} - 5\dfrac{1}{4}$
(b) 17. $3\dfrac{2}{3} + \dfrac{5}{6} + \dfrac{1}{2}$

Answer each question below.

18. What is $\dfrac{1}{3}$ of 21?
19. What is $\dfrac{2}{5}$ of 55?

(c) 20. What is $\dfrac{3}{7}$ of 84?
(d) 21. What is $\dfrac{4}{9}$ of 279?

Translate the word problem below into math; then solve.

(e) 22. Poor Rupert. He wanted to collect crazy straws, but every male in his family over the last seventy-five years has collected bottle caps instead. Oh, well. If Rupert now owns $\dfrac{2}{7}$ as many bottle caps as his dad, and his dad owns 224, how many does Rupert own?

Lesson 31—Multiplying Fractions

In the last couple of lessons, we've been multiplying a fraction and a whole number. But what about multiplying two fractions?

Multiply Tops and Bottoms Again

The good news is that the basic rule is the same: we just multiply the tops and bottoms. Let's go through an example.

$$\frac{1}{5} \times \frac{1}{3}$$

We just multiply the numerators: 1×1 equals 1. Then we multiply the denominators: 5×3 equals 15. So we end up with $\frac{1}{15}$. And that's fully reduced.

In the Real World

But here's a good question. What kinds of real-world problems would require us to multiply two fractions? Remember, we need to multiply a fraction and whole number when we're trying to finding a fraction of a whole number. The example from the last lesson asked us to figure out how many was $\frac{1}{5}$ of 450 bouquets. Well, here's a problem that involves multiplication of two fractions.

Betty gave one third of a delicious pan of lasagna to her mother. But her mother gave one fifth of that to the cat. What fraction of the lasagna pan did the cat get?

This problem is really asking us to find $\frac{1}{5}$ of $\frac{1}{3}$ of the lasagna pan. Instead of a fraction of a whole number we need to find a fraction of another fraction. We don't need to figure out how big the cat's piece of lasagna is either. Just what fraction it makes up of the total pan. All we have to do is multiply $\frac{1}{5}$ and $\frac{1}{3}$. And we already know the answer is $\frac{1}{15}$. But that's an example of a problem that requires multiplication of two fractions.

Fraction of a fraction problems are pretty tough. Sometimes looking at a picture can make them a little easier to understand. Check out the lasagna pans below. The pan on the left is cut into thirds. Let's say Betty gave the top third to her mom. Then on the right, that third is cut into fifths. And the cat's piece is in the upper corner.

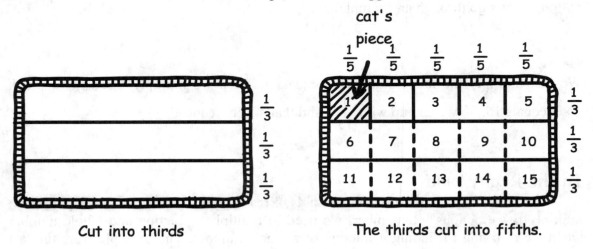

Cut into thirds   The thirds cut into fifths.

Now what if the other two thirds were also cut into fifths? That's shown by the dotted lines. Then the entire lasagna would be broken into 15 equal pieces. So the cat would have one out of those 15 pieces. That's $\frac{1}{15}$. Multiplying the two fractions gave us the right answer.

Practice 31

a. Multiply $\frac{1}{2} \times \frac{1}{5}$.

b. Multiply $\frac{7}{9} \times \frac{3}{5}$.

c. What is $\frac{1}{5}$ of $\frac{1}{10}$?

d. What is $\frac{3}{4}$ of $\frac{5}{12}$?

e. Translate the word problem below into math; then solve.

Super Duper Saver Grocery now sells guacamole by the gallon, the ounce, and everything in between. If Naomi bought $\frac{1}{2}$ of $\frac{1}{9}$ of a gallon, what fraction of a gallon did she buy?

Problem Set 31

Tell whether each sentence below is True or False.

1. To multiply fractions, just multiply their tops and bottoms.

   true

2. The easiest way to find $\frac{2}{5}$ of $\frac{3}{4}$ is to divide.

   False

Add or subtract each group of numbers below.

3.
```
    3,247
    1,245
    3,772
  + 9,923
```

4.
```
    89,451
  − 47,865
```

Multiply or divide each pair of numbers below.

5. $22\overline{)17{,}270}$

6.
```
    684
  × 502
```

Fully reduce each fraction below by factoring and canceling.

7. $\frac{27}{54}$

8. $\frac{12}{34}$

Find the lowest common denominator for each group of fractions below.

36

9. $\frac{2}{5}, \frac{3}{10}, \frac{7}{2}$

10. $\frac{1}{6}, \frac{1}{12}, \frac{5}{18}$

Add or subtract each pair of fractions below. Make sure your answers are fully reduced.

11. $\frac{5}{8} + \frac{1}{4}$

12. $\frac{3}{10} - \frac{1}{8}$

13. $\frac{14}{3} + \frac{5}{6}$

14. $3\frac{1}{7} - \frac{9}{14}$

15. $\frac{2}{5} + \frac{1}{6} + \frac{7}{10}$

16. $4 - 1\frac{3}{8}$

Multiply each pair of numbers below.

17. $6 \times \dfrac{2}{11}$ 　　　　**(a) 18.** $\dfrac{1}{4} \times \dfrac{1}{3}$ 　　　　**(b) 19.** $\dfrac{5}{4} \times \dfrac{2}{3}$

Answer each question below.

20. What is $\dfrac{1}{4}$ of 224? 　　**(c) 21.** What is $\dfrac{1}{3}$ of $\dfrac{2}{9}$?

(d) 22. What is $\dfrac{2}{5}$ of $\dfrac{3}{10}$?

Translate the word problem below into math; then solve.

(e) 23. Super Duper Saver Grocery recently replaced all of its "real beef" beef jerky with "beef-flavored" beef jerky. If Verne only bought $\dfrac{1}{2}$ of $\dfrac{1}{6}$ of a pound of beef-flavored beef jerky—just to give the stuff a try—how much of a whole pound did he buy?

Lesson 32—Canceling First

In the last lesson, we covered multiplying fractions and, as you remember (we hope!), the method is to multiply the tops and bottoms, which is pretty basic.

A Tougher Case

But now let's take a tougher case. Let's find $\frac{2}{9}$ of $\frac{3}{10}$. This is a fraction of a fraction problem. On these we're supposed to multiply the fractions, remember. That gives us this.

$$\frac{2}{9} \times \frac{3}{10}$$

Multiplying the 2 and 3 on top and the 9 and 10 on bottom, we get

$$\frac{6}{90}.$$

Answers should always be fully reduced, as you know. Since this fraction has pretty large numbers, it's probably reducible. We'll use the factoring and canceling method. The first step is to factor the top and bottom into prime numbers. The 6 on top factors as 2×3, and the 90 on bottom factors as 9×10. But 9 can be broken down further as 3×3 and 10 as 2×5. So we end up with this.

$$\frac{2 \times 3}{3 \times 3 \times 2 \times 5}$$

A pair of 2s and a pair of 3s will cancel. That leaves no factors at all on top, so we need to put a 1 up there. On bottom, there's a 3 and 5 left. Multiplying those gives us a denominator of 15. The final (fully reduced) answer is $\frac{1}{15}$.

$$\frac{\cancel{2} \times \cancel{3}}{3 \times \cancel{3} \times \cancel{2} \times 5}$$

Canceling 2s and 3s

$$\frac{1}{3 \times 5} \text{ or } \frac{1}{15}$$

Avoiding Extra Work

Did you notice in our example that we multiplied the tops and bottoms, but then had to "unmultiply" them again (meaning factor them) in order to reduce the answer?

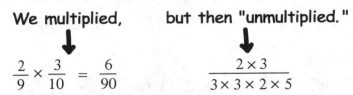

We multiplied,   but then "unmultiplied."

$$\frac{2}{9} \times \frac{3}{10} = \frac{6}{90} \qquad \frac{2 \times 3}{3 \times 3 \times 2 \times 5}$$

See, we multiplied the 2 and 3 to get 6. But then we had to take 6 and break it down as 2×3 again in the very next step. The same thing happened in the denominator. We multiplied 9 and 10 to get 90, but then 90 had to be factored back to 9×10 (and even further to $3 \times 3 \times 2 \times 5$).

This kind of multiplying and "unmultiplying" creates extra work. Is it possible to avoid it? Yes. What we can do is factor and cancel first—before multiplying. To show you how it works, let's do $\frac{2}{9} \times \frac{3}{10}$ again. Only this time, the very first step—before multiplying the tops and bottoms—is to factor.

We need to factor everything in both fractions into prime numbers. The numerators are already prime numbers, so we can't do anything with them. But we can break the denominators down: 9 factors as 3×3, of course, and 10 as 2×5.

$$\frac{2}{3 \times 3} \times \frac{3}{2 \times 5}$$

The next step is going to seem weird. What we're going to do is write the problem as a single fraction. We won't actually multiply anything. We'll just put the factors on top into a single numerator and the factors on bottom into a single denominator.

$$\frac{2 \times 3}{3 \times 3 \times 2 \times 5}$$

Look what happened. We've basically done the multiplication, because there's just one fraction. But our answer is factored, which means we're ready to cancel and reduce. The 2s and 3s cancel just like before to give $\frac{1}{15}$, which we know is right.

$$\frac{\cancel{2} \times \cancel{3}}{3 \times \cancel{3} \times \cancel{2} \times 5}$$

$$\frac{1}{15}$$

The main point is that by factoring *before* multiplying, we avoided having to multiply and then "unmultiply" again. We avoided the extra work. And the factoring step was a lot easier too, since we only had to factor small numbers (like 9 and 10) instead of bigger numbers (like 90).

Here's something else interesting. Most people cancel even before the two fractions are combined into one. They do it like this.

$$\frac{\cancel{2}}{3 \times \cancel{3}} \times \frac{\cancel{3}}{\cancel{2} \times 5} \qquad \text{Canceling when fractions are still separate.}$$

See, they cancel the 2s and 3s, even though they're in different fractions. This is legal, because the two fractions are going to be multiplied together in the very next step anyway. Then they'll be part of the same fraction. When canceling in this way, it's legal to cancel anything on top in either fraction with anything on bottom of either fraction.

And, once again, the advantage of canceling first is that it's faster and avoids some extra work. Another advantage is that you always know your answer is fully reduced, because you already canceled—before multiplying.

Practice 32

a. Multiply $2 \times \dfrac{3}{10}$. Factor and cancel first.

b. Multiply $\dfrac{3}{7} \times \dfrac{7}{4}$. Factor and cancel first.

c. Multiply $\dfrac{14}{5} \times \dfrac{1}{7}$. Factor and cancel first.

d. What is $\dfrac{4}{7}$ of $\dfrac{5}{8}$?

e. Translate the word problem below into math; then solve.

Baxter

Aunt Edna's ornery nephew was all smiles after being told that he had been included in her will. But the smile disappeared fast when he found out that she had left him only $\frac{1}{8}$ of $\frac{1}{10}$ of her estate. What fraction of Edna's estate did the nephew receive?

Problem Set 32

Tell whether each sentence below is True or False.

1. When multiplying fractions, it's easier to factor and cancel before multiplying.

    true

2. When you factor and cancel first, your answer is always fully reduced.

    true

Add or subtract each group of numbers below.

3.
$$\begin{array}{r} 1{,}789 \\ 5{,}336 \\ 3{,}024 \\ +\,8{,}590 \\ \hline \end{array}$$

4.
$$\begin{array}{r} 97{,}043 \\ -\,64{,}056 \\ \hline \end{array}$$

Multiply or divide each pair of numbers below.

5. $15\overline{)15{,}630}$

6.
$$\begin{array}{r} 763 \\ \times\,901 \\ \hline \end{array}$$

Fully reduce each fraction below by factoring and canceling.

7. $\dfrac{33}{99}$

8. $\dfrac{100}{150}$

Find the lowest common denominator for each group of fractions below.

9. $\dfrac{1}{8}, \dfrac{3}{5}, \dfrac{1}{2}$

10. $\dfrac{7}{10}, \dfrac{3}{14}, \dfrac{5}{21}$

Add or subtract each pair of fractions below. Make sure your answers are fully reduced.

11. $\dfrac{5}{3} + \dfrac{2}{3}$

12. $\dfrac{7}{8} + \dfrac{1}{4}$

13. $\dfrac{11}{14} + \dfrac{3}{10}$

14. $5\dfrac{2}{3} - 2\dfrac{1}{3}$

15. $\dfrac{5}{6} + \dfrac{1}{2} + \dfrac{1}{12}$

Multiply each pair of numbers below. Factor and cancel first.

(a) 16. $4 \times \dfrac{5}{12}$

(b) 17. $\dfrac{2}{5} \times \dfrac{5}{3}$

(c) 18. $\dfrac{10}{3} \times \dfrac{1}{5}$

Answer each question below.

19. What is $\dfrac{2}{3}$ of 990?

(d) 20. What is $\dfrac{3}{5}$ of $\dfrac{7}{12}$?

21. What is $\dfrac{3}{4}$ of $\dfrac{8}{9}$?

Translate the word problem below into math; then solve.

(e) 22. Aunt Edna's lazy and only somewhat loyal butler thought that Edna would surely leave him more money than she left her nephew (see practice problem e). Instead, the butler received only $\dfrac{1}{16}$ of $\dfrac{1}{10}$ of Edna's estate. What fraction of the estate did the butler get?

Lesson 33—Dividing Fractions

We've been multiplying with fractions, but now it's time to switch to division. We'll start by learning to divide a fraction by a whole number.

Dividing a Fraction by a Whole Number

Here's our first example.

$$\frac{1}{3} \div 2$$

The best way to see how to do this calculation is to compare it to another one that we already know how to do: $100 \times \frac{1}{2}$. To multiply 100 and $\frac{1}{2}$, we just put 100 over 1 and multiply the tops and bottoms of the fractions to get $\frac{100}{2}$ or 50.

$$\frac{100}{1} \times \frac{1}{2} = \frac{100}{2} = 50$$

So $100 \times \frac{1}{2}$ is really the same as 100 divided by 2. But if that's true, shouldn't $\frac{1}{3} \div 2$ be the same as $\frac{1}{3} \times \frac{1}{2}$? Yes. And we already know how to multiply two fractions. To multiply $\frac{1}{3}$ and $\frac{1}{2}$, we just multiply the tops and bottoms to get $\frac{1}{6}$.

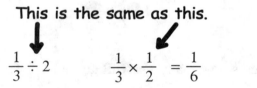

This is the same as this.

$$\frac{1}{3} \div 2 \qquad \frac{1}{3} \times \frac{1}{2} = \frac{1}{6}$$

But if $\frac{1}{3} \div 2$ and $\frac{1}{3} \times \frac{1}{2}$ are the same thing, then $\frac{1}{3} \div 2$ must also equal $\frac{1}{6}$. That makes sense, if you think about it. Check out these pictures.

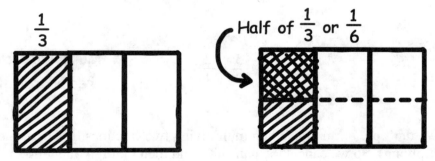

179

Cutting the whole into 3 equal pieces and shading 1 of them gives us $\frac{1}{3}$ (on the left). But dividing $\frac{1}{3}$ by 2 is the same as cutting that third in half. And that gives us $\frac{1}{6}$ (on the right). So $\frac{1}{6}$ is the correct answer.

Reciprocals

But notice something. The number 2 is the same as $\frac{2}{1}$, so we could have written our problem like this: $\frac{1}{3} \div \frac{2}{1}$. Then, to do the calculation, we could have just turned $\frac{2}{1}$ upside down and multiplied to get $\frac{1}{3} \times \frac{1}{2}$. That's the best way to divide a fraction. Just turn the second number upside down (or "invert") and multiply.

When we turn a number upside down, we get the **reciprocal** of the number. That means $\frac{2}{1}$ and $\frac{1}{2}$ are reciprocals, and so are $\frac{3}{4}$ and $\frac{4}{3}$, $\frac{5}{6}$ and $\frac{6}{5}$, and $\frac{4}{1}$ and $\frac{1}{4}$. The formal rule for dividing a fraction, then, is to multiply by the reciprocal of the second number.

Dividing Two Fractions

The same method will work when dividing two fractions. Look at this example.

$$\frac{5}{2} \div \frac{1}{2}$$

This problem is asking us how many $\frac{1}{2}$s will go into $\frac{5}{2}$. The answer is 5, because there have to be 5 halves in $\frac{5}{2}$. But let's see if our method works. We need to take the second number, $\frac{1}{2}$, and turn it upside down (to get its reciprocal) and multiply it by the first number, $\frac{5}{2}$.

$$\frac{5}{2} \times \frac{2}{1}$$

Multiplying by the reciprocal of $\frac{1}{2}$.

From here we multiply normally. When multiplying two fractions, it's best to cancel first (before multiplying). So we cancel the pair of 2s and then multiply the tops and bottoms.

$$\frac{5}{\cancel{2}_{1}} \times \frac{\overset{1}{\cancel{2}}}{1} = \frac{5}{1} \times \frac{1}{1} = \frac{5}{1} = 5 \qquad \text{Now multiply normally.}$$

That gives us 5, which is right.

Dividing a Whole Number by a Fraction

We also sometimes need to divide a whole number by a fraction. Here's one of those problems.

$$14 \div \frac{4}{5}$$

The method is exactly the same. First, we put 14 over 1. Next, we take the reciprocal of $\frac{4}{5}$, which is $\frac{5}{4}$, and multiply.

$$14 \div \frac{4}{5} = \frac{14}{1} \times \frac{5}{4} \qquad \text{Take the reciprocal of the second number and multiply.}$$

To carry out the actual multiplication, we factor and cancel first and then multiply the tops and bottoms.

$$\frac{14}{1} \times \frac{5}{4} = \frac{\cancel{2} \times 7}{1} \times \frac{5}{\cancel{2} \times 2} = \frac{35}{2} \qquad \text{Cancel the 2s, then multiply.}$$

We end up with $\frac{35}{2}$.

So it doesn't matter whether we're dividing a fraction by a whole number, two fractions, or a whole number by a fraction. The rule is the same: invert the second number and multiply.

Practice 33

a. Divide $\frac{1}{2} \div 3$.

b. Divide $\frac{3}{4} \div \frac{1}{5}$.

c. Divide $\frac{4}{7} \div \frac{4}{21}$.

 d. 50 has how many $\frac{1}{2}$'s in it?

e. Translate the word problem below into math; then solve.

Everybody loves Fiona's banana cream pie, but she never makes enough. For example, yesterday only $\frac{1}{4}$ of the pie was left, but 10 family members still wanted a piece. What fraction of the whole pie will each of the 10 family members have to settle for?

Problem Set 33

Tell whether each sentence below is True or False.

1. The reciprocal of a number is that number turned upside down.

2. To divide fractions, change the division to multiplication by the reciprocal.

Add or subtract each group of numbers below.

3.
$$\begin{array}{r} 436 \\ 5{,}232 \\ 6{,}948 \\ +\,733 \end{array}$$

4.
$$\begin{array}{r} 54{,}934 \\ -\,23{,}007 \end{array}$$

Multiply or divide each pair of numbers below.

5.
$$\begin{array}{r} 1{,}045 \\ \times\,802 \end{array}$$

6. $18)\overline{17{,}389}$

Fully reduce each fraction below by factoring and canceling.

7. $\dfrac{56}{24}$

8. $\dfrac{36}{81}$

Add or subtract each pair of fractions below. Make sure your answers are fully reduced.

9. $\dfrac{1}{7}+\dfrac{4}{7}$

10. $\dfrac{2}{3}-\dfrac{5}{9}$

11. $\dfrac{7}{5}-\dfrac{3}{4}$

12. $7\dfrac{1}{4}-5\dfrac{2}{3}$

13. $2\dfrac{1}{3}+\dfrac{7}{2}+\dfrac{5}{6}$

Multiply each pair of numbers below.

14. $\dfrac{7}{8}\times 16$

15. $\dfrac{2}{15}\times\dfrac{5}{4}$

16. $\dfrac{6}{35}\times\dfrac{7}{3}$

Divide each pair of numbers below.

(a) 17. $\dfrac{1}{3}\div 4$

(b) 18. $\dfrac{2}{5}\div\dfrac{1}{3}$

(c) 19. $\dfrac{3}{5}\div\dfrac{3}{10}$

Answer each question below.

20. What is $\dfrac{3}{8}$ of 136?

(d) 21. 100 has how many $\dfrac{1}{2}$ s in it?

Translate the word problem below into math; then solve.

(e) 22. Wendy has been pouring coffee refills all morning. If only $\dfrac{1}{5}$ of her decaf pitcher is left, and 7 people are asking for an immediate decaf refill, what fraction of the pitcher should each of the seven get?

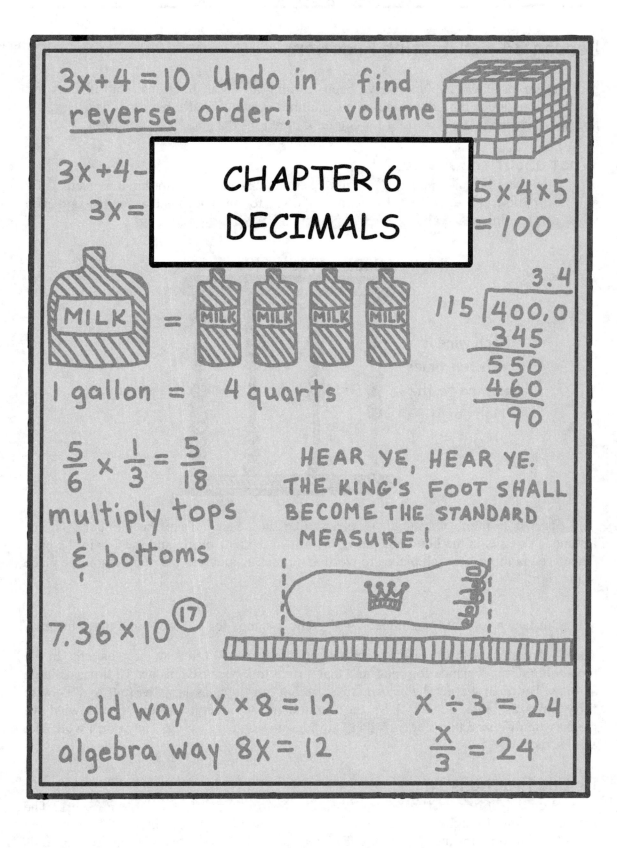

$3x + 4 = 10$ Undo in   find
reverse order!   volume

$3x + 4 -$

$3x =$

CHAPTER 6
DECIMALS

$5 \times 4 \times 5$
$= 100$

MILK $=$ MILK MILK MILK MILK

1 gallon $=$ 4 quarts

$$\begin{array}{r} 3.4 \\ 115 \overline{)400.0} \\ 345 \\ \hline 550 \\ 460 \\ \hline 90 \end{array}$$

$\dfrac{5}{6} \times \dfrac{1}{3} = \dfrac{5}{18}$

multiply tops
& bottoms

HEAR YE, HEAR YE.
THE KING'S FOOT SHALL
BECOME THE STANDARD
MEASURE!

7.36×10 (17)

old way $X \times 8 = 12$ $X \div 3 = 24$
algebra way $8X = 12$ $\dfrac{X}{3} = 24$

Lesson 34—Ill-Fitting Fractions

In the last few chapters, we've been learning all about fractions. And it turns out that fractions are a big advantage of our number system. That's because, unlike whole numbers, which can only be used for counting, fractions are good for measuring.

What about the Abacus?

However, there is one problem with fractions that you may not have noticed. They don't fit into the abacus system. Remember, the key to the abacus is that the balls on each wire have ten times the value of the balls on the wire to the right of them.

Each wire is worth ten times the wire to the right of it.

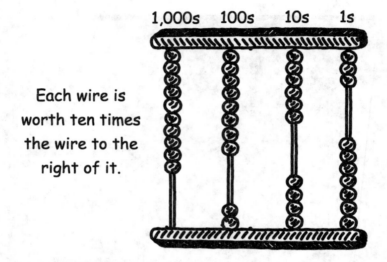

And our whole number system works just like the abacus. Take the number 247, for instance. The 2 is in the hundreds place; the 4 is in the tens place; and the 7 is in the ones place. The numbers in each place are worth ten times as much as the numbers in the place to the right.

But take a look at the number $247\frac{3}{4}$. The 2 stands for hundreds and the 4 for tens. That's consistent with the abacus, because hundreds are 10 times as large as tens. In the next column, the 7 stands for ones, and that's right too, because tens are 10 times as large as ones. But then we get 3 *fourths*. Ones are not ten times as large as fourths. (They're forty times as large, actually.) So the fraction messes everything up. That's what we meant when we said that fractions don't fit into our number system. They don't work like an abacus.

Fitting Fractions In

Wouldn't it be nice if we could get fractions to fit with all the whole numbers? The mathematicians thought so, and that's why they invented a new kind of fraction that would fit into the abacus. These new fractions are called decimal fractions, or **decimals** for short.[1] Regular fractions (like $\frac{3}{4}$) are actually called common fractions to distinguish them from decimal fractions. Of course, you've worked with decimals for years. But you may not have realized that the real difference between fractions (the regular kind) and decimals is that fractions don't work like an abacus but decimals do.

Here's how decimals work. To continue the abacus system with numbers less than one (fractions), we have to add another place to the right of the ones place, and ones have to be ten times the size of the numbers in that place. One is ten times bigger than $\frac{1}{10}$, so the place to the right of the ones is the tenths place. Next, we need to include another place to the right of the tenths. Tenths need to be ten times the size of the numbers in this place. The numbers in this place, then, need to be hundredths ($\frac{1}{100}$).[2] And we can keep adding places as long as we want, just as we can add as many places on the left as we want for the whole numbers.

...	100s	10s	1s	$\frac{1}{10}$	$\frac{1}{100}$	...
←	3	2	6	□	□	→

Once we have all these new places, it's easy to fit fractions into them. Take the number $326\frac{1}{2}$ as an example. It has 3 hundreds, 2 tens, 6 ones, and two *halves*. Obviously, the halves don't fit. So to use decimals here, we need to change halves to tenths. All we have to do is multiply the top and bottom of $\frac{1}{2}$ by 5. We know from the Law of Equivalent Fractions that that won't change the value of the fraction at all. But it will change the denominator to 10, which turns $\frac{1}{2}$ into five tenths.

$$\frac{1 \times 5}{2 \times 5} = \frac{5}{10}$$ **Multiplying top and bottom of $\frac{1}{2}$ by 5.**

Now our number is $326\frac{5}{10}$. The fraction is a tenth and it's in the tenth place, where it should be. But wait a minute. We don't write hundreds next to the 3 or tens next to the 2.

---

[1] The word decimal is from a Latin word for 10.

[2] Ones are ten times as big as tenths because 10 times $\frac{1}{10}$ equals 1. And tenths are ten times as big as hundredths because 10 times $\frac{1}{100}$ equals $\frac{1}{10}$.

So why do we need the denominator in $\frac{5}{10}$? The denominator is telling us that the 5 is a tenth. But we already know that, since the place next to ones always stands for tenths. So we can just put in a 5 to stand for 5 tenths and leave the denominator out.

The 5 stands for tenths.

3265

There's still a problem with this system. How do we tell which place is which? Somebody might think that 3265 means "three thousand two hundred sixty-five" mistaking the 5 for ones instead of tenths. We could try to fix this problem in several different ways. We could put a space between the 6 and 5, to show that the 5 stands for tenths.

326 5

But that might get confusing because people with sloppy handwriting might not make the space big enough. Another approach would be to put a slash between the two.

326/5

That would work okay. But, in the end, the mathematicians decided to use a dot instead of a slash. So in decimal form, $326\frac{1}{2}$ is written as 326.5.

The dot separates whole numbers from decimals

326.5

This number means 3 hundreds, two tens, 6 ones, and 5 tenths (which is the same as $\frac{1}{2}$). The dot shows very clearly which place is which, because the dot always goes between the ones and tenths place. As you know, the dot is actually called a **decimal point**.

By turning $\frac{1}{2}$ into $\frac{5}{10}$ and fitting it into the tenths place, we've made the number $326\frac{1}{2}$ work just like an abacus (326.5), where each place is worth ten times as much as the place to the right of it.

Leaving Off the Whole Numbers

Of course, decimals aren't always used to write numbers that are greater than one. We can also convert a pure fraction like $\frac{2}{5}$ (which doesn't have a whole number attached) into a decimal fraction. We just need to change $\frac{2}{5}$ to tenths. This is done by multiplying top and bottom by 2.

$$\frac{2 \times 2}{5 \times 2} = \frac{4}{10}$$

Multiplying top and bottom of $\frac{2}{5}$ by 2.

That gives us $\frac{4}{10}$. But we want to write this as a decimal, so we don't need the denominator of the fraction. All we have to do is put 4 in the tenths place. The decimal point should go to the left of it, like this: .4. But since the decimal point is hard to see, most people add a 0 in the ones column.

$$0.4.$$

The 0 doesn't change the value of the number, but it keeps people from confusing four tenths with four. So $\frac{2}{5}$ written as a decimal is 0.4.

Practice 34

a. 400 has how many $\frac{4}{3}$ s in it?

b. Write $\frac{3}{10}$ as a decimal fraction.

0.3

c. Write $\frac{3}{5}$ as a decimal fraction.

0.6 $\frac{3 \times 2}{5 \times 2}$ $\frac{6}{10}$

d. Write $3\frac{4}{5}$ as a decimal fraction.

e. Translate the word problem below into math; then solve.

Only $\frac{1}{2}$ of a slice of pizza was left and the 3 college roommates agreed to split it equally. What fraction of the slice did each get?

Problem Set 34

Tell whether each sentence below is True or False.

1. Decimals are special fractions that have been designed to fit the abacus system.

    true

2. A decimal point separates the ones column from the tenths column.

    ~~*false*~~ *true*

Add or subtract each group of numbers below.

3.
$$\begin{array}{r} 8{,}025 \\ 3{,}671 \\ 4{,}054 \\ +\,1{,}239 \end{array}$$

4.
$$\begin{array}{r} 89{,}705 \\ -\,47{,}846 \end{array}$$

Multiply or divide each pair of numbers below.

5.
$$\begin{array}{r} 8{,}308 \\ \times\,101 \end{array}$$

6. $32\overline{)24{,}389}$

Add or subtract each pair of fractions below. Make sure your answers are fully reduced.

7. $\dfrac{5}{9}+\dfrac{4}{9}$

8. $\dfrac{19}{20}-\dfrac{7}{10}$

9. $\dfrac{9}{14}+\dfrac{5}{12}$

10. $1\dfrac{1}{8}-\dfrac{2}{3}$

11. $4\dfrac{3}{4}+5\dfrac{1}{2}$

Multiply or divide each pair of numbers below.

12. $120\times\dfrac{2}{5}$

13. $\dfrac{2}{11}\div 5$

14. $\dfrac{3}{8}\times\dfrac{4}{9}$

15. $\dfrac{5}{3}\div\dfrac{2}{3}$

Answer each question below.

16. What is $\dfrac{6}{7}$ of $\dfrac{1}{12}$?

(a) 17. 300 has how many $\dfrac{2}{3}$'s in it?

(b) 18. Write $\dfrac{1}{10}$ as a decimal fraction.

(c) 19. Write $\dfrac{2}{5}$ as a decimal fraction.

(d) 20. Write $14\dfrac{1}{2}$ as a decimal fraction.

Translate the word problem below into math; then solve.

(e) 21. The 87 person rescue squadron was stuck in the middle of the desert with only $\dfrac{1}{2}$ of a water cooler left. What fraction of the water cooler should each member of the squadron get?

191

Lesson 35—Hundredths, Thousandths, ...

In the last lesson, we learned about decimals. To refresh your memory, the main advantage of decimals is that they allow us to fit fractions into our number system. Whole numbers work like an abacus and so do decimals.

Going Beyond Tenths

We changed a couple of fractions into tenths in the previous lesson. And it was a pretty simple process. Sometimes, though, a fraction can't be written with a denominator of 10, which means that it just won't fit into the tenths place. Here's an example.

$$28\frac{3}{4}$$

To make this a tenth, we would need to multiply the top and bottom of $\frac{3}{4}$ by some number that would change the 4 into a 10. The problem is that there's no whole number that will do that. So we can't change $\frac{3}{4}$ into a tenth.

That's no big deal, though. Not all whole numbers will fit into the ones place either. For instance, the number 28 can't be written with just ones. It uses the tens place too. It works the same way with some fractions. When a fraction can't be written as a tenth, we have to use the next place over, which is the hundredths place.

So to change $\frac{3}{4}$ to a decimal, instead of thinking of a number that we can multiply 4 by to get 10, let's think of a number we can multiply 4 by to get 100. That number is 25. So we should multiply the top and bottom of $\frac{3}{4}$ by 25.

$$\frac{3\times 25}{4\times 25} = \frac{75}{100}$$

Multiplying top and bottom of $\frac{3}{4}$ by 25.

That gives us $\frac{75}{100}$. Notice that the number on top has two digits instead of one, so it won't fit into a single place. How do we handle that? What we can do is split $\frac{75}{100}$ into two separate fractions.

$$\frac{75}{100} = \frac{70}{100} + \frac{5}{100}$$

Split $\frac{75}{100}$ into two fractions.

Then, since $\frac{70}{100}$ reduces to $\frac{7}{10}$, that means $\frac{75}{100}$ equals $\frac{7}{10}+\frac{5}{100}$. But that's just 7 tenths and 5 hundredths. Both of those fit perfectly into our decimal number system, with 7 going in the tenths place and 5 in the hundredths place. So $28\frac{3}{4}$ becomes 28.75.

We wanted to show you the splitting-the-fraction step, because that explains why $\frac{3}{4}$ is the same as 7 tenths and 5 hundredths. But it would be a real hassle to have to split a fraction every time we change a fraction to a decimal. Is there a shorter way to do it? Yes. Once we make the denominator of a fraction equal to 100 (like $\frac{75}{100}$), then if the numerator has two numbers (as in 75), we know automatically that the first digit is the tenth and the second is the hundredth. If the numerator has just one digit (like $\frac{2}{100}$), then that digit is a hundredth, and a zero needs to go in the tenths place (0.02). With this shortcut, we know at a glance that $\frac{43}{100}$ means 4 tenths and 3 hundredths (0.43). And we know that $\frac{7}{100}$ means 7 hundredths (0.07). No fraction splitting is necessary.

Going Beyond Hundredths

Some fractions won't fit completely into the tenths and the hundredths place. Even some simple fractions can't be squeezed into those two positions. Take $\frac{1}{8}$, for instance. It won't fit into tenths and hundredths, because there's no whole number that can be multiplied by 8 to get 10 or 100. What we have to do is go to the next place over, which is thousandths. To make the denominator of $\frac{1}{8}$ equal 1,000, we just have to multiply top and bottom by 125.

$$\frac{1\times125}{8\times125}=\frac{125}{1,000}$$

Multiplying top and bottom of $\frac{1}{8}$ by 125.

To turn $\frac{125}{1,000}$ into a decimal, we could break it down into three fractions: $\frac{100}{1,000}+\frac{20}{1,000}+\frac{5}{1,000}$. Then, the first two fractions could be reduced to get $\frac{1}{10}+\frac{2}{100}+\frac{5}{1,000}$. That comes out to 1 tenth, 2 hundredths, and 5 thousandths. All three of these fit into our number system, so $\frac{1}{8}$ becomes 0.125.

Fortunately, we can change $\dfrac{125}{1,000}$ to a decimal without any fraction splitting. Here's the shortcut for a denominator of 1,000. If the numerator has three digits (like 125), the first digit is the tenth, the second digit is the hundredth, and the third digit is the thousandth. If the numerator has two digits (like $\dfrac{21}{1,000}$), then the first digit is the hundredth and the second digit is the thousandth. There's no tenth, so a zero goes in the tenths place. So $\dfrac{21}{1,000}$ actually equals 0.021. If the numerator has just one digit (like $\dfrac{3}{1,000}$), then that digit goes in the thousandths place, with zeros in the tenths and hundredths place. Therefore, $\dfrac{3}{1,000}$ equals 0.003.

Finally, there are some fractions that require places even farther to the right than thousandths, such as ten thousandths, hundred thousandths, and on up. The method for converting them to decimal form is exactly the same.

Practice 35

a. Write $14\dfrac{9}{100}$ as a decimal fraction.

b. $\dfrac{3}{8}$ has how many $\dfrac{1}{4}$s in it?

c. Write $2\dfrac{5}{8}$ as a decimal fraction.

d. Write $\dfrac{1}{5}$ as a decimal fraction.

e. Translate the word problem below into math; then solve.

One half of the motocross racers said they had banged up their shins. One fifth of those said they had bruised their elbows too. What fraction of the racers had banged up their shins <u>and</u> bruised their elbows?

Problem Set 35

Tell whether each sentence below is True or False.

1. Some fractions cannot fit in the tenths column alone.

2. All fractions can fit into either the tenths or hundredths column.

Add or subtract each group of numbers below.

3.
$$\begin{array}{r} 899 \\ 2,212 \\ 3,923 \\ +1,205 \\ \hline \end{array}$$

4.
$$\begin{array}{r} 65,134 \\ -33,201 \\ \hline \end{array}$$

Multiply or divide each pair of numbers below.

5.
$$\begin{array}{r} 4,008 \\ \times 305 \\ \hline \end{array}$$

6. $14\overline{)28,764}$

Add or subtract each pair of fractions below. Make sure your answers are fully reduced.

7. $\dfrac{2}{3} + \dfrac{1}{6}$

8. $\dfrac{3}{4} - \dfrac{1}{7}$

9. $\dfrac{3}{8} + \dfrac{5}{9}$

10. $6\dfrac{1}{2} - 3\dfrac{2}{5}$

Multiply or divide each pair of numbers below.

11. $\dfrac{1}{3} \times \dfrac{3}{11}$

12. $\dfrac{3}{7} \div 6$

13. $1\dfrac{1}{4} \times \dfrac{8}{9}$

14. $\dfrac{9}{10} \div \dfrac{1}{2}$

Answer each question below.

15.   What is $\dfrac{1}{5}$ of 320?

16.   150 has how many $\dfrac{2}{7}$'s in it?

(a) 17.   Write $24\dfrac{7}{100}$ as a decimal fraction.

(b) 18. $\dfrac{7}{9}$ has how many $\dfrac{1}{3}$'s in it?

(c) 19.   Write $10\dfrac{3}{8}$ as a decimal fraction.

(d) 20.   Write $\dfrac{1}{4}$ as a decimal fraction.

Translate the word problem below into math; then solve.

(e) 21.   One fourth of the villains nabbed by the second-rate superhero were jaywalkers. One ninth of those were illegal double parkers too. What fraction of the nabbed villains were both jaywalkers <u>and</u> illegal double parkers?

Lesson 36—Adding and Subtracting Decimals

For the last few lessons, you may have been asking yourself why anyone would bother changing regular fractions to decimals (like $\frac{1}{8}$ to 0.125). Maybe the mathematicians get excited about putting all numbers (whole and fractional) into abacus form, but is there any practical reason for doing it? Absolutely. The reason for making the change is that fractions become much easier to add and subtract when they're written as decimals. It's a lot like going from Roman numerals (which are hard to add and subtract) to our modern numbers (which are easy to add and subtract). Let us explain.

Lining Up the Decimal Points

Remember from arithmetic courses what a pain it was to add mixed numbers with different denominators, like $4\frac{2}{5}+3\frac{1}{2}$. First, you have to convert each mixed number to an improper fraction. Then you have to find a lowest common denominator (LCD). Next, you have to change both of the denominators to the LCD and add their numerators. Finally, you might even have to reduce the answer. That's a lot of work.

But what if $4\frac{2}{5}+3\frac{1}{2}$ were converted to decimals first? We know that $4\frac{2}{5}$ is 4.4 and $3\frac{1}{2}$ is 3.5, so that gives us $4.4+3.5$. With both numbers in decimal form, they can be added vertically, just like whole numbers (and like pulling down balls on an abacus).

$$
\begin{array}{r}
4.4 \\
+\ 3.5 \\
\hline
7.9
\end{array}
$$

Add vertically and bring the decimal point down.

The answer is 7.9.[3] See how easy that was? That's the big advantage of converting fractions to decimals. By making fractions fit into the number system, they can be added or subtracted using the same basic methods that you've already learned for whole numbers. So even though you learned how to add decimals a long time ago, you may not have known what the purpose was.

Notice that the decimal points in 4.4 and 3.5 are lined up. And the decimal point in the answer 7.9 is directly below them. That's important because that's how we make sure we're adding ones to ones and tenths to tenths, and so on. When adding and subtracting decimals, then, the decimal points must always be lined up.

---

[3] The answer 7.9 could be changed back to a mixed number to get $7\frac{9}{10}$. But it isn't necessary to do this.

Carrying with Decimals

Sometimes when adding decimals, the tenths, hundredths, or another one of the fractional columns, will add to equal a number more than 10. Here's an example.

$$25.81$$
$$+14.73$$

Both of these numbers have fractional parts (0.81 and 0.73). But since the fractions are written as decimals, we can add the two numbers as if they were whole numbers. We just add the columns vertically. But notice that when adding the tenths column, we get 15. But all we have to do is put the 5 down below and carry the 1, just as we do with whole numbers. From there we finish by adding the other columns in the normal way. And, of course, the decimal points need to be all lined up.

$$\begin{array}{r} \mathbf{1\ 1} \\ 25.81 \\ +\ 14.73 \\ \hline 40.54 \end{array}$$

Add vertically and carry when necessary.

Even though adding decimals is so easy that you can do it without thinking, it's helpful to understand how the process actually works. When we added the tenths column to get 15, that was really 15 tenths or $\frac{15}{10}$. That's the same as $1\frac{5}{10}$. We then wrote down the 5 in the tenths column and carried the 1 into the ones column. The system worked perfectly. That's the beauty of decimals. We can handle fractions as easily as whole numbers.

A Subtraction Example

Here's a subtraction example.

$$887.616$$
$$-352.372$$

First, we have to make sure that the decimal points are all lined up vertically, with hundreds over hundreds, tens over tens, ones over ones, and tenths over tenths, etc. Next, we just subtract each column. The procedure is exactly the same as with whole numbers. When a number on top is smaller then the one below it then we have to regroup. In this problem, we need to group in the hundredths column by bringing over 1 tenth.

$$\begin{array}{r} \mathbf{5\ 11} \\ 887.6\cancel{1}6 \\ -\ 352.372 \\ \hline 535.244 \end{array}$$

Subtract vertically and regroup when necessary.

Make sure you understand what we did in that regrouping step. We had 1 hundredth minus 7 hundredths. But then we brought 1 tenth over, which makes 11 hundredths. And that left only 5 tenths on top in the tenths column. But, once again, the great thing about decimals is that you don't even have to think about whether you're subtracting tenths, hundredths, or anything else. It all works just like whole numbers.

We don't have room to show any more examples, but it's possible to add more than 2 numbers with decimals. And the procedure is exactly the same as the one we use for whole numbers, except for making sure that the decimal points are lined up.

Practice 36

a. Write $2\dfrac{7}{1,000}$ as a decimal.

b. Write $\dfrac{3}{5}$ as a decimal.

c. Subtract
$$\begin{array}{r} 68.742 \\ -35.393 \\ \hline \end{array}$$

d. Add
$$\begin{array}{r} 456.923 \\ +138.729 \\ \hline \end{array}$$

e. Translate the word problem below into math; then solve.

One fourth of the Thai recipes were too spicy for Brenda's taste buds and $\dfrac{1}{2}$ of the ones that were too spicy for Brenda were also too spicy for her husband. What fraction of the recipes were too spicy for Brenda's husband?

Problem Set 36

Tell whether each sentence below is True or False.

1. Fractions are easier to add and subtract when they are written as decimals.

2. When adding or subtracting decimals, the decimal points of the numbers should always be lined up.

Write each number below as a decimal.

3. $12\dfrac{7}{100}$

(a) 4. $3\dfrac{5}{1,000}$

(b) 5. $\dfrac{2}{5}$

Add or subtract each pair of numbers below.

6.
$$\begin{array}{r} 25.13 \\ +43.62 \\ \hline \end{array}$$

7.
$$\begin{array}{r} 9.75 \\ -3.23 \\ \hline \end{array}$$

8.
$$\begin{array}{r} 464.15 \\ +302.71 \\ \hline \end{array}$$

(c) 9.
$$\begin{array}{r} 46.563 \\ -24.275 \\ \hline \end{array}$$

(d) 10.
$$\begin{array}{r} 526.663 \\ +193.478 \\ \hline \end{array}$$

Multiply or divide each pair of numbers below.

11.
$$\begin{array}{r} 864 \\ \times 92 \\ \hline \end{array}$$

12. $18\overline{)9,846}$

Add or subtract each pair of fractions below. Make sure your answers are fully reduced.

13. $\dfrac{1}{8} + \dfrac{3}{4}$

14. $\dfrac{4}{5} - \dfrac{2}{3}$

15. $5\dfrac{1}{4} + 2\dfrac{1}{6}$

16. $7 - \dfrac{1}{5}$

Multiply or divide each pair of numbers below.

17. $\dfrac{2}{5} \times \dfrac{10}{12}$

18. $5 \div \dfrac{2}{7}$

19. $\dfrac{2}{9} \div \dfrac{4}{3}$

Answer each question below.

20.   What is $\dfrac{3}{4}$ of 264?

21. $\dfrac{5}{6}$ has how many $\dfrac{1}{12}$s in it?

Translate the word problem below into math; then solve.

(e) 22.   After seventy-seven failed attempts, the hockey team finally won the championship. Now $\dfrac{1}{2}$ of the fans think the city should name a street after the winning coach, and $\dfrac{1}{12}$ of those believe he should also be appointed mayor. What fraction of the fans believe the coach should be appointed mayor?

Lesson 37—Filling the Holes

In the last lesson, we learned how to add and subtract decimals. But here's an addition problem that's a little different. Suppose we tried to add the decimals 79.2 and 82.43.

$$
\begin{array}{r}
79.2 \\
+\ 82.43 \\
\end{array}
$$

Filling Holes when Adding

We've got the decimal points lined up vertically, as we should. But notice that there's a hole in the hundredths column. Is that a problem? Not really. It just means that 79.2 doesn't have any hundredths. But just so we have a number in every place, it's a good idea to fill the hole with a 0.

$$
\begin{array}{r}
79.20 \\
+\ 82.43 \\
\end{array}
$$
← Fill in the hole with a 0.

The extra zero makes it clear that the hundredths column is being treated just like all the others. Even more importantly, it helps us avoid the mistake of getting the decimal points out of line. For instance, without that extra 0, we might have mistakenly written the problem like this.

The decimal points aren't lined up.

↓

$$
\begin{array}{r}
79.2 \\
+\ 82.43 \\
\end{array}
$$

See, the decimal points are out of line, and that could cause us to add tenths with hundredths or tenths with ones, which would be totally wrong. Putting in that extra zero is kind of like putting a zero in front of .7 to get 0.7. It doesn't change the value of the number, it just makes things easier. But here's our problem worked out correctly (with the extra 0).

$$
\begin{array}{r}
\overset{1}{} \\
79.20 \\
+\ 82.43 \\
\hline
161.63 \\
\end{array}
$$
Adding normally.

Filling Holes when Subtracting

Filling the holes with an extra 0 is even more important when we're subtracting decimals. For example, to subtract 23.14 from 85.7 vertically, we really need to put a zero in the hundredths place of 85.7 to get 85.70.

$$85.70$$
$$-\ 23.14$$

What makes the 0 really necessary here is that we're going to have to regroup to subtract the hundredths (since 0 is smaller than 4). Without the 0, regrouping would be kind of tough. Here's the way it should work.

$$
\begin{array}{r}
85.\overset{6\ 10}{\cancel{70}} \\
-\ 23.14 \\
\hline
62.56
\end{array}
$$

The 0 helps with regrouping.

Filling More than One Hole

Sometimes, we have to fill more than one hole. Look at this problem.

$$896.9$$
$$-\ 53.324$$

See, we have two holes to fill on top. One in the hundredths place and one in the thousandths place. All we do is put an extra 0 in each place and subtract normally.

$$
\begin{array}{r}
896.\overset{\ \ \ \ 9}{\overset{8\ 10\ 10}{\cancel{900}}} \\
-\ 53.324 \\
\hline
843.576
\end{array}
$$

Subtract normally, regrouping twice.

We could have even filled the hole in the hundreds column of 53.324. Then the problem would have looked like this.

$$896.900$$
$$-053.324$$

But we're so used to working with whole numbers that it's not really necessary to fill in a hole to the left of the decimal point. It's probably enough just to fill in the holes on the right side of the point.

Practice 37

a. Write $\dfrac{189}{1,000}$ as a decimal.   **b.** Write $6\dfrac{5}{8}$ as a decimal.

c. Add $\begin{array}{r} 649.58 \\ +\,285.4 \\ \hline \end{array}$ **d.** Subtract $\begin{array}{r} 67.8 \\ -\,53.43 \\ \hline \end{array}$

e. Translate the word problem below into math; then solve.

One half of the outfielders who were surveyed said that air-conditioned baseball caps were a great idea, and $\dfrac{1}{15}$ of those said that foot-massage cleats would be even better. What fraction of those who were surveyed would prefer foot-massage cleats to air-conditioned caps?

Problem Set 37

Tell whether each sentence below is True or False.

1. When adding numbers, putting zeros in for empty places helps avoid getting the decimal points out of line.

2. It is never necessary to put in extra zeros when subtracting decimals.

Write each number below as a decimal.

(a) 3. $\dfrac{142}{1,000}$ **4.** $7\dfrac{23}{100}$ **(b) 5.** $10\dfrac{3}{8}$

Add or subtract each pair of numbers below.

6. $\begin{array}{r} 46.95 \\ +\,21.62 \\ \hline \end{array}$ **7.** $\begin{array}{r} 8.63 \\ -\,4.81 \\ \hline \end{array}$ **(c) 8.** $\begin{array}{r} 573.68 \\ +\,391.6 \\ \hline \end{array}$

(d) 9. $\begin{array}{r} 89.7 \\ -\,65.25 \\ \hline \end{array}$ **10.** $\begin{array}{r} 57.346 \\ +\,33.579 \\ \hline \end{array}$

Multiply or divide each pair of numbers below.

11.
$$\begin{array}{r} 1708 \\ \times 130 \\ \hline \end{array}$$

12. $22\overline{)15{,}432}$

Add or subtract each pair of fractions below. Leave your answer in fractional form, but make sure the fraction is fully reduced.

13. $\dfrac{5}{11} + \dfrac{4}{11}$

14. $8\dfrac{1}{3} - 2\dfrac{1}{7}$

15. $5 + \dfrac{9}{4}$

16. $3 - \dfrac{6}{5}$

Multiply or divide each pair of numbers below.

17. $\dfrac{1}{9} \times \dfrac{3}{5}$

18. $\dfrac{7}{8} \div 14$

19. $\dfrac{3}{2} \div \dfrac{1}{8}$

Answer each question below.

20. What is $\dfrac{1}{8}$ of 480?

21. 56 has how many $\dfrac{2}{3}$'s in it?

Translate the word problem below into math; then solve.

(e) 22. One half of the islanders thought the hammock was the greatest invention since fire, but $\dfrac{1}{7}$ of those said that wind-resistant grass huts would be even better. What fraction of the islanders would prefer wind-resistant grass huts to hammocks?

Lesson 38—Money and Decimals

In this lesson, we're going to talk about one of the most common ways that people use decimals, and that's to work with money. You may have never thought of this, but everybody uses decimals when money is involved.

Quarters and Nickels and Decimals

As an example, what if we wanted to add a $5 bill and a quarter to a $10 bill and a nickel? A quarter is the same as 25 cents and that's written as 0.25. A nickel is the same as 5 cents or 0.05. What we would probably do is combine the 5 dollars and the quarter to get 5.25. Then we would combine the 10 dollars and the nickel to get 10.05. Since these are decimals, we would add them vertically, making sure to line up the decimal points like this.

$$
\begin{array}{r}
\overset{\mathbf{1}}{5}.25 \\
+\,10.05 \\
\hline
\mathbf{15.30}
\end{array}
$$

Convert cents to decimal and add vertically.

The answer comes out to 15.30, which is just 15 dollars and 30 cents.

Everybody knows how to add money in that way. But if you think about it, the whole procedure was designed to avoid using fractions with different denominators. After all, a quarter is a fourth of a dollar (that's where the name "quarter" comes from), and a nickel is a twentieth of a dollar.[4] So we could have done the problem like this instead.

$$ 5\frac{1}{4} + 10\frac{1}{20} $$

It would have been a lot harder, though, because we would have had to convert the mixed numbers to improper fractions, then find a lowest common denominator, and so on. By converting the quarter and nickel into decimal form, we avoided the messy fractions entirely. And since we're so used to working with quarters and nickels, we even did the conversions in our head. (You were probably required to memorize those in earlier basic math courses.) But no one would ever dream of doing a money calculation using $\frac{1}{4}$ for a quarter and $\frac{1}{20}$ for a nickel, because decimals are so much easier. So money is just another example of why decimals are so helpful.

---

[4] This is because it takes 20 nickels to make $1.

A Handy Table

Just as a review, here are the most common amounts of money and their decimal forms. You can look back at this whenever you're doing money problems in your assignments.

Common Money Amounts in Dollars

amount	fraction	decimal
half dollar	$\frac{1}{2}$	0.5
quarter	$\frac{1}{4}$	0.25
dime	$\frac{1}{10}$	0.10
nickel	$\frac{1}{20}$	0.05
penny	$\frac{1}{100}$	0.01

Practice 38

a. Write $\frac{23}{1,000}$ as a decimal.

b. Write the following amount of money as a decimal number (in dollars): Two $5 bills, three $1 bills, two quarters, and two dimes.

c. Write the following amount of money as a decimal number (in dollars): Two quarters, one dime, four nickels, and three pennies.

d. Add $\begin{array}{r} 88.37 \\ + 43.945 \\ \hline \end{array}$

e. Translate the word problem below into math; then solve.

Just before heading off to her palatial winter getaway, Madame Pompadour purchased her 43rd pair of mink earmuffs for $3,900.45 and her 27th pair of mink leg warmers for $5,230.58. What was the total bill for these two items?

Problem Set 38

Tell whether each sentence below is True or False.

1. We use decimal numbers when doing calculations with money.

2. Another way to do calculations with money is to convert everything into cents.

Write each number below as a decimal.

3. $\dfrac{17}{100}$

(a) 4. $\dfrac{52}{1,000}$

5. $18\dfrac{3}{10,000}$

Write each amount of money as a decimal number (in dollars).

(b) 6. Three \$5 bills, two \$1 bills, one quarter, and one dime.

(c) 7. One quarter, two dimes, three nickels, and four pennies.

Add or subtract each pair of numbers below.

8. $\begin{array}{r} 11.25 \\ +6.76 \\ \hline \end{array}$

9. $\begin{array}{r} 36.61 \\ -15.72 \\ \hline \end{array}$

10. $\begin{array}{r} 467.58 \\ -56.19 \\ \hline \end{array}$

(d) 11. $\begin{array}{r} 99.05 \\ +37.211 \\ \hline \end{array}$

Multiply or divide each pair of numbers below.

12. $\begin{array}{r} 3200 \\ \times 405 \\ \hline \end{array}$

13. $26\overline{)20,384}$

Add or subtract the fractions below. Leave your answer in fractional form, but make sure the fraction is fully reduced.

14. $\dfrac{1}{2}+\dfrac{5}{2}$

15. $\dfrac{5}{6}-\dfrac{7}{9}$

16. $12\dfrac{3}{4}-11\dfrac{3}{8}$

Multiply or divide each pair of numbers below.

17. $6 \times \dfrac{7}{12}$ **18.** $\dfrac{7}{8} \div \dfrac{1}{4}$ **19.** $\dfrac{2}{5} \times 4\dfrac{1}{2}$

Answer each question below.

20. What is $\dfrac{1}{4}$ of $\dfrac{2}{3}$?   **21.** $\dfrac{3}{4}$ has how many $\dfrac{1}{16}$ s in it?

Translate the word problem below into math; then solve.

(e) 22. Madame Pompadour recently purchased a velvet-lined doggie basket and a diamond-studded flea collar as birthday gifts for her beloved pet poodle. If the two items cost $3,215.90 and $5,850.25 respectively, what was the total bill?

Lesson 39—Multiplying Decimals

Now that we've learned about adding and subtracting decimals, let's talk about multiplying them. Take a look at this example.

$$1.25 \times 7.5$$

Since 1.25 is the same as $1\frac{1}{4}$ and 7.5 is the same as $7\frac{1}{2}$, we could multiply these as mixed numbers. But that would be pretty messy. Multiplying them as decimals is actually much easier, because decimals can be multiplied using basically the same method we use for multiplying whole numbers. The tenths and hundredths can be treated just like the ones. So it's not just addition and subtraction that are made easier by using decimals, but multiplication too. That's another advantage of using decimals to make fractions (like $\frac{1}{4}$ and $\frac{1}{2}$) fit into our number system, so they can be treated like balls on an abacus.

Just Like Whole Numbers Again

Let's go through the steps for multiplying 1.25 and 7.5. First, we need to write the numbers vertically (just as with long multiplication of whole numbers).

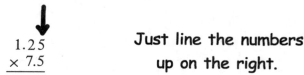

$$\begin{array}{r} 1.2\,5 \\ \times\ 7.5 \\ \hline \end{array}$$

Just line the numbers up on the right.

Notice, though, that the decimal points aren't lined up. That's one of the differences between addition and subtraction with decimals and multiplication with decimals. When multiplying, we don't have to worry about lining up the decimal points. All we have to do is make the digits that are farthest to the right line up (the 5s, in this case) and let the rest of the digits (and the decimal points) take care of themselves. The next step is to multiply the numbers normally, completely ignoring the decimal points. We just pretend they aren't even there at this point.

$$\begin{array}{r} \overset{\mathbf{3}}{\underset{1}{1}}\overset{\mathbf{2}}{} \\ 1.2\,5 \\ \times\ 7.5 \\ \hline {}_{1}625 \\ 8750 \\ \hline 9375 \end{array}$$

Multiply normally, ignoring the decimal points.

We end up with 9375. But that isn't the final answer, because we still need to place the decimal point. But where should it go? We can't write it underneath the other decimal points, because they aren't lined up. Here's how we figure out where to put the decimal point.

Counting the Digits

We count the number of digits to the right of the decimal point in each of the numbers being multiplied. In 1.25, there are two digits to the right of the decimal point (2 and 5). In 7.5, there is one digit to the right of the decimal point (5). Then we add up the total number of digits: 2+1 equals 3.

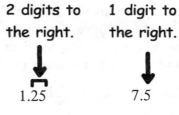

Add them up: 2 + 1 = 3

Next comes the key step. We go to 9375 (our answer) and put the decimal point in a position so that there are exactly 3 digits to the right of it. That means the decimal point needs to go between the 9 and 3 like this.

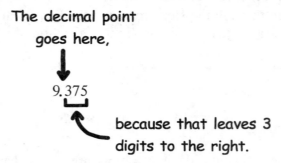

So our final answer is 9.375. That's all there is to it.

Decimal x Whole Number Too

To multiply a decimal by a whole number, we use the exact same method. Here's a simple example.

$$\begin{array}{r} 7.4 \\ \times\ 8 \\ \hline \end{array}$$

We already have the numbers lined up along the right. So the first step is to multiply, ignoring the decimal point.

3
7.4
$\times$ 8
———
592

Multiply normally, ignoring the decimal point.

Now to place the decimal point in the answer, we just count the number of digits to the right of the decimal points in 7.4 and 8. There's 1 digit to the right of the point in 7.4. What about 8, though? No decimal point is showing. But, remember, every whole number actually has a decimal point on the far right, even if it isn't shown. Yet since there's no digit to the right of the point, we still get 0 digits for 8.[5] Next, we need to add those digits up: 1+0 equals 1. The final step is to place the decimal point in 592 so that there is 1 digit to the right of it. That means the point goes between the 9 and 2 like this.

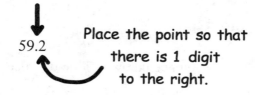

59.2   Place the point so that there is 1 digit to the right.

No Hole Filling

Another nice thing about multiplication is that we don't have to fill up holes with zeros (the way we do when adding and subtracting decimals). For example, when multiplying 5.34 times 2.2, we can just write the problem like this.

5.34
$\times$2.2

We don't have to fill the hundredths place in 2.2 to get 2.20. That's not necessary because we're not lining up the decimal points. All we have to do is line the numbers up on the right and start multiplying. Here's this problem all worked out.

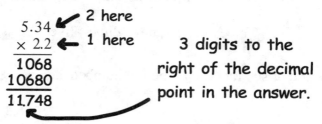

5.34   ← 2 here
$\times$ 2.2 ← 1 here
———
1068
10680
———
11.748

3 digits to the right of the decimal point in the answer.

Since there are 2 digits to the right of the decimal point in 5.34 and 1 digit to the right of the point in 2.2, we place the decimal point so that there are 3 digits to the right in the answer. That gives us 11.748.

---

[5] It's wrong to write 8 as 8.0 and then say there's 1 digit to the right of the decimal point. With that method, you could create as many digits to the right of the point as you wanted: 8.00 or 8.000 or 8.0000 and so on.

Practice 39

a. Write $\dfrac{409}{10,000}$ as a decimal.

b. Multiply
$$\begin{array}{r} 3.8 \\ \times\,0.77 \\ \hline \end{array}$$

c. Multiply
$$\begin{array}{r} 0.547 \\ \times\,2.6 \\ \hline \end{array}$$

d. Multiply
$$\begin{array}{r} 422.4 \\ \times\,23 \\ \hline \end{array}$$

e. Translate the word problem below into math; then solve.

Rocky Raccoons were on sale for $3.30 per pound. If Mrs. Gargantua bought 4.5 pounds worth for tonight's dinner, what was her total bill?

Problem Set 39

Tell whether each sentence below is True or False.

1. Decimals can be multiplied with the same basic method that is used for multiplying whole numbers.

2. When multiplying decimals, both decimal points must be lined up.

Write each number below as a decimal.

(a) 3. $\dfrac{101}{10,000}$

4. $\dfrac{11}{50}$

Write each amount of money as a decimal number (in dollars).

5. One $10 bill, one $1 bill, two quarters, two dimes, and four pennies.

6. Three quarters, three dimes, five nickels, and one penny.

Add or subtract each group of numbers below.

7.
$$\begin{array}{r} 86.32 \\ -\,8.25 \\ \hline \end{array}$$

8.
$$\begin{array}{r} 156.3 \\ 54.8 \\ +\,8.9 \\ \hline \end{array}$$

9.
$$\begin{array}{r} 24.402 \\ -\,5.285 \\ \hline \end{array}$$

10.
$$\begin{array}{r} 738.254 \\ +\,95.05 \\ \hline \end{array}$$

Multiply or divide each pair of numbers below.

11.
$$\begin{array}{r} 27.657 \\ \times 0.8 \\ \hline \end{array}$$

(b) 12.
$$\begin{array}{r} 2.4 \\ \times 0.99 \\ \hline \end{array}$$

(c) 13.
$$\begin{array}{r} 0.839 \\ \times 1.9 \\ \hline \end{array}$$

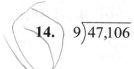
14. $9\overline{)47,106}$

(d) 15.
$$\begin{array}{r} 251.7 \\ \times 12 \\ \hline \end{array}$$

Add or subtract each pair of fractions below. Make sure your answers are fully reduced.

16. $\dfrac{2}{14} + \dfrac{3}{7}$

17. $\dfrac{7}{18} - \dfrac{1}{12}$

Multiply or divide each pair of numbers below.

18. $10 \times \dfrac{4}{5}$

19. $\dfrac{8}{15} \div 4$

20. $\dfrac{2}{9} \times 3 \times \dfrac{1}{4}$

Answer each question below.

21. What is $\dfrac{3}{8}$ of 256?

22. 500 has how many $\dfrac{5}{9}$ s in it?

Translate the word problem below into math; then solve.

(e) 23. Hippo lard sells for $1.20 per ounce. If Mrs. Gargantua bought 8.5 ounces worth for her Saturday brunch, what was her total bill?

Lesson 40—Dividing Decimals

We covered multiplication of decimals in the last lesson. What about division? Well, it turns out that decimals can be divided in basically the same way we divide whole numbers. So decimals allow us to add, subtract, multiply, and divide fractions as if they were plain old whole numbers. Pretty amazing.

Turning the Divisor into a Whole Number

Let's go through a division example.

$$2.5\overline{)15.75}$$

We could just divide the numbers by ignoring the decimal points at first and then figuring out where to put the decimal in our answer. Doing the problem that way, the rule is the reverse of the rule for multiplying. Instead of adding up the digits to the right of the decimal points, we would have to subtract them. But we won't show you that method, because nobody actually divides decimals that way.[6]

There's an easier method that everybody uses. With this one, the first step is to make a change to the decimal points. This change is easier to understand if the problem is written as a fraction, so let's do that.

$$\frac{15.75}{2.5}$$

We multiply the bottom number by 10 or 100 or 1,000, or etc. in order to turn it into a whole number. In this case, we need to multiply 2.5 by 10 to make it 25. To avoid changing the value of the fraction, we have to multiply the top by 10 as well.

$$\frac{15.75 \times 10}{2.5 \times 10} = \frac{157.5}{25}$$

**Make the number
on bottom
a whole number.**

The important thing to understand is that the answer to the problem hasn't changed. We've just made the denominator a whole number. That will make the division a little easier.

---

[6] However, it is kind of interesting that this method is the reverse of the one for multiplying with decimals.

The next step is to write the problem as a normal long division problem again and then carry out the division.[7] And we don't need to pay any attention to the decimal point in 157.5 at this stage.

$$
\begin{array}{r}
63 \\
25\overline{)157.5} \\
150\downarrow \\
\overline{75} \\
75 \\
\overline{0}
\end{array}
$$

Divide normally, ignoring the decimal point.

That gives us 63, but we still have to figure out where to put the decimal point. Since we changed 2.5 to 25 (and 15.75 to 157.5), all we have to do is put the decimal point directly above the point in 157.5. That means the point goes directly between the 6 and 3 to get 6.3.

$$
\begin{array}{r}
6.3 \\
25\overline{)157.5} \\
150 \\
\overline{75} \\
75 \\
\overline{0}
\end{array}
$$

The point goes directly above the point in 157.5.

If we hadn't changed 2.5 to 25, then we would have had to count the number of digits to the right of the decimal point in both numbers and subtract the digits and so on. But this method is a lot easier.

Here are all the steps again for dividing with decimals.

Dividing with Decimals

1.	Multiply top and bottom by 10, 100, 1,000 or etc. to make the bottom number (divisor) a whole number.
2.	Do normal long division, ignoring the decimal point.
3.	Put the decimal point in the answer directly above the point in the number underneath (dividend).

---

[7] Keep in mind that $25\overline{)157.5}$ has the same answer as $2.5\overline{)15.75}$, so whatever answer we get here will also be the answer to our original problem.

Doing it in Your Head

Let's do one more example.

$$0.18\overline{)9.36}$$

The first step is to write the problem as a fraction ($\frac{9.36}{0.18}$) and turn 0.18 (the divisor) into a whole number. We can do that by multiplying 0.18 and 9.36 by 100, which will change the bottom to 18 and the top to 936. You probably know that most people don't bother writing the problem as a fraction. They do this step in their head. They just move the decimal point in 0.18 until it's all the way to the right (to become 18) and then move the decimal point in 9.36 the same number of places, which is 2 places to the right, for 936. But this is the same thing as multiplying the top and bottom of $\frac{9.36}{0.18}$ by 100 (even though most people don't know it).

By the way, an easy way to multiply and divide numbers by 10, 100, 1,000, and so on is to just move the decimal point. You may remember these shortcuts from earlier math courses but here they are again.

Multiplying and Dividing by Moving the Decimal Point

1.	When multiplying a decimal by 10, 100, 1,000, etc., move the decimal point in the number to the right as many places as there are 0s.
2.	When dividing a decimal by 10, 100, 1,000, etc., move the decimal point in the number to the left as many places as there are 0s.

When people move the decimal point in 0.18 as many places as in 9.36, they're just using shortcut number 1.

But getting back to our problem, we now have it in the form $18\overline{)936}$. This is now a really easy problem, because it's just division of two whole numbers. We won't even bother working it out. The answer is 52. Make sure you understand, though, that since $18\overline{)936}$ and $0.18\overline{)9.36}$ are the same, 52 is also the answer to $0.18\overline{)9.36}$, which was our original problem.

Practice 40

a. Write $\dfrac{8}{25}$ as a decimal.

b. Add
$$\begin{array}{r} 0.24 \\ 9.3 \\ +15.87 \\ \hline \end{array}$$

c. Divide $0.5\overline{)11.85}$.

d. Divide $0.12\overline{)6.24}$.

e. Translate the word problem below into math; then solve.

Pretty in Pink Lemonade costs $1.24 per bottle. If Shirley bought $19.84 worth, how many bottles did she buy?

Problem Set 40

Tell whether each sentence below is True or False.

1. When dividing two decimals, the first step is to change the divisor to a whole number.

2. When dividing a decimal number by a whole number, the decimal point stays in the same spot in the answer.

Write each number below as a decimal.

3. $\dfrac{9}{10}$

(a) 4. $\dfrac{1}{25}$

Add or subtract each group of numbers below.

5.
$$\begin{array}{r} 12.96 \\ +11.07 \\ \hline \end{array}$$

6.
$$\begin{array}{r} 125.145 \\ -33.268 \\ \hline \end{array}$$

(b) 7.
$$\begin{array}{r} 0.88 \\ 5.1 \\ +18.56 \\ \hline \end{array}$$

8.
$$\begin{array}{r} 72.427 \\ -43.634 \\ \hline \end{array}$$

Multiply or divide each pair of numbers below.

(c) 9. $0.4\overline{)31.24}$

10. $\begin{array}{r} 801.7 \\ \times 2.3 \\ \hline \end{array}$

11. $1.2\overline{)6{,}278.4}$

12. $\begin{array}{r} 35.01 \\ \times 0.75 \\ \hline \end{array}$

(d) 13. $0.15\overline{)7.245}$

Add or subtract each pair of fractions below. Make sure your answers are fully reduced.

14. $\dfrac{1}{3} + \dfrac{2}{3} + \dfrac{1}{4}$

15. $\dfrac{2}{33} + \dfrac{4}{11} + \dfrac{1}{3}$

Multiply or divide each pair of numbers below.

16. $\dfrac{1}{6} \times \dfrac{3}{7}$

17. $1\dfrac{1}{2} \div 4$

18. $3 \times \dfrac{1}{5} \times \dfrac{2}{3}$

Answer each question below.

19. What is $\dfrac{2}{3}$ of $\dfrac{3}{14}$?

20. $10\dfrac{1}{2}$ has how many $\dfrac{1}{2}$'s in it?

Translate the word problem below into math; then solve.

(e) 21. Redder than Red Cranberry Juice costs \$1.56 per bottle. If Amanda bought \$10.92 worth, how many bottles did she buy?

Lesson 41—Decimal Remainders

When dividing whole numbers, a lot of answers have a remainder. For example, when dividing 125 by 4, we get 31 with a remainder of 1.

$$\begin{array}{r} 31 \\ 4\overline{)125} \\ -12 \\ \hline 05 \\ 4 \\ \hline 1 \end{array}$$

The answer is 31 with a remainder of 1.

You remember from arithmetic that one way to show an answer with a remainder is to put the answer followed by a capital R and then the remainder: 31 R1 Another way to show a remainder, though, is with a fraction. What we do is put the remainder over the number we're dividing by (the divisor). For our example problem, $4\overline{)125}$, the remainder is 1 and the divisor is 4, so that gives us this.

$$31\frac{1}{4}$$

⟵ **Remainder on top.**

⟵ **Divisor on bottom.**

Put in a Decimal Point and Zero

There is a third way to show a remainder. It's to turn it into a decimal. And the great thing about this approach is that all we have to do is keep dividing. We'll show you how it works on $4\overline{)125}$. After we've brought down the last number and subtracted to get the remainder, we put in a decimal point to the right of 125 (the dividend) and write a zero after it. This is perfectly legal because it doesn't change the value of 125.

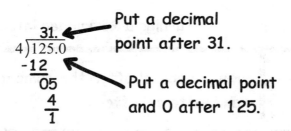

Put a decimal point after 31.

Put a decimal point and 0 after 125.

The next step is to put a decimal point in 31 (our answer) directly above the point in 125 (the dividend), as we always do when dividing a decimal by a whole number.

Just Keep Dividing

From here, we just continue the division process by bringing down the 0, as if it were part of the original division problem. And since we already have the decimal point properly positioned in the answer, there's no need to worry about it anymore at all.

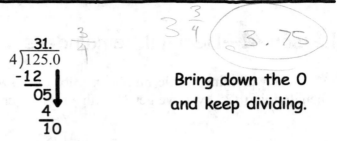

$$4\overline{)125.0}$$ = 31.
−12
05
4
10

Bring down the 0
and keep dividing.

Now we divide 4 into 10 to get 2. The 2 goes on top above the 0. Then since 2×4 equals 8, we put an 8 below the 10 and subtract. That gives us a remainder of 2, though. We can't allow that, because we're converting the remainder into a decimal. So we have to put another 0 after 125.0 and bring it down. And the division process continues until we finally end up with a remainder of 0.

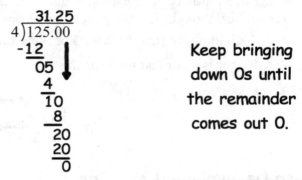

$$4\overline{)125.00}$$ = 31.25
−12
05
4
10
8
20
20
0

Keep bringing
down 0s until
the remainder
comes out 0.

As you can see, it took two more steps to get to that point. The answer comes out to 31.25. That makes sense, because $31\frac{1}{4}$ is the same as 31.25. So by continuing to divide (bringing down another 0 each step) we automatically turned $\frac{1}{4}$ into its decimal form, 0.25. Here are all the steps for turning a remainder into a decimal.

Turning a Remainder into a Decimal

1.	Put a decimal after the number being divided (dividend) and write a 0 after it.
2.	Put a decimal point directly above in the answer.
3.	Keep dividing (and bringing down more 0s) until you get a 0 remainder.

Practice 41

a. Divide $6\overline{)723}$. Write any remainder in decimal form.

b. Divide $8\overline{)6,269}$. Write any remainder in decimal form.

c. Divide $12\overline{)2,793}$. Write any remainder in decimal form.

d. What is $\dfrac{1}{4}$ of $13\dfrac{1}{3}$?

e. Translate the word problem below into math; then solve.

The Golden Spud sells plain baked potatoes for $1.82 each. If the restaurant sold $203.84 worth of plain baked potatoes at lunchtime, how many of them did they sell?

Problem Set 41

Tell whether the sentence below is True or False.

1. A remainder can be turned into a decimal by just continuing the long division process.

2. A remainder can be turned into a fraction by putting it over the divisor.

Add or subtract each group of numbers below.

3.
$$
\begin{array}{r}
248.3 \\
+\,69.92 \\
\hline
\end{array}
$$

4.
$$
\begin{array}{r}
7.325 \\
-\,0.142 \\
\hline
\end{array}
$$

5.
$$
\begin{array}{r}
551.34 \\
+\,924.06 \\
\hline
\end{array}
$$

Multiply or divide each pair of numbers below. Write any remainders in decimal form.

(a) 6. $4\overline{)526}$

7.
$$
\begin{array}{r}
4.25 \\
\times\,6.1 \\
\hline
\end{array}
$$

(b) 8. $8\overline{)7,325}$

9.
$$
\begin{array}{r}
387.6 \\
\times\,0.15 \\
\hline
\end{array}
$$

(c) 10. $16\overline{)4,054}$

11.
$$
\begin{array}{r}
5.03 \\
\times\,2.4 \\
\hline
\end{array}
$$

Add or subtract each pair of fractions below. Make sure your answers are fully reduced.

12. $\dfrac{3}{7} + \dfrac{1}{4}$

13. $\dfrac{7}{10} - \dfrac{1}{6}$

Multiply or divide each pair of numbers below.

14. $18 \div \dfrac{2}{9}$

15. $\dfrac{3}{5} \times \dfrac{5}{2}$

16. $\dfrac{1}{8} \div \dfrac{7}{4}$

Answer each question below.

17. What is $\dfrac{9}{11}$ of $\dfrac{5}{18}$?

18. 24 has how many $\dfrac{3}{4}$'s in it?

(d) 19. What is $\dfrac{1}{5}$ of $52\dfrac{1}{2}$?

Translate the word problem below into math; then solve.

(e) 20. Hamster Accessories Incorporated sells eight-inch skateboards for $6.75 each. If the company sold $317.25 worth of eight-inch skateboards, how many did they sell?

Lesson 42—Converting Fractions to Decimals

Now that you know all about division with decimals, we can show you a quick way to change a fraction to decimal form. Take the fraction $\frac{1}{5}$ as an example. We've learned to convert $\frac{1}{5}$ to a decimal by multiplying the top and bottom of the fraction by 2 to get $\frac{2}{10}$, or 0.2. This method works fine, but another way to do it is to use the methods for dividing decimals that we've been learning.

Divide the Bottom into the Top

With this new method, the first step is to change the 1 in the numerator to 1.0 to get $\frac{1.0}{5}$. Basically, we've just turned the numerator into a decimal. The next step is to divide the bottom (5) into the top (1.0), according to the rules for dividing decimals. The decimal point in the answer has to be directly above the point in 1.0. So we put the point in the proper position and then divide, ignoring the decimal points completely. And we just keep dividing until we get a 0 remainder.

$$
\begin{array}{r}
.2 \\
5{\overline{)1.0}} \\
-\underline{10} \\
0
\end{array}
$$

Divide the bottom into the top.

The result comes out to .2 (or 0.2 to show the decimal point more clearly), which is the same answer we got by multiplying the top and bottom by 2.

So now we have two methods for converting a fraction to a decimal. The first is to multiply the top and bottom by the same number to make the denominator equal to 10, 100, 1,000, etc. The second is to make the numerator a decimal by putting a point to its right, and then divide the bottom of the fraction into the top, using long division.

Dividing Is Often Easier

Since $\frac{1}{5}$ is a simple fraction, it's just about as easy to convert it by multiplying the top and bottom of the fraction (by 2) as it is to use long division. But for some fractions, the division approach is a lot easier. For example, remember that to convert $\frac{1}{8}$ the old way, we have to change the denominator to 1,000. Figuring out what number will make the bottom equal 1,000 can take awhile. It's actually 125. After multiplying the top and bottom of $\frac{1}{8}$ by 125 the fraction becomes $\frac{125}{1,000}$. That turns out to be 0.125 in decimal form. But the process is pretty long.

It's faster to convert $\frac{1}{8}$ using long division. All we have to do is change the 1 on top to 1.0 and then divide until we get a 0 remainder (bringing down more 0s as necessary).

$$\begin{array}{r} .125 \\ 8\overline{)1.000} \\ -8 \\ \hline 20 \\ -16 \\ \hline 40 \\ -40 \\ \hline 0 \end{array}$$

Keep dividing until the remainder is 0.

We end up with 0.125, which is the same answer we got by multiplying the top and bottom of $\frac{1}{8}$. But the long division approach was faster, because we didn't have to brainstorm about what number to multiply 8 (and 1) by.

Big, Messy Numbers Mean It's Better to Divide

Here's another example of a fraction that's a whole lot easier to convert using long division: $\frac{128}{4,096}$. Think of how hard it would be to convert this fraction into decimal form using the old method. We'd have to change the denominator to some huge number like 10000000000…. And how would we ever figure out what number to multiply the top and bottom by? But by using long division, we could change the fraction to a decimal fairly quickly. We would just put a decimal point after 128, and another point directly above that one, in the answer. And it would probably make sense to stick in several zeros at the end, since the division is likely to take several steps.[8]

$$4,096\overline{)128.0000}$$

The next step would be to divide normally, ignoring the decimal points, until we get a 0 remainder. We won't show you the steps, but the answer turns out to be 0.03125. That's the decimal form of $\frac{128}{4,096}$. The main point, though, is that whenever the numerator and

---

[8] Since 4,096 is so much bigger than 128, we have to add at least 2 zeros to 128 because the smallest whole number that 4,096 can divide into in this problem is 12,800.

denominator of a fraction are large, it's almost always easier to convert it to a decimal by using long division.

Converting Decimals into Fractions

We've been converting fractions into decimals, but what about converting a decimal back into a regular (common) fraction? We already learned how to do that. Say, for example, that we want to change 0.42 to a fraction. We just rewrite the decimal as a fraction with a denominator of 100. The digits 42 go on top and the 100 on bottom to get $\frac{42}{100}$. But then we have to make sure that the answer is fully reduced. For $\frac{42}{100}$, we can factor and cancel to reduce it down to $\frac{21}{50}$. So $\frac{21}{50}$ is the fraction form of 0.42.

Generally, to convert decimals into fractions we can just look at the last digit in the decimal. If the last digit is tenths, then the denominator will be 10, if it's hundredths, the denominator will be 100, and so on. Once we have the denominator, we write the digits that make up the decimal in the numerator (forgetting about any zeros to the left). So, in the last example, since the 2 in 0.42 is in the hundredths spot, that means that the denominator has to equal 100 and the numerator has to equal 42.

Here's another quick one. To convert 0.051 to a fraction, we first need to recognize that the 1 is in the thousandths place, which means that the denominator has to equal 1,000. Then we ignore zeros to the left and write 51 in the numerator to get $\frac{51}{1,000}$.

Practice 42

a. Divide $4\overline{)4,973}$.   b.   Multiply $\frac{5}{27} \times \frac{9}{25} \times \frac{5}{9}$.

c. Convert $\frac{7}{8}$ into decimal form using long division.

d. Convert 0.295 into a fraction. Make sure your answer is fully simplified.

e. Translate the word problem below into math; then solve.

Big Hans is 188.5 cm (or 6 ft. 2 in.) tall. Little Hans is 94 cm (or 3 ft. 1 in.) tall. How many centimeters taller is Big Hans than Little Hans?

Problem Set 42

Tell whether each sentence below is True or False.

1. A fraction can be converted into decimal form using long division.

2. It is not possible to convert decimals into fractions.

Add or subtract each group of numbers below.

3. $\begin{array}{r} 36.005 \\ +18.756 \\ \hline \end{array}$

4. $\begin{array}{r} 157.24 \\ -104.51 \\ \hline \end{array}$

5. $\begin{array}{r} 23.65 \\ 14.72 \\ +30.9 \\ \hline \end{array}$

6. $\begin{array}{r} 903.75 \\ -646.32 \\ \hline \end{array}$

Multiply or divide each pair of numbers below. Write any remainders in decimal form.

7. $3.2\overline{)13.76}$

8. $\begin{array}{r} 75.4 \\ \times 9.6 \\ \hline \end{array}$

9. $2.4\overline{)300.48}$

10. $\begin{array}{r} 77.42 \\ \times 0.52 \\ \hline \end{array}$

(a) 11. $4\overline{)5,235}$

Add or subtract each group of fractions below. Make sure your answers are fully reduced.

12. $\dfrac{1}{2}+\dfrac{3}{4}+\dfrac{1}{5}$

13. $\dfrac{5}{14}-\dfrac{2}{7}$

Multiply or divide each group of numbers below.

14. $24\times\dfrac{5}{6}$

15. $\dfrac{4}{5}\div 8$

(b) 16. $\dfrac{3}{8}\times\dfrac{4}{9}\times\dfrac{3}{4}$

Convert each fraction below into decimal form using long division.

17. $\dfrac{2}{5}$ **(c) 18.** $\dfrac{3}{8}$

Convert each decimal below into a fraction. Make sure your answers are fully reduced.

19. 0.23 **(d) 20.** 0.145

Translate the word problem below into math; then solve.

(e) 21. In early August, the bag where the Happy Valley Post Office keeps all the letters to Santa weighed only 2.8 pounds, but by late September it weighed 4.7 pounds. How many pounds were added in between?

Lesson 43—Never-Ending Decimals

For quite a few lessons now, we've been telling you how great decimals are, but the truth is, decimals do have some drawbacks.

It Just Keeps Going and Going ...

To show you, let's convert the fraction $\frac{1}{3}$ into decimal form. We'll use the long division method. We change the 1 on top to 1.0 and then divide. A decimal point should be placed in the answer (above the point in 1.0).

$$
\begin{array}{r}
.333\ldots \\
3\overline{)1.000} \\
-9 \\
\hline
10 \\
-9 \\
\hline
10 \\
-9 \\
\hline
1
\end{array}
$$

We never get a remainder of 0.

As always, we need to divide until the remainder comes out 0. But notice that we've gotten into a pattern. Every time we bring down another 0, 3 goes into 10 3 times, and 3 times 3 is 9, which leaves a remainder of 1 (not 0). So we're never going to get a 0 remainder. It will just be 3s forever. What does this mean? It means that the only way to get a decimal fraction that is exactly equal to $\frac{1}{3}$ is to let the 3s go on without stopping. In other words, $\frac{1}{3}$ is exactly equal to $\frac{3}{10}+\frac{3}{100}+\frac{3}{1,000}+\frac{3}{10,000}$ and on and on forever.

Believe it or not, there's no simpler way to fit $\frac{1}{3}$ into our modern number system.[9]

$$\frac{1}{3} = \frac{3}{10} + \frac{3}{100} + \frac{3}{1,000} + \frac{3}{10,000} + \frac{3}{100,000} + \cdots \text{ forever}$$

Since we can't keep writing numbers forever, we write a line over the 3 like this: $0.\overline{3}$.

$$0.3333\ldots \text{ is written as } 0.\overline{3}$$

The line simply means that the digit 3 repeats forever. Decimals like $0.\overline{3}$ are called **repeating decimals**, and decimals that stop (like 0.5) are called **terminating decimals.**

---

[9] That just means there's no number that you can multiply by 3 to get 10, 100, 1,000, etc.

Lots of Repeaters

So the one big drawback of decimals is that not all fractions will fit nicely into the decimal system. There are some fractions where the digits have to go on forever to fit. It's kind of surprising that a fraction as simple as $\frac{1}{3}$ is like that. Even worse, there are a lot of other repeating decimals. For instance, if we try to convert $\frac{2}{9}$ into decimal form, we get 0.222..... (In other words, $\frac{2}{9}$ is equal to $\frac{2}{10}+\frac{2}{100}+\frac{2}{1,000}+\frac{2}{10,000}$ and on and on.) Of course, the proper way to write 0.222... is $0.\overline{2}$.

Here's another repeater: $\frac{1}{6}$. If we try to convert this one into a decimal using long division, the result is 0.1666.... Notice that there's a 1 in the tenths place, but then it's 6s forever after that. So $\frac{1}{6}$ actually equals $\frac{1}{10}+\frac{6}{100}+\frac{6}{1,000}+\frac{6}{10,000}$ and on and on. The short way to write 0.1666... is $0.1\overline{6}$. The line goes over only the repeating digit, the 6.

Sometimes more than one digit repeats. For example, if we try to convert $\frac{1}{7}$ into a decimal by long division, we'll get this: 0.142857142857142857.... There are actually six digits that are repeating. And they just go on and on. The correct way to write this is to put a line over all six digits like this: $0.\overline{142857}$.

Even though repeating decimals can be a pain, they're worth it, because they allow us to add, subtract, multiply, and divide fractions in the same way as whole numbers. That's a huge advantage, especially when solving practical problems.

Rounding Off Repeating Decimals

But that raises an important question. How do we handle a repeating decimal if it pops up as the answer to a practical problem? For instance, what if we were measuring something and ended up with 0.333... feet? We wouldn't want to wrestle with never ending digits on a practical problem like that. One way out would be just to use the fraction form, $\frac{1}{3}$. But what if we wanted to use a decimal to make our calculations simpler? Then we could use a decimal estimate by rounding off 0.333....

Here's the way rounding works. Instead of writing $\frac{1}{3}$ as 0.333333...., we first decide how many digits we really need. That's determined by how accurate the answer needs to be. The more 3s we use, the more accurate the estimate is (because the closer the decimal's value gets to $\frac{1}{3}$). The number 0.33333 is closer to $\frac{1}{3}$ than the number 0.333. But neither one is exactly equal to $\frac{1}{3}$. That would require 3s going on forever. But let's say we only need an answer accurate to tenths. Then we can just use 0.3. That's not equal to $\frac{1}{3}$ (it's actually equal to $\frac{3}{10}$), but it may be close enough for our problem. If we need the answer to be a little more accurate, then we could use an estimate to hundredths. That would be 0.33 (which isn't exactly right either).

Actually, to be technically correct when rounding a number, we have to look at the digit to the right of the one we're rounding to. For instance, if we want to round 0.166666..., which is the decimal form of $\frac{1}{6}$, to the hundredths place, we look at the thousandths place. If that digit is 5 or greater, then we increase the hundredths digit by 1. In 0.166666...., there's a 6 in the thousandths place, so we need to change 0.16 to 0.17 to correctly round.

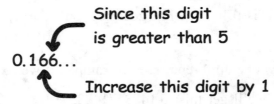

Since this digit
is greater than 5

0.166...

Increase this digit by 1

That means 0.1666 rounded to hundredths (2 decimal places) = 0.17

If the digit to the right (of the spot we're rounding to) is less than 5, then we leave the digit we're rounding to alone. An example is $\frac{2}{9}$, which equals 0.2222.... To round this to the tenths (1 place), we look at the hundredths place. Since it's below 5, we keep the tenths digit the same, leaving us with 0.2. Here are the formal rules for rounding.

Rounding a Decimal

1.	When the digit to the right of the one you're rounding to is 5 or greater, round up (increase by 1).
2.	When the digit to the right of the one you're rounding to is less than 5, leave the number alone.

One more point. Rounding is really common when dealing with money. Nobody wants to mess with a fraction of a cent. For instance, if a money calculation resulted in an answer like $14.166666...., we would round it off to the nearest hundredths place, because a penny is the smallest kind of coin (it equals $\frac{1}{100}$ of a dollar). But since the number next to the hundredths place is greater than 5, we have to round up, which means the answer would have to be $14.17.

Practice 43

a. Divide $0.22\overline{)48.4}$. Write any remainders in decimal form.

b. Divide $18\overline{)7,842}$. Write any remainders in decimal form.

c. Convert $\frac{4}{9}$ into decimal form.

d. Round $0.2\overline{8}$ to two digits.

e. Translate the word problem below into math; then solve.

Howie has decided to grow a beard. If his beard grows at a rate of 0.001 inches each week, how many inches long will it be in 12 weeks?

Problem Set 43

Tell whether each sentence below is True or False.

1. A decimal that goes on forever is called a terminating decimal.

2. When solving a practical problem, repeating decimals are often rounded.

Add or subtract each group of numbers below.

3. $\begin{array}{r} 909.64 \\ +132.15 \\ \hline \end{array}$

4. $\begin{array}{r} 42.89 \\ -21.375 \\ \hline \end{array}$

5. $\begin{array}{r} 576.5 \\ 149.7 \\ +250.9 \\ \hline \end{array}$

Multiply or divide each pair of numbers below. Write any remainders in decimal form.

6.
$$128.1 \\ \underline{\times 0.5}$$

(a) 7. $0.25\overline{)75.5}$

8.
$$6.806 \\ \underline{\times 4.3}$$

(b) 9. $12\overline{)5,648}$

10.
$$504.1 \\ \underline{\times 0.07}$$

Add or subtract each pair of fractions below. Make sure your answers are fully reduced.

11. $4\dfrac{2}{3} + \dfrac{8}{9}$

12. $\dfrac{5}{3} - \dfrac{3}{2}$

Multiply or divide each pair of numbers below.

13. $\dfrac{3}{7} \div \dfrac{9}{14}$

14. $\dfrac{5}{8} \times 56$

15. $\dfrac{6}{7} \div 3$

Convert each fraction below into decimal form.

16. $\dfrac{7}{20}$

(c) 17. $\dfrac{1}{9}$

Convert each decimal below into a fraction. Make sure your answers are fully reduced.

18. 0.62

19. 0.008

Round each decimal below to two digits (hundredths).

20. $0.\overline{4}$

(d) 21. $0.5\overline{7}$

Translate the word problem below into math; then solve.

(e) 22. Howie's hero, his uncle Thornton, has a beard that grows at a rate of 0.075 inches per week. How many inches will Thornton's beard grow in 12 weeks?

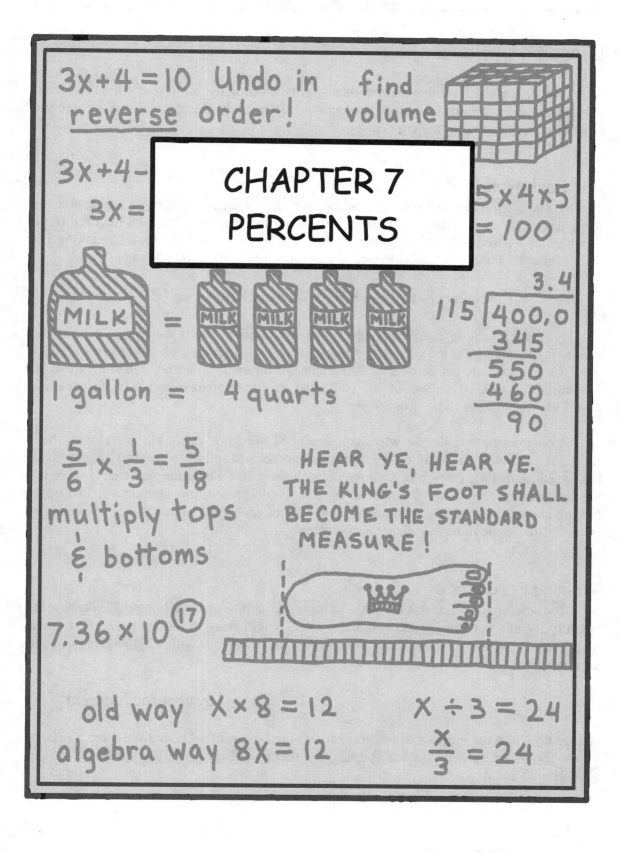

CHAPTER 7 PERCENTS

$3x+4=10$ Undo in reverse order!

find volume

$3x+4-$

$3x=$

$5\times4\times5=100$

MILK $=$ MILK MILK MILK MILK

1 gallon $=$ 4 quarts

$$\begin{array}{r} 3.4 \\ 115\overline{\smash{\big)}400.0} \\ 345 \\ \hline 550 \\ 460 \\ \hline 90 \end{array}$$

$\dfrac{5}{6}\times\dfrac{1}{3}=\dfrac{5}{18}$

multiply tops & bottoms

HEAR YE, HEAR YE. THE KING'S FOOT SHALL BECOME THE STANDARD MEASURE!

7.36×10^{17}

old way $\quad X\times8=12$

algebra way $\quad 8X=12$

$X\div3=24$

$\dfrac{X}{3}=24$

Lesson 44—Percents

We've studied fractions and decimals pretty thoroughly, so now it's time to turn to percents. And even though you did percents in earlier math courses, we'll try to give you a better understanding of the concept.

For Each Hundred

The word **percent** actually means "per hundred." Or another way of saying it is "for each hundred."[1] For example, one percent of a number means 1 for each hundred in the number. So 1 percent of 500 is 5, since there are 5 hundreds in 500, and we're taking 1 in each of those 5 hundreds. Using the same logic, one percent of 900 has to be 9.

Percent really means "for each hundred."

You can also take more than one percent of a number. For instance, two percent just means 2 for each hundred, and since there are 2 hundreds in 200, 2 percent of 200 is $2+2$ or 4. Likewise, ten percent of 200 means 10 for every hundred, and since there are 2 hundreds in 200, 10 percent of 200 is $10+10$ or 20. Another example is 30 percent of 200. That would have to be $30+30$ or 60.

You may be wondering why we even need percents. After all, we already have fractions and decimals. Why do we need percents too? Mainly it's because people find it easy to think in 100s (which is what we do with percents). For example, what if there is a big political meeting and 10 out of every 25 people present are Democrats. Instead of talking about 10 out of 25, most people think it's easier to talk about 40 out of every 100 (which is the same thing). And that's 40 percent.

Writing Percents

It's important to know how to write a percent. Fortunately, we don't have to actually write out the word percent. That would take a long time. But since mathematicians like symbols better than words, they came up with a symbol for percent. Of course, you've used it for years. Here it is.

%   Symbol for "percent"

All we do is put the number of the percent and then the symbol goes right after it (as you know). So one percent is written as 1%, 2 percent is written as 2%, 30 percent is written as 30%, and so on.

[1] "Cent" is from a Latin word for hundred.

Practice 44

a. Convert the fraction $\frac{1}{7}$ into decimal form. If it's a repeating decimal, round to two digits (hundredths).

b. Convert the fraction $\frac{13}{14}$ into decimal form. If it's a repeating decimal, round to two digits (hundredths).

c. Convert 0.017 into a fraction. Make sure your answer is fully reduced.

d. What is 2% of 300?

e. Translate the word problem below into math; then solve.

A rickshaw is a small, two-wheeled carriage that is pulled by a human being instead of a horse. Some rickshaw drivers in other countries get paid an amount equal to only $\frac{1}{2}$ of a penny for every block they travel. How many pennies will a driver earn after he travels 94 blocks?

Problem Set 44

Tell whether each sentence below is True or False.

1. The word percent means "per hundred."

2. A percent is shown using the symbol "&."

Add or subtract each group of numbers below.

3.
$$\begin{array}{r} 99.35 \\ +75.82 \\ \hline \end{array}$$

4.
$$\begin{array}{r} 503.2 \\ -14.19 \\ \hline \end{array}$$

5.
$$\begin{array}{r} 8.034 \\ +4.125 \\ \hline \end{array}$$

Multiply or divide each pair of numbers below. Write any remainders in decimal form.

6.
$$\begin{array}{r} 18.75 \\ \times 4.3 \\ \hline \end{array}$$

7. $1.5\overline{)4.575}$

8.
$$\begin{array}{r} 542.1 \\ \times 0.7 \\ \hline \end{array}$$

9. $9\overline{)6,333}$

10. $\begin{array}{r} 73.8 \\ \times 12 \\ \hline \end{array}$

Add or subtract each pair of numbers below. Make sure your answers are fully reduced.

11. $11 - \dfrac{9}{2}$

12. $3\dfrac{3}{10} + \dfrac{5}{2}$

Multiply or divide each pair of numbers below. Make sure your answers are fully reduced.

13. $\dfrac{2}{11} \times 22$

14. $\dfrac{1}{3} \div \dfrac{1}{2}$

Convert each fraction below into decimal form. Round any repeating decimals to two digits (hundredths).

15. $\dfrac{3}{5}$

(a) 16. $\dfrac{4}{7}$

(b) 17. $\dfrac{11}{14}$

Convert each decimal below into a fraction. Make sure your answers are fully reduced.

18. 0.8

(c) 19. 0.029

Answer each question below.

20. What is 1% of 600?

(d) 21. What is 3% of 700?

Translate the word problem below into math; then solve.

(e) 22. In some countries, a shoe shine boy might earn an amount equal to only $\dfrac{1}{4}$ of a penny for each shoe he shines. How many pennies will the boy earn after shining 128 shoes?

Lesson 45—Calculating Percents

In the last lesson we started learning about percents. We only did a few simple calculations, which is why we were able to do all of them in our heads. But there's also a pencil and paper way to calculate a percent. This method comes in handy when doing tougher percent problems.

Calculating a Percent Using a Fraction

To show you how the method works, let's go through an example.

Find 2% of 400.

The first step is to turn the percent into a fraction. All we have to do is drop the percent symbol, and then put 2 in the top (numerator) and 100 in the bottom (denominator) of the fraction.

$$2\% \text{ equals } \frac{2}{100} \text{ as a fraction}$$

The next step is to multiply the fraction by the number (400).

$$\frac{2}{100} \times 400$$

To carry out the multiplication, we write the 400 over 1 and then multiply the two fractions.

$$\frac{2}{100} \times \frac{400}{1}$$

$$\frac{800}{100}$$

Now we reduce the fraction by factoring and canceling.

$$\frac{2 \times 2 \times 2 \times 2 \times 5 \times 2 \times 5}{2 \times 5 \times 2 \times 5}$$

$$\frac{\cancel{2} \times \cancel{2} \times 2 \times 2 \times \cancel{5} \times 2 \times \cancel{5}}{\underset{1}{\cancel{2} \times \cancel{5} \times \cancel{2} \times \cancel{5}}}$$

$$\frac{8}{1}$$

That leaves us with $\frac{8}{1}$ or just 8. That makes sense, if you think about it. Percent means "out of one hundred," and 1% of 400 is 4 (1 for each 100), so 2% must be 8.

So to find the percent of a number, we can change the percent to a fraction and then multiply the fraction by the number normally.

Calculating a Percent Using a Decimal

We can also calculate a percent using a decimal. Going back to the problem 2% of 400, instead of using $\frac{2}{100}$, we just use the decimal form, which is 0.02.

$$\frac{2}{100} \text{ written as a decimal is } 0.02.$$

Next, we multiply the decimal (0.02) by 400 to get 8.

$$0.02 \times 400 = 8$$

And that's the same answer we got before.

Actually, there's a quick way to change a percent to a decimal, without having to write it as a fraction first. You probably remember the method from arithmetic, but we'll go over it quickly.

Every whole number has a decimal point. So 2% is the same as 2.0%. But compare 2.0% with the decimal form 0.02. The only difference is that the percent symbol has been dropped and the decimal point has been moved two places to the left. That's always the way it works, which means that to change a percent to a pure decimal all we have to do is drop the percent symbol and move the decimal point 2 places to the left.[2]

Move the decimal point
two places to the left.

2.0% equals 0.02

Converting percents into decimals is important because most people think it's easier to calculate the percent of a number using a decimal (instead of a fraction). That's

---

[2] By the way, the reason this works is that dividing by 100 always moves the decimal point 2 places to the left.

particularly true now that we all have calculators. With a calculator, you can punch in a decimal really fast.

A Quick Example

Just to make sure you're understanding the concept, let's do a quick example.

Lower Transylvania had never witnessed bravery equal to that displayed by the Seventeenth Brigade's Third Battalion. Amazingly, 17% of the Battalion's 800 men were awarded their country's highest military honor. How many received the honor?

To solve this, we need to find 17% of 800. Let's go through the formal method. The first step is to change 17% to a decimal. We could change it into a fraction, but a decimal is probably easier (as we said). All we have to do is drop the percent symbol and move the decimal point 2 places to the left. That turns 17% into 0.17.

17% equals 0.17

Next, we just multiply 0.17 by 800.

$$0.17 \times 800 = 136$$

That gives us 136, which means that 136 soldiers must have received the country's highest military honor.

Practice 45

a. Divide $6\overline{)1,271}$. Write any remainders in decimal form.

b. Convert $\dfrac{7}{11}$ into decimal form. If your answer is a repeating decimal, round to two digits (hundredths).

c. Convert 0.64 into a fraction. Make sure your answer is fully reduced.

d. What is 18% of 900?

e. Translate the word problem below into math; then solve.

All the clowns who were surveyed said they had dreamed of becoming a clown when they grew up, but only 15% said they had dreamed of becoming a rodeo clown. If 200 clowns were surveyed, how many of those said they had dreamed of becoming a rodeo clown?

Problem Set 45

Tell whether each sentence below is True or False.

1. To calculate the percent of a number, change the percent to a fraction or decimal and multiply.

2. The shortcut for changing a percent to a decimal is to drop the percent symbol and move the decimal point two places to the left.

Add or subtract each group of numbers below.

3.
$$\begin{array}{r} 306.74 \\ +265.81 \\ \hline \end{array}$$

4.
$$\begin{array}{r} 8.214 \\ -3.93 \\ \hline \end{array}$$

5.
$$\begin{array}{r} 68.6 \\ 73.1 \\ +90.5 \\ \hline \end{array}$$

Multiply or divide each pair of numbers below. Write any remainders in decimal form.

6. $2.4\overline{)134.4}$

7. $\begin{array}{r} 2.465 \\ \times 3.7 \\ \hline \end{array}$

(a) 8. $6\overline{)1,885}$

9. $14\overline{)1,197}$

Add or subtract each pair of fractions below. Make sure your answers are fully reduced.

10. $\dfrac{5}{7}-\dfrac{5}{14}$

11. $\dfrac{7}{8}+\dfrac{1}{6}$

Multiply or divide each pair of numbers below. Make sure your answers are fully reduced.

12. $\dfrac{3}{5}\times 95$

13. $12\div\dfrac{4}{9}$

Convert each fraction below into decimal form. Round any repeating decimals to two digits (hundredths).

14. $\dfrac{7}{8}$

15. $\dfrac{5}{6}$

(b) 16. $\dfrac{9}{11}$

Convert each decimal below into a fraction. Make sure your answers are fully reduced.

17. 0.11

(c) 18. 0.32

19. 0.701

Answer each question below.

20. What is 14% of 300?

(d) 21. What is 22% of 800?

Translate the word problem below into math; then solve.

(e) 22. All the sailors who were surveyed said they had dreamed of crossing the ocean when they grew up, but only 5% said they had dreamed of crossing the ocean in a submarine. If 400 sailors were surveyed, how many of those said they had dreamed of crossing the ocean in a submarine?

Lesson 46—Percent of Any Number

We've been learning how to figure the percent of a number. But you may have noticed that all the numbers in our examples were simple ones that ended with zeros—like 400 and 800. Most of these calculations can be done in your head.

Percent of an Ordinary Number

But what about finding a percent of an ordinary number like 82 or 25 or 46? These are often too hard to do in your head, and that's when the method we showed you in the last lesson comes in really handy. Let's go through one of these harder examples.

Find 25% of 85.

The first step is to change the percent into a fraction or decimal. Since the decimal is easier, we'll use that. There's actually a decimal point after the 25 in 25%, so it could be written as 25.0%. But to change the percent to a decimal, what we do is drop the percent symbol and move the decimal point two places to the left.

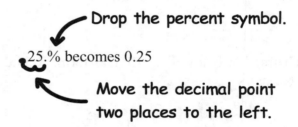

Drop the percent symbol.

25.% becomes 0.25

Move the decimal point two places to the left.

So the decimal form of 25% is 0.25. (We put the 0 in just to make it easier to see the point.) The next step is to multiply 0.25 by the number, which is 85.

$$\begin{array}{r} 85 \\ \times\, 0.25 \\ \hline 425 \\ 1700 \\ \hline 21.25 \end{array}$$

25% of 85 is 21.25.

The answer turns out to be 21.25, so that's 25% of 85. If we had tried to do that in our heads it probably would have taken awhile.

Percent of a Fraction

This method for finding a percent of a number works on even the toughest problems. For instance, what if we needed to find the percent of a fraction? That may sound kind of tricky. But we can just apply the same method that we've been using. Here's an example.

$$\text{Find } 40\% \text{ of } \frac{1}{2}.$$

We could write 40% as the fraction $\frac{40}{100}$ and then multiply it by $\frac{1}{2}$. That turns out to equal $\frac{1}{5}$ (since $\frac{40}{100}$ reduces to $\frac{2}{5}$ and $\frac{2}{5} \times \frac{1}{2}$ equals $\frac{1}{5}$). So that works. But, as we've said, decimals are usually easier to use. And that's probably true even in this case, where the number is a fraction. But to use decimals on this problem, we have to change both 40% and $\frac{1}{2}$ into decimal form. To convert 40%, we go through the usual procedure. We drop the percent symbol and move the decimal point two places to the left. That gives us 0.40. Then $\frac{1}{2}$ as a decimal is 0.5.

Change both to decimal form.

$$40\% \text{ is the same as } 0.40 \qquad\qquad \frac{1}{2} \text{ is the same as } 0.5$$

Now we just multiply 0.40 and 0.5. We won't show the calculation, but it turns out to equal 0.2. But interestingly, 0.2 is the same as $\frac{2}{10}$, which reduces to $\frac{1}{5}$. So using decimals, we ended up with the decimal form of $\frac{1}{5}$, which is the same answer we got before.

Practice 46

a. Convert $\frac{11}{12}$ into decimal form. If your answer is a repeating decimal, round to two digits (hundredths).

b. What is 20% of 34?

c. What is 45% of 18?

d. What is 30% of $\frac{2}{5}$?

e. Translate the word problem below into math; then solve.

Salespeople at Silky Shiny Wigs Incorporated earn a 25% commission. How much will Suzanne make in commission if she sells a wig for $98?

Problem Set 46

Tell whether each sentence below is True or False.

1. It is possible to calculate the percent of numbers that do not end in zeros.

2. It is not possible to calculate the percent of a number that is less than one.

Add or subtract each group of numbers below.

3.
$$205.9$$
$$+\,732.24$$

4.
$$64.5$$
$$-\,17.325$$

5.
$$5.14$$
$$+\,9.703$$

Multiply or divide each pair of numbers below. Write any remainders in decimal form.

6. $5.3\overline{)445.2}$

7.
$$92.37$$
$$\times\,4.1$$

8. $12\overline{)582}$

9. $9\overline{)2{,}279}$

Add or subtract each pair of fractions below. Make sure your answers are fully reduced.

10. $\dfrac{7}{9} - \dfrac{2}{3}$

11. $\dfrac{3}{10} + \dfrac{8}{15}$

Multiply or divide each pair of numbers below. Make sure your answers are fully reduced.

12. $\dfrac{7}{8} \times \dfrac{4}{14}$

13. $\dfrac{1}{6} \div \dfrac{1}{12}$

Convert each fraction below into decimal form. Round any repeating decimals to two digits (hundredths).

14. $\dfrac{1}{16}$ **(a) 15.** $\dfrac{5}{12}$

Convert each decimal below into a fraction. Make sure your answers are fully reduced.

16. 0.012   **17.** 0.65

Answer each question below.

18. What is 12% of 500?   **(b) 19.** What is 30% of 28?

(c) 20. What is 65% of 16?   **(d) 21.** What is 20% of $\dfrac{3}{4}$?

Translate the word problem below into math; then solve.

(e) 22. The salespeople at the Livin' Doll Cosmetics Company get paid a 15% commission on everything they sell. How much will Linda make in commission if she sells $275 worth of cosmetics?

Lesson 47—Fractional Percents

In the last lesson, we learned that we can calculate the percent of all sorts of numbers, even whole numbers that don't end in zero and fractions. But is it possible for a percent itself to be fractional? For example, does it make sense to have something like $4\frac{1}{2}\%$? There's nothing wrong with that at all. Actually, $4\frac{1}{2}\%$ just means "four and one half for each hundred." So $4\frac{1}{2}\%$ of 100 is $4\frac{1}{2}$, and $4\frac{1}{2}\%$ of 200 is $4\frac{1}{2}+4\frac{1}{2}$ or 9.

Calculating Fractional Percents

Here's another important question: can we calculate the percent of a number even when the percent has a fraction in it? Fortunately, yes. We'll show you how with an example.

$$\text{What's } 4\frac{1}{2}\% \text{ of } 88?$$

The basic method is the same. We want to multiply the percent by the number. Before moving the decimal point, we should change $4\frac{1}{2}\%$ to 4.5%. Now we drop the percent symbol and move the decimal point two places to the left to get 0.045.

$$4\frac{1}{2}\% \ = \ 04.5 \ = \ 0.045$$

drop

move 2 places

Next, we multiply 0.045 and 88 to get 3.96. That's $4\frac{1}{2}\%$ of 88. So we can calculate the fractional percent of a number in basically the same way that we calculate regular percents. We just need to change $4\frac{1}{2}\%$ to 4.5% first.

And to be honest, we didn't have to change $4\frac{1}{2}\%$ to 4.5%. We could change $4\frac{1}{2}\%$ to a fraction. All we have to do is put $4\frac{1}{2}$ over 100 to get $\dfrac{4\frac{1}{2}}{100}$. The mixed number on top can then be changed to an improper fraction: $\dfrac{\frac{9}{2}}{100}$. From here, we invert and multiply to get $\frac{9}{2} \times \frac{1}{100}$ or $\frac{9}{200}$. So $4\frac{1}{2}\%$ written as a fraction is $\frac{9}{200}$. Then we can just multiply $\frac{9}{200}$ and 88 to get 3.96, which is the same answer as before. But notice that this second method is more complicated. That's why most people prefer to change a fractional percent (like $4\frac{1}{2}\%$) to a decimal. There are lots of other examples of fractional percents. Here are a few.

$15\frac{1}{4}\%$ is the same as 15.25%
$36\frac{1}{5}\%$ is the same as 36.2%
$75\frac{5}{8}\%$ is the same as 75.625%

Repeating Decimals Again

Sometimes, the fractional part of a percent is a repeating decimal. An example is $12\frac{1}{3}\%$. Since $\frac{1}{3}$ is the same as 0.333..., $12\frac{1}{3}\%$ is equal to 12.333...% or $12.\overline{3}\%$. But what if we need to do a calculation with this? How do we handle the repeating decimal? Well, one option is to round it off. That's a good option if the answer doesn't need to be exact (as with many practical problems). Rounding $12.\overline{3}\%$ to tenths would give us 12.3%.

$12.\overline{3}\%$ rounded to tenths equals 12.3%   **Can round off repeaters**

That might be close enough. Or if we wanted to round to hundredths, we could use 12.33%.

But if the answer had to be exact, we could change the percent to a fraction (as we did with $4\frac{1}{2}\%$ above). We just drop the percent symbol in $12\frac{1}{3}\%$ and put $12\frac{1}{3}$ over 100.

$$12\frac{1}{3}\% = \frac{12\frac{1}{3}}{100}$$ **Drop percent symbol and put over 100.**

But $\dfrac{12\frac{1}{3}}{100}$ is the same as $\dfrac{\frac{37}{3}}{100}$. Then inverting and multiplying gives us $\dfrac{37}{3} \times \dfrac{1}{100}$, or $\dfrac{37}{300}$. From there, we could multiply $\dfrac{37}{300}$ by whatever number we were trying to find $12\frac{1}{3}\%$ of. Using the fractional form is more complicated than rounding, but it does give an exact answer. So here are the two ways of dealing with a percent that contains a repeating decimal.

Can Handle a Percent with a Repeating Decimal in Two Ways

1.	Round off the repeating decimal to the right digit (depending on required accuracy).
2.	Turn the percent into a fraction by dropping the percent symbol and putting over 100. (Make sure to reduce the fraction before using.)

Practice 47

a. Convert 3.5 into a fraction. Make sure your answer is fully reduced.

b. Convert $8\frac{1}{2}\%$ into decimal form.

c. What is 40% of $\frac{3}{5}$?　　　d. What is $2\frac{1}{4}\%$ of 80?

e. Translate the word problem below into math; then solve.

Sales tax in The Land of the Burgeoning Bureaucrats is $18\frac{1}{2}\%$. If Burl buys a stereo system for $974, how much will he have to pay in sales tax?

Problem Set 47

Tell whether each sentence below is True or False.

    1. It is possible for percents to contain fractions.

    2. Fractional percents can be converted into fractions but not into decimals.

Add or subtract each group of numbers below.

    3.
$$\begin{array}{r} 73.48 \\ + 25.13 \\ \hline \end{array}$$

    4.
$$\begin{array}{r} 825.75 \\ - 433.82 \\ \hline \end{array}$$

Multiply or divide each pair of numbers below. Write any remainders in decimal form.

    5. $0.21\overline{)15.435}$

    6.
$$\begin{array}{r} 45.8 \\ \times 6.2 \\ \hline \end{array}$$

    7. $5\overline{)2{,}113}$

Add or subtract each pair of numbers below. Make sure your answers are fully reduced.

    8. $\dfrac{4}{5} + \dfrac{2}{7}$

    9. $7 - \dfrac{9}{2}$

Multiply or divide each pair of numbers below. Make sure your answers are fully reduced.

    10. $24 \times \dfrac{3}{8}$

    11. $\dfrac{7}{11} \div 21$

Convert each fraction below into decimal form. Round any repeating decimals to two digits (hundredths).

    12. $\dfrac{9}{20}$

    13. $\dfrac{8}{9}$

Convert each decimal below into a fraction. Make sure your answers are fully reduced.

14. 0.205   **(a) 15.** 2.5

Convert each percent below into decimal form.

16. 15%   **(b) 17.** $6\frac{1}{2}\%$

Answer each question below.

18. What is 35% of 220?

(c) 19. What is 60% of $\frac{4}{5}$?

(d) 20. What is $7\frac{1}{4}\%$ of 56?

Translate the word problem below into math; then solve.

(e) 21. Sales tax in The Land of Contradictions is $6\frac{1}{2}\%$. If Connie buys a toothless comb for $8, how much will she have to pay in sales tax?

Lesson 48—Percents and Banking

We've been learning about percents, but how are they actually used in the real world? Well, it turns out that percents are used all the time, especially in areas where money is involved, like banking.

How a Bank Works

A bank will pay you to keep your money. You probably know that. But you might not know that the amount the bank agrees to pay is always a percent of the amount of money put in. Let's say we put $100 in a bank. The bank will pay us **interest** (that's what the payments are called) while it has our money, and if, for example, the bank pays a $5\frac{1}{2}$% interest rate, that means they'll pay $5\frac{1}{2}$% of what we have in the bank every year.

So for $100, they'll pay $5\frac{1}{2}$% of that each year (in interest).

To calculate how much that is, we just change $5\frac{1}{2}$% to 5.5%. Then we drop the percent symbol and move the decimal point two places to the left to get 0.055. Finally, we multiply 0.055 by 100 to get 5.5. Since 100 was in dollars, that means the bank would pay us $5.50 each year.[3] We could also take our $100 out at the end of the year if we wanted to.

Interest Rate	×	Amount in Bank	=	Interest
$5\frac{1}{2}$% (0.055)	×	100	=	$5.50

Here's another example. Say we put $1,640 in a bank that pays a $3\frac{1}{4}$% interest rate. To calculate the amount of interest we'd get after a year, we change $3\frac{1}{4}$% to 3.25% and then to 0.0325. Then, we multiply 0.0325 by 1,640 to get 53.3. So the amount of interest comes out to $53.30. That's all there is to it.

Interest on Interest

Here's something else that's interesting (no pun intended!). What if we want to leave our money in the bank for *more than* one year? Let's say we have $1,000 and want to put it in the bank for 3 years at a 5% interest rate. In the first year, we'd earn 5% on the 1,000, which is $0.05 \times 1,000$ or $50. But at the end of the year, we wouldn't take our money out. We would just leave the $1,000 in the bank. And let's assume that we're going to leave the $50 in interest in the bank too. That means for the second year, instead

---

[3] You may be wondering why the bank is willing to pay us for letting them hold our money. Well, it's because they're going to lend our money out to someone else and charge them even more interest. The bank will then keep the difference between what it pays us and what it earned from the amount it lent.

of having $1,000, we would have $1,000 + $50 or $1,050 in the bank. So how much interest would we earn in that year? Well, we'd make 5% of $1,050, which is $0.05 \times 1,050$. That's equal to 52.5, or $52.50.

1st Year Interest

5% of $1,000 = $50

2nd Year Interest

5% of $1,050 = $52.50

Notice what happened, we earned more interest in the second year than we did in the first. That's because we earned "interest on our interest." This is called **compound interest**, actually.

What about the third year? Well, the answer depends on whether we keep our interest in the bank again. If we did, we'd have $1,050 + $52.50, or $1,102.50 in the bank after the second year. So in the third year, we would earn 0.05 times 1,102.50, which equals 55.125, or $55.13 when it's rounded to cents. Notice that in the third year our interest is even higher. Of course, if we kept this up, our savings would grow faster and faster. This is why people always talk about how fast money can grow in the bank (or when it's invested somewhere else). The fast growth is caused by the "interest on interest" or compound interest.

Practice 48

a. Convert $55\dfrac{1}{8}\%$ into decimal form.

b. Convert 28% into a fraction. Make sure your answer is fully reduced.

c. Convert $3\dfrac{1}{3}\%$ into a fraction. Make sure your answer is fully reduced.

d. What is $12\dfrac{3}{5}\%$ of 320?

e. Translate the word problem below into math; then solve.

Mr. Stallworthy opened up a college savings account for his daughter at the local bank. He put $1,750 in the account, which pays $5\dfrac{1}{2}\%$ in yearly interest.

i.) How much will Mr. Stallworthy have earned in interest one year from now?

ii.) If he leaves his money <u>and</u> interest in the bank for another year, how much interest will he earn for the 2nd year? Round your answer to the nearest hundredths place.

Problem Set 48

Tell whether each sentence below is True or False.

1. Percents are used a lot in banking.

2. The "interest rate" is the percent the bank will pay you each year of the money they are holding for you.

3. "Compound interest" is interest earned on interest that you've already been paid.

Add or subtract each group of numbers below.

4.
$$6.145$$
$$+17.82$$

5.
$$93.22$$
$$-48.65$$

Multiply or divide each pair of numbers below. Write any remainders in decimal form.

6.
$$29.1$$
$$\times 0.64$$

7. $15\overline{)1,280}$

Add or subtract each pair of fractions below. Make sure your answers are fully reduced.

8. $\dfrac{3}{20} + \dfrac{1}{20}$

9. $\dfrac{6}{5} - \dfrac{7}{10}$

Multiply or divide each pair of numbers below. Make sure your answers are fully reduced.

10. $\dfrac{2}{9} \times \dfrac{3}{8}$

11. $\dfrac{5}{6} \div \dfrac{1}{2}$

Convert each fraction below into decimal form. Round any repeating decimals to two digits (hundredths).

12. $\dfrac{1}{15}$

13. $\dfrac{4}{25}$

Convert each decimal below into a fraction. Make sure your answers are fully reduced.

14. 0.085

15. 4.2

Convert each percent below into decimal form.

16. $14\frac{2}{5}\%$

(a) 17. $75\frac{1}{8}\%$

Convert each percent below into a fraction. Make sure your answers are fully reduced.

(b) 18. 38%

(c) 19. $5\frac{1}{3}\%$

Answer each question below.

20. What is 62% of 980?

(d) 21. What is $15\frac{3}{5}\%$ of 250?

Translate the word problem below into math; then solve.

(e) 22. Albert is trying to save enough money to buy his uncle's classic Thunderbird. Although he still has a long way to go, he now has $1,500 in a bank account that pays $6\frac{1}{2}\%$ in yearly interest.

    i.) How much will Albert have earned in interest one year from now?

    ii.) If he leaves his money <u>and</u> interest in the bank for another year, how much interest will he earn for the 2nd year? Round your answer to the nearest hundredths place.

Lesson 49—Finding the Percent

We've learned how to find the percent of a number, but what if we have two numbers and want to know what percent one is of the other? Here's an example.

What percent of 100 is 30?

This one is easy enough to do in your head: it's 30%. But how do we do the formal calculation? Well, we just put 30 over 100 and then convert the fraction to a percent by getting rid of the denominator and putting in the percent symbol.

$$\frac{30}{100} \text{ is equal to } 30\%$$

Put 30 over 100 and change to a percent.

By the way, it's important to make sure to get the right numbers on top and bottom. How did we know to put 30 on top and 100 on bottom? Well, the "of" number always goes on bottom and the "is" number always goes on top. That's the easy way to remember.

Using a Decimal

We used a fraction to figure out our example problem. But it's also possible to do the problem with a decimal. We still start with $\frac{30}{100}$. But then we divide 100 into 30 using long division to get 0.30. Next, we convert the decimal to a percent. But how do we do that? We know that a percent can be converted into a decimal by dropping the percent symbol and moving the decimal point two places to the left. It shouldn't surprise you that to convert a decimal into a percent, we just go backwards: we move the decimal point two places to the *right* (in the other direction) and put the percent symbol back in again. So 0.30 becomes 30%.

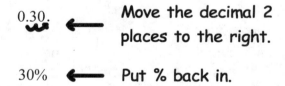

0.30. ⟵ **Move the decimal 2 places to the right.**

30% ⟵ **Put % back in.**

It's pretty easy to convert a fraction with a denominator of a 100 into a percent (whatever method we use). But on tougher problems, decimals are almost always easier to use than fractions. Here's an example.

What percent of 40 is 15?

The first step is to figure out what goes on top and what goes on bottom. Remember the rule: the "of" number goes on bottom and the "is" number goes on top. So it's 15 over 40.

"of" number goes $\dfrac{15}{40}$ ⬅ "is" number goes

on bottom ➡   on top

Since this fraction doesn't have a denominator of 100, it's not clear what the percent is. What we need to do is convert it into a decimal by dividing 40 into 15.

$$40\overline{)15.000}^{\;.375}$$ Convert $\dfrac{15}{40}$ into a decimal.

That gives us 0.375. Now we can move the decimal point two places to the right and put in the percent symbol for an answer of 37.5% or $37\dfrac{1}{2}\%$. So 15 is $37\dfrac{1}{2}\%$ of 40.

Even with Fractions

This method will even work with fractions. Take this example.

What percent of $\dfrac{1}{2}$ is $\dfrac{1}{4}$?

This problem would stump a lot of people. But now that you understand the method, it's actually not that tough. The "of" number is $\dfrac{1}{2}$, so that goes on bottom. The "is" number is $\dfrac{1}{4}$, which goes on top.

$$\dfrac{\dfrac{1}{4}}{\dfrac{1}{2}}$$ "Of" on bottom and "is" on top.

Inverting and multiplying, we get $\dfrac{1}{4}\times\dfrac{2}{1}$ or $\dfrac{2}{4}$, which reduces to $\dfrac{1}{2}$. Next, we could convert $\dfrac{1}{2}$ to a percent by changing it to $\dfrac{50}{100}$. That's the same as 50%. But most people would just use long division. They would divide 2 into 1 to get 0.5. (Actually, it's so simple they would do it in their heads.) But from 0.5, they would move the decimal point two places to the right for 50% again.

$$\dfrac{1}{2} = 0.5 = 50\%$$

Decimals Too

We can also find what percent one decimal is of another. Let's do this one.

What percent of 0.8 is 0.2?

The "of" number is 0.8, so it goes on bottom. The "is" number is 0.2, which goes on top.

$$\frac{0.2}{0.8} = 0.25 \qquad \textbf{Just divide.}$$

Then carrying out the division gives us 0.25. The next step is to change 0.25 to a percent by moving the decimal point two places to the right and putting the percent symbol back in.

$$0.25 = 25\% \qquad \textbf{Change decimal}$$
$$\textbf{to percent}$$

So 0.2 is 25% of 0.8.

The main point of this lesson is that the best way to find what percent one number is of another is to divide the numbers to get a decimal and then change the decimal to a percent.

Practice 49

a. Convert $\frac{6}{5}$ into decimal form. If your answer is a repeating decimal, round to two digits (hundredths).

b. What is $\frac{2}{5}$ of 450?

c. What percent of 40 is 12?

d. What percent of $\frac{4}{5}$ is $\frac{1}{5}$?

e. Translate the word problem below into math; then solve.

Gus thinks he can juggle 5 bottles of ketchup at once. Right now, he is juggling 3. What percent of his goal has been achieved?

Problem Set 49

Add or subtract each group of numbers below.

1.
$$\begin{array}{r} 48.03 \\ +21.55 \\ \hline \end{array}$$

2.
$$\begin{array}{r} 502.9 \\ -126.4 \\ \hline \end{array}$$

Multiply or divide each pair of numbers below. Write any remainders in decimal form.

3.
$$\begin{array}{r} 0.375 \\ \times 0.25 \\ \hline \end{array}$$

4. $4\overline{)3{,}931}$

5. $25\overline{)962}$

Add or subtract each pair of numbers below. Make sure your answers are fully reduced.

6. $5\dfrac{1}{2} - 3\dfrac{2}{3}$

7. $6\dfrac{2}{5} + 2\dfrac{3}{10}$

Multiply or divide each pair of numbers below. Make sure your answers are fully reduced.

8. $\dfrac{3}{7} \times \dfrac{14}{18}$

9. $15 \div \dfrac{5}{8}$

Convert each fraction below into decimal form. Round any repeating decimals to two digits (hundredths).

10. $\dfrac{7}{12}$

(a) 11. $\dfrac{5}{4}$

Convert each decimal below into a fraction. Make sure your answers are fully reduced.

12. 0.024

13. 0.48

Convert each percent below into decimal form.

14. 67%

15. $98\dfrac{1}{10}\%$

Answer each question below.

(b) 16. What is $\dfrac{3}{5}$ of 550?

17. What is 47% of 70?

18. What is 32.5% of 225?

(c) 19. What percent of 60 is 15?

(d) 20. What percent of $\dfrac{1}{2}$ is $\dfrac{2}{5}$?

Translate the word problem below into math; then solve.

(e) 21. Arnie plans to eat 4 Twinkies during his lunch break. So far he has eaten 3. What percent of his goal has been achieved?

Lesson 50—Calculating a Grade

Finding the percent one number is of another is something that most people need to do all the time in the real world. As a student, you've probably had to use this technique when calculating your grade on an assignment.

Grades are Based on Percents

That's because most grading systems are based on percents. If you get $100-90\%$ of the questions right you get an A. If you get $89-80\%$ right, you get a B, $79-70\%$ equals a C, $69-60\%$ equals a D, and 59% and below equals an F.

Just to show you how it works, let's do an example. What if you take a test that has 25 questions, and get 20 of them right? What should your grade be? Well, to figure this one out, all you have to do is calculate what percent of 25 is 20. The "of" number is 25, which goes on bottom. The "is" number is 20, so it goes on top.

$$\frac{20}{25} \qquad \text{"of" on bottom; "is" on top}$$

Next, we divide 25 into 20 using long division to get 0.8.

$$\frac{20}{25} = 0.8 \qquad \textbf{Divide to get a decimal}$$

Now we just change 0.8 to a percent by moving the decimal point two places to the right and putting in the percent symbol to get 80%. That's just barely a B. Of course, as you probably know, instead of saying 80%, some people will just say "I got an 80." But that means 80 out of 100, which is 80 percent.

Worth More than One Point?

Sometimes each question on an assignment is worth more than one point. That tends to confuse people, but it really shouldn't, because the method for calculating the grade is basically the same. Say you did an assignment that had 50 questions and each one was worth 3 points. If you got 45 right, then you could calculate your percentage grade in one of two ways. First, you could just divide the number of questions you got right by the total number of questions. Since $\frac{45}{50}$ is equal to 0.90, or 90%, your grade would be an A (That's the same method we used above). That method will work just fine, as long as each question is worth the same number of points. The second method is to do the calculation using points. Since you got 45 right and each problem counted for 3 points, you earned 45 times 3, or 135 points out of a total of 50 times 3, or 150 points. So dividing the two point totals leaves $\frac{135}{150}$ (with the "of" number on bottom and the "is" number on top). That comes out to 0.90, which converts to 90%, the same answer we got with the first method. The two methods are the same if the problems are all worth the same amount. The point method is the one to use if the problems are worth different amounts. We won't do an example like that. But all you do is add up the points you got and divide that by the total points possible.

The simplest method for calculating a grade, though, is to divide the number of questions you got right by the total number of questions on the assignment. After you've done that, just change the decimal to a percent.

Practice 50

   a. Convert 2.16 into a common fraction. Make sure your answer is fully reduced.

   b. Convert 110% into decimal form.

   c. What is $8\frac{2}{5}\%$ of 75?

   d. What percent of $\frac{1}{3}$ is $\frac{1}{6}$?

   e. Translate the word problem below into math; then solve.

       The toddler only got 1 out of 3 questions right on his "Stop, Drop, and Roll" test. What percentage of the questions did he get right? Write your answer as a fractional percent.

Problem Set 50

Tell whether each sentence below is True or False.

   1. Percents are never used in grading.

   2. To calculate a grade, divide the number of questions answered correctly by the total number of questions (and convert the answer into a percent).

Add or subtract each group of numbers below.

3.
$$\begin{array}{r} 19.25 \\ 27.39 \\ +14.52 \\ \hline \end{array}$$

4.
$$\begin{array}{r} 24.65 \\ -14.38 \\ \hline \end{array}$$

Multiply or divide each pair of numbers below. Write any remainders in decimal form.

5.
$$\begin{array}{r} 1.825 \\ \times 0.4 \\ \hline \end{array}$$

6. $0.22\overline{)14.19}$

7.
$$\begin{array}{r} 6.58 \\ \times 1.2 \\ \hline \end{array}$$

Add or subtract each pair of fractions below. Make sure your answers are fully reduced.

8. $\dfrac{7}{8} + \dfrac{1}{4}$

9. $\dfrac{9}{14} - \dfrac{1}{14}$

Multiply or divide each pair of numbers below. Make sure your answers are fully reduced.

10. $\dfrac{5}{12} \times 144$

11. $\dfrac{3}{2} \div \dfrac{3}{16}$

Convert each fraction below into decimal form. Round any repeating decimals to two digits (hundredths).

12. $\dfrac{17}{20}$

13. $\dfrac{7}{6}$

Convert each decimal below into a fraction. Make sure your answers are fully reduced.

14. 0.45

(a) 15. 4.12

Convert each percent below into decimal form.

16. $62\dfrac{1}{4}\%$

(b) 17. 120%

Answer each question below.

18. What is $\dfrac{2}{7}$ of 490?

(c) 19. What is $4\dfrac{1}{5}\%$ of 50?

(d) 20. What percent of $\dfrac{2}{3}$ is $\dfrac{1}{6}$?

Translate the word problem below into math; then solve.

(e) 21. The trainer kept trying to teach her dolphins how to play baseball, but after a year's worth of practice, only 4 out of 15 knew the difference between a "strike" and a "ball." What percentage of the dolphins knew the difference between a "strike" and a "ball"? Write your answer as a fractional percent.

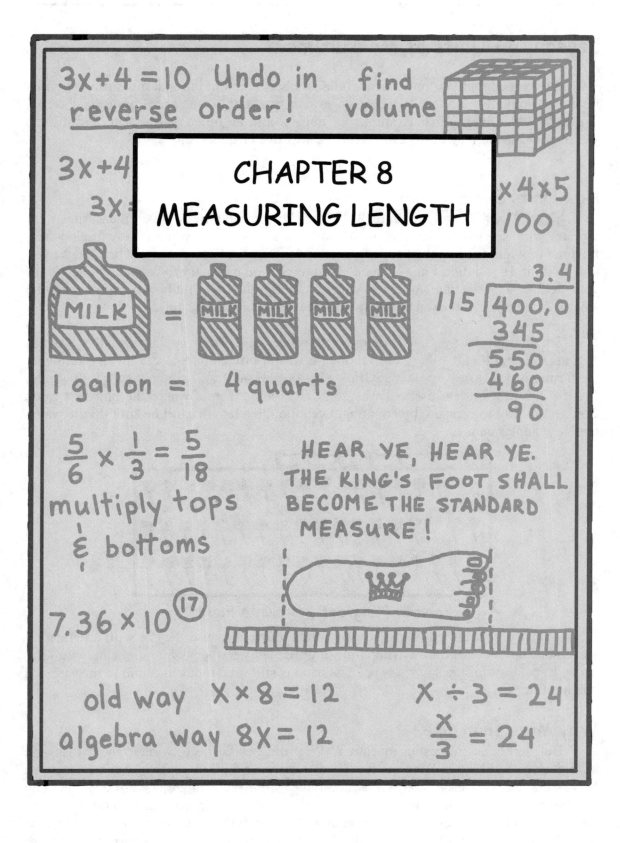

CHAPTER 8
MEASURING LENGTH

Lesson 51—Units of Measurement

We learned that you only need whole numbers to count but that measuring requires fractions. Actually, though, it takes more than fractions to measure things in the real world. We also need **units**. Examples of units would be miles, yards, feet, and inches. We're going to learn all about units over the next two chapters.

How Units Got Started

How did units ever get started? Well, the first people to do much measuring were farmers who needed to measure their land. This was no easy thing way back when. Imagine how hard it might be to measure the length of a field if nobody had taught you how to do it. If you didn't know much about math, you might try to "count" the length of your field (since counting worked so well on other problems). But how could you count a length. A length isn't broken up into pieces the way a basket of apples is.

So units probably first started when some clever farmer figured out a way to "count" the length of his field, even though it wasn't broken into pieces. In all likelihood, the farmer just measured how many times his foot would fit along the length of the field. If it fit 252 times, then his field was 252 "feet" long. That's where the unit feet came from. It's a way to measure by counting, even though a length can't be split up the way a bunch of apples can.

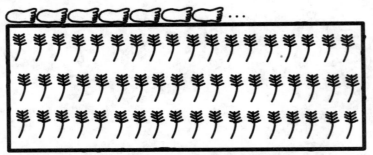

Farmer ("Bigfoot") Brown's Field

Actually, feet turned out to be good units to use, because they're with a person all the time. They never go away (hopefully). Other body parts, such as the hand and arm, began to be used for the same reason. The hand is still used today as a unit to measure the height of horses.

Why More than One?

But here's an interesting question? Why did people need to have more than one kind of unit to measure? Why not just always use your feet? Well, there are two reasons. First, some units are easier to use for certain measurements than others. For example, you wouldn't want to measure the length of a tilled garden with your arm. You'd have to crawl around on the ground, which would make you really dirty. Your foot would be far better for that kind of job. However, if you were measuring fabric, your arm would work much better than your foot because you can just pull the fabric right along your arm to measure it. If you used your foot to measure fabric, you'd have to walk all over it.

The second reason we need different units is that some lengths are much longer than others. The longer the length, the longer the unit you want to use. You wouldn't want to measure the distance from New York to California in inches. That would be crazy. The measurement would turn out to equal a gigantic number, which would be really hard to work with. And you wouldn't want to measure the length of an atom in miles. It would be such a tiny number that it would be hard to work with.

Practice 51

a. Convert 2.9 into a fraction.

b. Convert 14% into a fraction.

c. Convert $2\frac{1}{4}$% into a fraction.

d. What percent of 7.5 is 0.3?

e. Translate the word problem below into math; then solve.

Alana got 22 out of 25 right on her French exam. What percent of the questions did she get right?

Problem Set 51

Tell whether each sentence below is True or False.

1. Units of measurement were probably first used by farmers who wanted to measure their land.

2. There is no good reason why we have more than one unit of measurement.

Add or subtract each group of numbers below.

3.
$$386.50$$
$$+941.47$$

4.
$$802.3$$
$$-341.2$$

Multiply or divide each pair of numbers below. Write any remainders in decimal form.

5.
$$7.03$$
$$\times 2.5$$

6. $1.4\overline{)12.18}$

7.
$$955$$
$$\times 0.06$$

Add or subtract each pair of fractions below. Make sure your answers are fully reduced.

8. $\dfrac{3}{4} + \dfrac{1}{8}$ **9.** $\dfrac{17}{20} - \dfrac{7}{20}$

Multiply or divide each pair of numbers below. Make sure your answers are fully reduced.

10. $\dfrac{4}{5} \times \dfrac{10}{12}$ **11.** $\dfrac{9}{11} \div 6$

Convert each fraction below into decimal form. Round any repeating decimals to two digits (hundredths).

12. $\dfrac{2}{11}$ **13.** $\dfrac{3}{50}$

Convert each decimal below into a common fraction. Make sure your answers are fully reduced.

14. 0.82   **(a) 15.** 2.7

Convert each percent below into a common fraction. Make sure your answers are fully reduced.

(b) 16. 26%   **(c) 17.** $3\dfrac{1}{4}\%$

Answer each question below.

18. What is $\dfrac{2}{3}$ of 900?   **19.** What is $6\dfrac{1}{2}\%$ of 80?

(d) 20. What percent of 2.5 is 0.2?

Translate the word problem below into math; then solve.

(e) 21. Bradford got 72 out of 80 right on his underwater basket weaving exam. What percent of the questions did he get right?

Lesson 52—Standard Measures

In the last lesson, we learned about units of measurement and how they got started with body parts. But one drawback of using body parts for measuring is that everyone has a different shaped body. How can we ever agree on the exact measurement of a field if my foot is bigger than your foot?

People got around this problem by creating **standard measures**. A standard measure is a physical object like a stick that represents a unit of measurement. Then everybody agrees that the stick is the correct length of the unit, which eliminates all the confusion.

The King's Foot

But how did people decide what the standard should be? Interestingly, the first standards were based on a King's body parts. For example, the first "foot" was the length of the great French King Charlemagne's foot, and (supposedly) the length of the yard was first determined by the distance between the nose and fingertip of Henry I of England.

King's foot becomes the standard measure

Even after people came up with standard units, there was still a problem. Everybody couldn't share one single measuring stick. That's why a lot of copies of the standard stick had to be made and passed around so everybody could use them. These copies are called **secondary standards**. For instance, you probably own a ruler or a yardstick. Those are secondary standards. The original standard is kept safely under lock and key to make sure that nobody tampers with it. In fact, there are government officials who make sure that secondary standards (copies) are made properly. Otherwise, it would be really tempting for some people to whittle down the length of their yardsticks a bit. They could use the shorter yardsticks to cheat customers who bought goods (like fabric) by the yard.

Feet and Inches on the Same Stick

Eventually somebody got the idea of putting more than one unit on the secondary standards. That meant a yardstick would have marks for feet and inches on it. Here's why that's useful. With different units on the same stick, fractional measurements are easier to make. For example, if you're measuring something that's over 2 feet long, you can just read off your yardstick that the object is 2 feet and so many inches.

269

Adjusting the Units

There was one drawback of putting more than one unit on a single yardstick, though. What if the smaller unit didn't divide into the larger one evenly? Not surprisingly, this was pretty common. After all, why should the length of Charlemagne's foot divide evenly into the length from Henry I's nose to his fingertip? The way around the problem was to adjust the units a bit. For instance, you can make the inch a little smaller or larger until a certain number of inches equals a foot exactly. This is why there are exactly 12 inches in a foot and exactly 3 feet in a yard today.

Practice 52

a. Convert $\frac{1}{7}$ into decimal form. If your answer is a repeating decimal, round to two digits (hundredths).

b. Convert 185% into decimal form.

c. What is 12.5% of 42?

d. What percent of 4 is $\frac{3}{5}$?

e. Translate the word problem below into math; then solve.

Of the 400 people who were surveyed, only 20% said the governor should not sign the bill against lobbying. How many of those surveyed thought the governor should not sign the bill against lobbying?

Problem Set 52

Tell whether each sentence below is True or False.

1. A standard measure is a physical object like a stick or rod that represents a unit of measurement.

2. The first standards for units of measure were based on the body parts of kings.

3. All units of measure have been exactly the same throughout history.

Add or subtract each group of numbers below.

4.
$$709.02 \\ +552.16$$

5.
$$8.125 \\ -4.03$$

Multiply or divide each pair of numbers below. Write any remainders in decimal form.

6.
$$850 \\ \times 42$$

7. $0.3\overline{)758}$

8.
$$2.21 \\ \times 0.8$$

Add or subtract each pair of numbers below. Make sure your answers are fully reduced.

9. $\dfrac{7}{3} + \dfrac{1}{2}$

10. $2 - \dfrac{6}{5}$

Multiply or divide each pair of fractions below. Make sure your answers are fully reduced.

11. $\dfrac{1}{3} \times \dfrac{9}{10}$

12. $\dfrac{2}{5} \div \dfrac{4}{5}$

Convert each fraction below into decimal form. Round any repeating decimals to two digits (hundredths).

13. $\dfrac{7}{8}$

(a) 14. $\dfrac{2}{7}$

Convert each decimal below into a common fraction. Make sure your answers are fully reduced.

15. 0.95

16. 0.2

Convert each percent below into decimal form.

17. $18\dfrac{1}{10}\%$

(b) 18. 225%

Answer each question below.

19. What is $\dfrac{2}{9}$ of 180?

(c) 20. What is 15.5% of 36?

(d) 21. What percent of 2 is $\dfrac{2}{5}$?

Translate the word problem below into math; then solve.

(e) 22. Of the 1,250 people who were surveyed, only 30% said the longtime city councilman should not run for mayor. How many of those surveyed thought the councilman should not run for mayor?

Lesson 53—Unit Conversions

We've been learning about units of measurements. Sometimes we have to add or subtract two measurements. What do we do with the units in a case like that? Well, the rule is that we can always add or subtract two measurements, as long as the units are the same for both. Here's a simple example.

$$2 \text{ feet} + 7 \text{ feet}$$

We can always add (or subtract) measurements, as long as the units are the same. In our example feet are added to feet. All we have to do, then, is add the numbers and keep the units the same to get 9 feet.

Feet to Inches

But what if the units are different? For example, what if we need to add 3 feet and 24 inches?

$$3 \text{ feet} + 24 \text{ inches}$$

Since one measurement is in feet and the other is in inches, we can't add the measurements the way they are right now. Adding 3 feet to 24 inches to get 27 feet (or 27 inches) is obviously wrong. What we do is change one unit into another, so that the units are the same. Then they can be added. Changing or "converting" one unit into another is actually called a **unit conversion**.

To do a unit conversion, we have to know how the two units are related. For example, we know that there are 12 inches in 1 foot. Using that knowledge, we can convert 3 feet to inches. Since there are 12 inches in each of the 3 feet, we *multiply* 3 by 12 to get 36 inches.

$$3 \times 12 = 36$$

Multiply by 12 to convert feet to inches.

Next, we put 36 inches in for 3 feet in our problem. With both measurements in the same units (inches), we can add normally.

$$36 \text{ inches} + 24 \text{ inches} = 60 \text{ inches}$$

Inches to Feet

As you probably know, that's not the only way to do our problem.

$$3 \text{ feet} + 24 \text{ inches}$$

273

Instead of converting everything into inches, we can convert into feet. Since there are 12 inches in a foot, we can convert 24 inches into feet by *dividing* 24 by 12 to get 2 feet.

$$24 \div 12 = 2$$

Divide by 12 to convert inches to feet.

With the units the same, we can add normally.

$$3 \text{ feet} + 2 \text{ feet} = 5 \text{ feet}$$

These may seem like different answers to the same problem, but they're really the same. If we convert 5 feet into inches by multiplying by 12 we get 60 inches ($5 \times 12 = 60$), which is the same answer we got by doing the problem in inches.

When to Multiply/When to Divide

Did you notice that in going from feet to inches, we multiplied, but in going from inches to feet, we divided? Those are really important rules. We always convert larger units (like feet) into smaller units (like inches) by multiplying. It doesn't matter what the units are. That's because multiplying increases the number, and there are always more smaller units in any measurement than there are larger units. (A yardstick has just 3 feet, but it has 36 inches).

Going in the other direction, we always convert smaller units (like inches) into larger units (like feet) by dividing. This also works no matter what units are involved. That's because dividing decreases the number, and there are always fewer larger units in any measurement than there are smaller units.

Rules for Unit Conversions

1.	When converting larger units to smaller units *multiply*.
2.	When converting smaller units to larger units *divide*.

Conversion Factors

Unit conversions are easy as long as we know how the units relate. In math, the numbers telling us how the units relate are called **conversion factors**. Here are the conversion factors between the major units of length.

Some Conversion Factors
(for lengths)

12 inches = 1 foot
3 feet = 1 yard
1,760 yards = 1 mile

Practice 53

a. Convert 5 feet into inches.

b. Convert 70 yards into feet.

c. Convert 6 miles into yards.

d. What percent of 12.5 is 4?

e. Translate the word problem below into math; then solve.

Mr. Shaw is 6 feet tall, and the stool he is standing on is 36 inches. How many *inches* high is Mr. Shaw plus the stool?

Problem Set 53

Tell whether each sentence below is True or False.

1. Changing or "converting" one unit into another is called a unit conversion.

2. Larger units (like feet) are always converted into smaller units (like inches) by dividing.

Add or subtract each group of numbers below.

3.
$$
\begin{array}{r}
24,381 \\
+\,92,903 \\
\hline
\end{array}
$$

4.
$$
\begin{array}{r}
44.75 \\
-\,28.29 \\
\hline
\end{array}
$$

Multiply or divide each pair of numbers below. Write any remainders in decimal form.

5. $3.2\overline{)52}$

6.
$$
\begin{array}{r}
4.7 \\
\times\,7.5 \\
\hline
\end{array}
$$

7. $12\overline{)8,025}$

275

Add or subtract each group of fractions below. Make sure your answers are fully reduced.

8. $\dfrac{1}{2} + \dfrac{2}{5} + \dfrac{1}{4}$ **9.** $\dfrac{11}{14} - \dfrac{2}{7}$

Multiply or divide each pair of numbers below.

10. $8 \times \dfrac{3}{16}$ **11.** $6 \div \dfrac{2}{5}$

Convert each fraction below into decimal form. Round any repeating decimals to two digits (hundredths).

12. $\dfrac{9}{5}$ **13.** $\dfrac{1}{3}$

Convert each percent below into decimal form.

14. $12\dfrac{4}{5}\%$ **15.** 340%

Do each unit conversion below. (Conversion factors: 12 inches = 1 foot; 3 feet = 1 yard; 1,760 yards = 1 mile.)

(a) 16. Convert 6 feet into inches.   **(b) 17.** Convert 80 yards into feet.

(c) 18. Convert 2 miles into yards.

Answer each question below.

19. What is 22% of 480?   **(d) 20.** What percent of 12.5 is 8?

Translate the word problem below into math; then solve.

(e) 21. The 5 foot tall circus performer is balancing a stack of containers on her head. If the stack is 24 inches high, how many *inches* high is the woman plus the stack?

Lesson 54—Skipping Around

In the last lesson, we learned how to convert a measurement from one unit to another. The main thing we need to know is the proper conversion factor. That's the number that tells us how the units relate. Here are the conversion factors for the major units of length again.

$$12 \text{ inches} = 1 \text{ foot} \qquad 3 \text{ feet} = 1 \text{ yard} \qquad 1{,}760 \text{ yards} = 1 \text{ mile}$$

Miles to Feet and Back

Using these conversion factors, it's easy to convert between inches and feet, or between feet and yards, or between yards and miles. But what if we need to convert from miles all the way down to feet? The list of conversion factors doesn't tell us how many feet are in a mile. Is there a good way to do the conversion? Yes. We'll show you how it works with a specific example.

How many feet are in 4 miles?

We can do this problem in steps. The first step is to figure out how many yards there are in 4 miles. Since we know that $1{,}760 \text{ yards} = 1 \text{ mile}$, that's easy. We just multiply 4 by 1,760. (Remember, we multiply since we're going from larger to smaller units.)

$$4 \times 1{,}760 = 7{,}040 \qquad \textbf{Converting miles to yards.}$$

That gives us 7,040 yards. We're not finished, because we're trying to find how many feet are in 4 miles. The second step, then, is to convert 7,040 yards to feet. Since we know that $3 \text{ feet} = 1 \text{ yard}$, this is easy too. We just have to multiply 7,040 by 3. (We multiply, because we're going from larger to smaller units again.)

$$7{,}040 \times 3 = 21{,}120 \qquad \textbf{Converting yards to feet.}$$

Our answer is 21,120 feet. That's how many feet are in 4 miles. The main point is that we converted miles into feet by going in steps: from miles to yards and then from yards to feet.

Inches to Miles

Let's do one more tough example where the units are far apart.

How many *miles* are in 76,032 *inches*?

We're skipping units again. We're going from miles all the way to inches. Only this time, we're starting with smaller units and going to larger units. That means we have to *divide* each time.

The first step is to convert inches to feet by dividing 76,032 by 12.

$$76{,}032 \div 12 = 6{,}336 \qquad \textbf{Converting inches to feet.}$$

That gives us 6,336 feet. The second step is to convert feet to yards by dividing 6,336 by 3.

$$6{,}336 \div 3 = 2{,}112 \qquad \textbf{Converting feet to yards.}$$

We end up with 2,112 yards. The last step is to convert yards to miles by dividing 2,112 by 1,760.

$$2{,}112 \div 1{,}760 = 1.2 \qquad \textbf{Converting yards to miles.}$$

We get 1.2, which means that 76,032 inches equals 1.2 miles.

The main point of this lesson, then, is that we can skip around between units that are far apart in size by going in steps. We just convert one unit at a time.

Practice 54

a. Convert 0.45% into decimal form.   **b.** How many inches are in 8 yards?

c. Convert 6 miles into feet.   **d.** How many miles are in 95,040 inches?

e. Translate the word problem below into math; then solve.

It is 671 miles from Paris to Berlin, how far is this in feet?

Problem Set 54

Add or subtract each group of numbers below.

1.
$$\begin{array}{r} 80.57 \\ +\,46.11 \\ \hline \end{array}$$

2.
$$\begin{array}{r} 6{,}004 \\ -\,2{,}573 \\ \hline \end{array}$$

Multiply or divide each pair of numbers below. Write any remainders in decimal form.

3. $9\overline{)1{,}708}$

4.
$$\begin{array}{r} 520 \\ \times\,7.3 \\ \hline \end{array}$$

5. $0.25\overline{)3.65}$

Add or subtract each pair of fractions below. Make sure your answers are fully reduced.

6. $\dfrac{3}{2} + \dfrac{1}{2}$

7. $\dfrac{5}{6} - \dfrac{3}{4}$

Multiply or divide each pair of numbers below.

8. $\dfrac{6}{5} \times \dfrac{10}{9}$

9. $\dfrac{1}{4} \div \dfrac{7}{8}$

Convert each fraction below into decimal form. Round any repeating decimals to two digits (hundredths).

10. $\dfrac{35}{10}$

11. $\dfrac{1}{6}$

Convert each decimal below into a common fraction. Make sure your answers are fully reduced.

12. 0.05

13. 0.14

Convert each percent below into decimal form.

14. $8\dfrac{1}{2}\%$

(a) 15. 0.75%

Do each unit conversion below. (Conversion factors: 12 inches = 1 foot; 3 feet = 1 yard; 1,760 yards = 1 mile.)

(b) 16. How many inches are in 9 yards?

(c) 17. Convert 5 miles into feet.

(d) 18. How many miles are in 158,400 inches?

Answer each question below.

19. What is 32% of 60?

20. What percent of 40 is 5?

Translate the word problem below into math; then solve.

(e) 21. It is 800 miles from Seattle to San Francisco, how far is this in feet?

Lesson 55—Making a Table

In the last lesson, we learned a method for converting units that aren't right next to each other (like going from miles all the way down to inches). We just do the conversion in steps. The only drawback of this method is that it takes a long time, especially when the units are very different in size.

Converting in a Single Step

There's actually a faster way to do conversions between units that are really far apart. Instead of going step by step from inches to miles, we can figure out the conversion factor for inches to miles directly. And we can do the same thing for miles to feet, inches to yards, and all of the other combinations. That allows us to convert between any two units in a single step. It helps to write all these conversion factors down neatly. Most people put them in a table, called (not surprisingly!) a **unit conversion table**. Here's a unit conversion table for all of the major units of length.

Unit Conversion Table (for lengths)

	mile	yard	foot	inch
mile	1	1,760	5,280	63,360
yard	$\frac{1}{1,760}$	1	3	36
foot	$\frac{1}{5,280}$	$\frac{1}{3}$	1	12
inch	$\frac{1}{63,360}$	$\frac{1}{36}$	$\frac{1}{12}$	1

Here's how this table is used. Say we want to convert 4 yards to inches. Instead of having to convert yards to feet first and then feet to inches, all we have to do is look at our table for the yards to inches conversion factor. When looking up a conversion factor, we always begin on the left. Since we're starting with yards, we go to the yard row. Then we move to the right until we run into the inch column. The number in that spot is the conversion factor for yards to inches. It happens to be 36 because there are 36 inches in 1 yard. So all we have to do is multiply 4 by 36 to get 144 inches and we're done!

The Table Tells it All

The other neat thing about this table is that when using it, we don't have to worry about whether we should multiply or divide when converting from one unit to another. Assume, for example, that we want to convert feet to miles. That's going from smaller to larger units, which means we should divide. But watch what happens when we use the conversion table. To find the conversion factor, we start on the left and then go down to the foot row. Next, we move to the right until we hit miles. The number in that box is the fraction $\frac{1}{5,280}$. That's the conversion factor we need. Now all we have to do is *multiply* by $\frac{1}{5,280}$ to convert feet to miles.

But wait a minute. Aren't we supposed to divide when going from smaller to larger units? Well, yes, but we haven't broken any rules, because multiplying by $\frac{1}{5,280}$ is actually the same as dividing by 5,280. For instance, if we were converting 10,000 feet to miles, multiplying 10,000 by $\frac{1}{5,280}$ would give us this: $\frac{10,000}{1} \times \frac{1}{5,280}$ or $\frac{10,000}{5,280}$. But 10,000 over 5,280 is the same as dividing by 5,280.

The main point is that when using the table, we multiply every time—whether we're going from larger to smaller units or from smaller to larger units. Since the table has fractions in all the right places, it decides whether the number should be multiplied or divided for us.[1] We don't have to remember a thing.

It Pays to Memorize

Of course, you won't always have a unit conversion table in front of you when doing a unit conversion. So it's still smart to memorize as many conversion factors as possible. And it's definitely still worth remembering the rule about multiplying when going from larger to smaller units and dividing when going from smaller to larger units. If you're without a conversion table, that rule really helps.

Practice 55

a. Convert 10 yards into inches. Use the table below problem 18.

b. Convert 16,896 feet into miles. Use the table below problem 18.

---

[1] If you look closely, you'll see that every box that has a fraction in it is a case of converting from smaller to larger units. And when we multiply by that fraction, we're really dividing by the number on the bottom of the fraction.

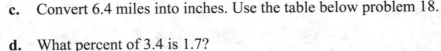

c. Convert 6.4 miles into inches. Use the table below problem 18.

d. What percent of 3.4 is 1.7?

e. Translate the word problem below into math; then solve.

The team had only 9 inches to go to get a first down. How many yards is that?

Problem Set 55

Tell whether each sentence below is True or False.

1. A unit conversion table contains the conversion factors between all units.

2. A unit conversion table tells you whether you are supposed to multiply or divide to do a particular conversion.

Add or subtract each group of numbers below.

3.
$$573.1$$
$$+98.9$$

4.
$$901.42$$
$$-854.26$$

Multiply or divide each pair of numbers below. Write any remainders in decimal form.

5.
$$13.4$$
$$\times 2.1$$

6. $0.8\overline{)235}$

7.
$$390$$
$$\times 61$$

Add or subtract each pair of numbers below. Make sure your answers are fully reduced.

8. $\dfrac{3}{7}+\dfrac{4}{7}$

9. $6\dfrac{2}{5}-2\dfrac{9}{10}$

Multiply or divide each pair of fractions below.

10. $\dfrac{3}{8}\times\dfrac{4}{5}$

11. $\dfrac{5}{16}\div\dfrac{5}{4}$

Convert each fraction below into decimal form. Round any repeating decimals to two digits (hundredths).

12. $\dfrac{5}{8}$ **13.** $\dfrac{5}{6}$

Convert each percent below into decimal form.

14. $77\dfrac{1}{4}\%$ **15.** 500%

Do each unit conversion below using the unit conversion table:

(a) 16. Convert 12 yards into inches.   **(b) 17.** Convert 18,480 feet into miles.

(c) 18. Convert 7.2 miles into inches.

	mile	yard	foot	inch
mile	1	1,760	5,280	63,360
yard	$\dfrac{1}{1,760}$	1	3	36
foot	$\dfrac{1}{5,280}$	$\dfrac{1}{3}$	1	12
inch	$\dfrac{1}{63,360}$	$\dfrac{1}{36}$	$\dfrac{1}{12}$	1

Answer each question below.

19. What is 25% of 14?   **(d) 20.** What percent of 7.5 is 1.5?

Translate the word problem below into math; then solve.

(e) 21. The man with the largest bicep in the world has a bicep which measures 30 inches when cold. How many yards is this?

283

Lesson 56—The Common System

The units of length that we've been studying so far are all part of what's called the **English system** or **common system** of measurements. So inches, feet, yards, miles, etc. all go together. This system is called "English" because it originated in England, and it's called "common" because for a long time, units like inches, feet, yards, and miles were the ones most often used in "common," everyday measurements. But today only English speaking countries, like the U.S., Britain, Australia, and New Zealand, still use the common system at all. The other 200 or more countries in the world use a different system, which we'll learn about in the next lesson.

Too Complicated

Why isn't the common system more popular? Well, since the common system was the first system of measurement, it arose gradually. And the original units were based on body parts. Remember, the foot was actually set to equal the length of the French King Charlemagne's foot. The original yard was based on the distance between the nose and fingertip of King Henry I of England. And the other units are just as random. With such weird beginnings, it's not surprising that the whole system turned out to be pretty complicated. Even though some of the units were later adjusted a bit so that they would fit together better (the foot was made to equal 12 inches exactly instead of $11\frac{1}{2}$ or $12\frac{1}{2}$ inches), that still didn't help all that much.

Too Much to Memorize

For example, think of how many different numbers we have to memorize when using the common system of measurements. There are 12 inches in a foot, so we need to remember the number 12. But then there are only 3 feet in a yard, so we have to remember the number 3 as well. There are 1,760 yards in a mile, and we wouldn't want to forget that. Then it also makes sense to remember that there are 5,280 feet in a mile. So with only a handful of units, we have to do a lot of memorizing. The other problem is that since everything is based on body parts, the numbers aren't related to one another in any simple way. No wonder we need a table to remember all of the conversion factors!

So the common system isn't all that popular, because it's so complex. Wouldn't it be nice if there were a simpler system where all the numbers fit together nicely? Then there wouldn't be so much to memorize. Stay tuned.

Practice 56

a. Convert 504 inches into yards. Use the table below problem 17.

b. Convert $\frac{1}{8}$ of a mile into inches. Use the table below problem 17.

c. 108 has how many $\frac{1}{4}$ s in it?

d. Add 47 inches and 6 feet and put your answer in inches.

e. Translate the word problem below into math; then solve.

The second-rate superhero tried to bend the steel bars on the windows, but, as usual, he couldn't. Now the only way for the hero to escape from the tower is to try to slide his skinny body through the bars and lower himself to the ground using a rope made with bed sheets. If each bed sheet will extend $7\frac{1}{2}$ feet, how many will he need to reach the ground which is 90 feet below?

Problem Set 56

Tell whether each sentence below is True or False.

1. The English or common system of units is still used for everyday measurements in English-speaking countries (like the U.S. and Britain).

2. The common system of units is not popular today because it is too logical and scientific.

Add or subtract each group of numbers below.

3.
$$\begin{array}{r} 524.6 \\ +103.4 \\ \hline \end{array}$$

4.
$$\begin{array}{r} 88.23 \\ -57.65 \\ \hline \end{array}$$

Multiply or divide each pair of numbers below. Write any remainders in decimal form.

5.
$$\begin{array}{r} 72.6 \\ \times 0.12 \\ \hline \end{array}$$

6. $3.2\overline{)180}$

Add or subtract each pair of fractions below. Make sure your answers are fully reduced.

7. $\frac{5}{16}+\frac{1}{16}$

8. $\frac{3}{2}-\frac{1}{5}$

Multiply or divide each pair of numbers below. Make sure your answers are fully reduced.

9. $3\dfrac{1}{2} \times \dfrac{2}{3}$

10. $\dfrac{5}{8} \div \dfrac{3}{4}$

Convert each fraction below into decimal form. Round any repeating decimals to two digits (hundredths).

11. $\dfrac{9}{20}$

12. $\dfrac{14}{15}$

Convert each decimal below into a common fraction. Make sure your answers are fully reduced.

13. 0.99

14. 0.8

Do each unit conversion below using the unit conversion table:

(a) 15. Convert 612 inches into yards.

16. Convert 7.1 miles into feet.

(b) 17. Convert $\dfrac{1}{4}$ of a mile into inches.

	mile	yard	foot	inch
mile	1	1,760	5,280	63,360
yard	$\dfrac{1}{1,760}$	1	3	36
foot	$\dfrac{1}{5,280}$	$\dfrac{1}{3}$	1	12
inch	$\dfrac{1}{63,360}$	$\dfrac{1}{36}$	$\dfrac{1}{12}$	1

Answer each question below.

(c) 18. 102 has how many $\frac{1}{3}$ s in it?

19. What is 72% of 250?

(d) 20. 52 inches + 8 feet (Put your answer in inches.)

Translate the word problem below into math; then solve.

(e) 21. The garden bug has a dream that some day she will be able to leave The Land of Boring Lettuce and travel to The Land of Sweet Potatoes. If the garden bug can travel $5\frac{1}{4}$ inches each day, and The Land of Sweet Potatoes is 294 inches away, how many days will it take the bug to get there?

Lesson 57—The Metric System

We talked about how nice it would be to have a simpler system of units. Well, in the 17th and 18th centuries—a time of great scientific discoveries—people began to wonder about whether such a system could actually be created.

Based on Nature

With so much science going on, there was a need for more accurate measurements than you could get by using the common system. (Scientists usually want their measurements to be as precise as possible.) People were also getting frustrated with having to remember all those conversion factors: 12 inches to a foot, 3 feet to a yard, and so on.

There was another reason that many of the scientifically-minded intellectuals of Europe wanted to dump the common system. They thought that units of measure should be based not on the length of a dead King's foot but on a fact of nature. Thomas Jefferson (the 3rd president of the U.S.) agreed with this thinking and was interested in creating a new system of units for America too. The only problem was that people had gotten so used to the old common units that changing to something new seemed really hard.

It wasn't until after the French Revolution (when the French king was thrown out and killed) that a new system was actually invented. The revolutionaries who took over from the king decided to recruit a group of scientists and give them the assignment of creating a complete new system of measurement. They asked the scientists to make the new system as logical as possible.

Finding the Basic Unit

The scientists first had to decide on a basic unit for their system. It would be the unit that all the other units are based upon. (The basic unit of the common system is the foot.) As we said, they wanted this unit to come from nature, because that seemed more logical and intelligent to them. After doing quite a bit of thinking, they ended up choosing the distance around the earth itself. Actually, instead of the distance all the way around the earth, they measured from the equator to the North Pole, which is a fourth of the way around the earth.

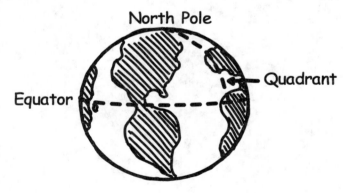

This length is called a **quadrant** ("quad" means four). Since the scientists were French, they measured along a line that ran right through the city of Paris (from the equator to the North Pole).

The only problem with the quadrant is that it's too long to be used in everyday measurements. A basic unit really should be short enough to fit on a stick. So the last step for the scientists was to divide the quadrant into 10 million pieces. One 10 millionth of the quadrant then became the basic unit of measure. This unit was given the name **meter**, and it's only a little longer than a yard (which is a great length for a stick).[2]

A meter stick

The complete length is a little over a yard.

Of course, if the scientists' measurements had been exact, it would take precisely 10 million meters to go from the equator to the North Pole through Paris, and the distance all the way around the earth would be 4 times that or 40 million meters. But those first measurements were a little off, so today's meter is not precisely equal to this length, even though it's very close.

Giving the System a New Name

Once the meter was decided upon, the French scientists created other units to go along with it. All of these were fit together into a new system of measurement that was extremely logical, and since the meter was its basic unit, the new set of measurements was called the **metric system**. We'll learn more about the metric system in the next few lessons.

Practice 57

a. Convert 162 inches into yards. (Conversion factors: 12 inches = 1 foot; 3 feet = 1 yard; 1,760 yards = 1 mile.)

b. How many feet are in $5\frac{1}{2}$ miles?

c. $\frac{7}{2}$ has how many $\frac{1}{8}$ s in it?

---

[2] There isn't enough room on the page to show the entire stick.

d. 4 miles − 3,960 feet (Put your answer in miles.)

e. Translate the word problem below into math; then solve.

Mr. and Mrs. Gibbons are trying to save enough money to buy their daughter a harp. They have already saved $1,200 and it still isn't enough. (Harps are expensive!) If their $1,200 in savings is sitting in a bank account that pays $5\frac{1}{2}$ % in yearly interest.

i.) How much will Mr. and Mrs. Gibbons have earned in interest one year from now?

ii.) If they leave their money <u>and</u> interest in the bank for another year, how much interest will they earn for the 2nd year? Round your answer to the nearest hundredths place.

Problem Set 57

Tell whether each sentence below is True or False.

1. In the 18th century, scientists created a more logical system of units called the metric system.

2. The basic unit of measurement in the metric system is the inch.

Add or subtract each group of numbers below.

3.
$$\begin{array}{r} 1,850 \\ + 7,042 \\ \hline \end{array}$$

4.
$$\begin{array}{r} 9.056 \\ - 4.135 \\ \hline \end{array}$$

Multiply or divide each pair of numbers below. Write any remainders in decimal form.

5. $\begin{array}{r} 236 \\ \times\,4.2 \\ \hline \end{array}$

6. $0.5\overline{)11.75}$

7. $\begin{array}{r} 8.5 \\ \times\,1.7 \\ \hline \end{array}$

Add or subtract each pair of numbers below. Make sure your answers are fully reduced.

8. $1\dfrac{1}{4} + 2\dfrac{5}{6}$

9. $\dfrac{8}{9} - \dfrac{2}{3}$

Multiply or divide each pair of fractions below.

10. $\dfrac{17}{18} \times \dfrac{18}{17}$

11. $\dfrac{9}{10} \div \dfrac{1}{5}$

Convert each fraction below into decimal form. Round any repeating decimals to two digits (hundredths).

12. $\dfrac{3}{5}$

13. $\dfrac{6}{11}$

Do each unit conversion below. (Conversion factors: 12 inches = 1 foot; 3 feet = 1 yard; 1,760 yards = 1 mile.)

14. How many inches are in 34 feet?

(a) 15. Convert 126 inches into yards.

(b) 16. How many feet are in $4\dfrac{1}{2}$ miles?

Answer each question below.

(c) 17. $\dfrac{5}{2}$ has how many $\dfrac{1}{4}$ s in it?

18. What is $\dfrac{2}{5}$ of 205?

19. What is 14.5% of 30?

(d) 20. 3 miles $-$ 2,640 feet (Put your answer in miles.)

Translate the word problem below into math; then solve.

(e) 21. Mr. Randall opened up a college savings account for his son at the local bank. He put \$3,000 in the account, which pays $7\frac{1}{2}$% in yearly interest.

    i.) How much will Mr. Randall have earned in interest one year from now?

    ii.) If he leaves his money <u>and</u> interest in the bank for another year, how much interest will he earn for the 2nd year? Round your answer to the nearest hundredths place.

Lesson 58—It's All in a Name

As we talked about in the last lesson, the metric system is based on the meter. But there are also lots of other units of different sizes in the metric system. We'll learn about the major ones in this lesson.

Finally, a Simple System

Before getting into the names of the other units, though, we should talk a little about how they're all related. The common system's biggest weakness is that the conversion factors are hard to remember. You have to remember that there are 12 inches in a foot, 3 feet in a yard, 1,760 yards in a mile, and so on. Since the metric system was created from scratch (by logically-minded scientists), its units are related in a much simpler way. In the metric system, each unit is 10 times (or one tenth of) the next unit. So, for example, the meter is 10 times the unit that is just smaller than it in size. And the unit that is just bigger than the meter is 10 times the meter's length. All the units are related this way. Everything goes up by 10s. As we'll see later, this makes a huge difference in doing unit conversions.

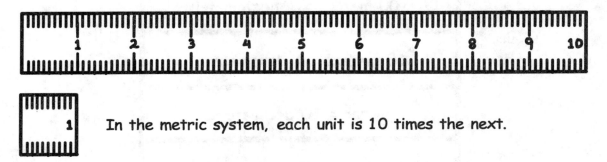

In the metric system, each unit is 10 times the next.

Smaller than a Meter

What about the names of these other units? Let's start with the smaller ones. These come from breaking down the meter into smaller lengths. The unit that is one tenth of the meter is called the **decimeter**. It's about 4 inches long. And since the decimeter is one tenth of the meter, it takes 10 decimeters to equal 1 meter.

To get the unit just smaller than the decimeter, we have to break it down into ten pieces. This gives us the **centimeter**. It takes 10 centimeters to equal 1 decimeter and 100 centimeters to equal 1 meter. The centimeter is less than half an inch in length.

Next in line comes the **millimeter**, which as you might expect is one tenth of a centimeter. The millimeter is only about as wide as a pinhead. It takes 1,000 millimeters to equal 1 meter.

Bigger than a Meter

The decimeter, centimeter, and millimeter are units that are smaller than a meter—and the ones used most often. But what about the units that are bigger than a meter? Well, the first one is 10 times the meter in length, and it's called the **dekameter**. Notice that everything is still by 10s, by the way. That holds true for all the units of the metric system (small and large). The dekameter is over 30 feet long.

The next biggest unit is the **hectometer**, and it is 10 times the dekameter, which means that it's equal to 100 meters. A hectometer is longer than a football field.

Following the hectometer, we have the **kilometer**, which is 10 times the hectometer. The kilometer is equal to 1,000 meters and is a little over half a mile in length. Here are all of the major units of the metric system shown together.

Major Metric Units (for length)

1,000 meters = 1 kilometer
100 meters = 1 hectometer
10 meters = 1 dekameter
1 meter = 10 decimeters
1 meter = 100 centimeters
1 meter = 1,000 millimeters

The important point to remember is that each unit is 10 times as big as the one below it. The kilometer is the largest on the list, so it's 10 times as big as the hectometer. The hectometer is 10 times as big as the dekameter, and so on. That's what makes the metric system so simple.

The Name Tells the Size

The other big advantage of the metric system is that the names of the units tell you how big they are compared to the meter. The prefix "kilo" means 1,000, and a kilometer is 1,000 times a meter. The prefix "hecto" means 100, and the hectometer is 100 times the size of the meter. "Deka" means 10, because a dekameter is 10 times the meter. For the smaller units, "deci" means $\frac{1}{10}$, because a decimeter is $\frac{1}{10}$ the length of a meter. "Centi" means $\frac{1}{100}$, since a centimeter is $\frac{1}{100}$ the length of a meter. And "milli" means $\frac{1}{1,000}$, since a millimeter is $\frac{1}{1,000}$ as long as a meter. The whole system is set up to be as simple as possible, so that we don't have to memorize so much. It's totally different from the common system, where the word inch, for example, doesn't tell us anything about the size of that unit.

Practice 58

a. Convert 0.65% into decimal form.

b. Convert 7 yards 3 feet to inches. (Conversion factors: 12 inches = 1 foot; 3 feet = 1 yard; 1,760 yards = 1 mile.)

c. 14 feet 6 inches + 10 feet 3 inches (Put your answer in feet.)

d. 3 miles + 7,568 yards + 1,056 feet (Put your answer in miles.)

e. Translate the word problem below into math; then solve.

By the most exact measurements, the Empire State Building is said to be 1,453 feet 9 inches high. If a (very brave) person 5 feet 6 inches tall stood on the very tip of the building's antenna, how many <u>feet</u> high would the person plus the building be?

Problem Set 58

Tell whether each sentence below is True or False.

1. In the metric system, each unit is ten times the size of the next unit.

2. In the metric system, the size of each unit can be determined by the prefix of its name.

Complete each sentence below with the best of the choices given.

3. A meter is equal to 10 _____ .

    A. kilometers   B. hectometers   C. dekameters
    D. decimeters   E. centimeters

4. 1,000 millimeters equals 1 _____.

      A. kilometer   B. dekameter   C. meter
      D. decimeter   E. centimeter

5. A kilometer is equal to 10 _____.

      A. hectometers   B. dekameters   C. meters
      D. decimeters   E. centimeters

Add or subtract each group of numbers below.

6.
$$\begin{array}{r} 31.25 \\ +\,9.375 \\ \hline \end{array}$$

7.
$$\begin{array}{r} 85{,}204 \\ -\,23{,}810 \\ \hline \end{array}$$

Multiply or divide each pair of numbers below. Write any remainders in decimal form.

8.
$$\begin{array}{r} 0.58 \\ \times\,0.12 \\ \hline \end{array}$$

9. $4\overline{)372.5}$

Add or subtract each pair of fractions below. Make sure your answers are fully reduced.

10. $\dfrac{3}{8}+\dfrac{1}{4}$

11. $\dfrac{4}{5}-\dfrac{1}{2}$

Multiply or divide each pair of numbers below.

12. $21\times\dfrac{5}{7}$

13. $32\div\dfrac{8}{9}$

Convert each percent below into decimal form.

14. $52\dfrac{1}{2}\%$

(a) 15. 0.75%

Answer each question below. (Conversion factors: 12 inches = 1 foot; 3 feet = 1 yard; 1,760 yards = 1 mile.)

16. How many feet are in 1,800 inches?

(b) 17. Convert 6 yards 5 feet to inches.

(c) 18. 11 feet 6 inches + 12 feet 3 inches (Put your answer in feet.)

(d) 19. 6 miles + 9,152 yards + 1,320 feet (Put your answer in miles.)

Translate the word problem below into math; then solve.

(e) 20. The limo measured 19 feet and 6 inches; then the driver added a special back bumper that was 1 foot 3 inches long (just to keep the photographers even farther back). How many <u>feet</u> long is the limo now if you include the new back bumper?

Lesson 59—Everything by 10

Just as we sometimes have to convert feet to inches (or yards), it's also often necessary to convert from one metric unit into another. But it's in converting units that the metric system is at its best. That's because the whole system is based on the number 10 (just like our number system), and this makes converting from one unit to another incredibly easy.

Just Move the Decimal Point

For example, let's say we want to change 5.2 dekameters into meters. Since the dekameter is the next bigger unit after the meter, we just need to multiply by 10. Since $5.2 \times 10 = 52$, we know that 5.2 dekameters equals 52 meters.

Actually, we don't even need to go through the formal multiplication process. Since multiplication by 10 only affects the position of the decimal point, 5.2 dekameters can be converted to meters just by moving the decimal point one place to the right to get 52.0 meters.

5.2 dekameters = 52.0 meters   **Move decimal point one place to the right.**

Converting from a smaller unit to a larger one is just as easy. For instance, to change 18 decimeters into meters, all we have to do is divide by 10. And we can do that by moving the decimal point (after the 8) one place to the left to get 1.8.

18.0 decimeters = 1.8 meters   **Move decimal point one place to the left.**

Larger to Smaller Still Means Multiply

Notice that the same rules about when to multiply and when to divide also apply to the metric system. When converting larger units (dekameters) into smaller units (meters), we multiply by 10, but when converting smaller units (meters) to larger units (dekameters), we divide by 10. It's just that with the metric system, multiplying and dividing are a lot easier, because it's always by 10.

The next page shows a complete list of all the metric units that we've learned about. To go up the list, we move the decimal point one place to the left, and to go down the list, we move the decimal point one place to the right.

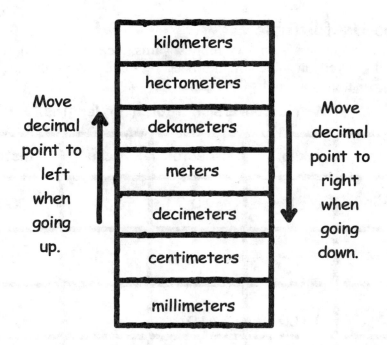

From Kilometers to Millimeters

Just to prove to you once and for all how much better metric is, let's convert 1.4 kilometers (because kilometers is at the top of the list) to millimeters, which is all the way at the bottom. We have to do the same kind of thing sometimes with common units. For example, we might have to convert miles (which are really long) into inches (which are really short). And you remember that that can be pretty tough.

But watch how much easier it is to go from kilometers all the way down to millimeters. All we have to do is count how many unit conversions are needed to go from kilometers to millimeters. Starting on top with kilometers, we need to make 6 conversions to get to millimeters. Next, we just move the decimal point that many places. Since we're going down, we move the decimal point 6 places to the right.[3]

1.400000 kilometers

= 1,400,000 millimeters

Move decimal point 6 places to the right.

So 1.4 kilometers equals 1,400,000 millimeters.

Going from really small units to really large units is just as easy. We just move the decimal point a certain number of places to the *left*. For example, to convert 950 centimeters to hectometers, we would need 4 conversions (count them yourself in the chart above). That means we need to move the decimal point 4 places to the left to get 0.095 hectometers. It's that easy.

---

[3] We've added some zeros to the right of 1.4 to make it easier to move the decimal point.

The Not-So-Useful Table

As with the common system (with miles, yards, feet, and inches), it's also possible to create a unit conversion table for the metric system. Here's the part of the metric conversion table that includes units from meters on up.

Metric Conversion Table (for lengths)

	kilo	hecto	deka	meter
kilo	1	10	100	1,000
hecto	$\frac{1}{10}$	1	10	100
deka	$\frac{1}{100}$	$\frac{1}{10}$	1	10
meter	$\frac{1}{1,000}$	$\frac{1}{100}$	$\frac{1}{10}$	1

Notice the difference between this table and the unit conversion table for the common system. Everything is based on 10s here. It's all 1, 10, 100, 1,000 and fractions with 10, 100, and 1,000 on bottom.

We use this table in the same way we use the common system table. We find the unit we're starting with on the left, and then move to the right to find the direct unit conversion. Next, we multiply by the number in the box. Of course, when the conversion factor is a fraction, that's actually the same as dividing by the denominator.

This section is titled "The Not-So-Useful Table." Why isn't the table useful? There's nothing wrong with it, really. It works just like our other table. But the metric system is so simple that we don't really need a unit conversion table. The easiest way to convert from one unit to another in the metric system is just by moving the decimal point. What more could anybody ask for?

Practice 59

a. 42 yards 2 feet + 37 yards 1 foot (Put your answer in feet.)

b. How many centimeters are in 5 dekameters?

c. Convert 415 meters to kilometers.

✓ **d.** How many hectometers are in 292 meters?

✓ **e.** Translate the word problem below into math; then solve.

Some South American plants have leaves so big that their leaf blades are 20 meters long. How many centimeters is this?

Problem Set 59

Tell whether each sentence below is True or False.

1. Converting from one unit to another is more difficult in the metric system than it is in the common system.

2. The old rules about when to multiply and divide when doing unit conversions do not apply in the metric system.

Complete each sentence below with the best of the choices given.

✓ **3.** A kilometer is equal to 10,000 _____.

A. hectometers   B. dekameters   C. meters
D. decimeters   E. centimeters

✓ **4.** 100 centimeters equals 1 _____.

A. kilometer   B. dekameter   C. meter
D. decimeter   E. millimeter

✓ **5.** 10,000 millimeters is equal to 1 _____.

A. kilometer   B. dekameter   C. meter
D. decimeter   E. centimeter

Add or subtract each group of numbers below.

6. 5,231
      +970

7. 7.884
      − 0.952

Multiply or divide each pair of numbers below. Write any remainders in decimal form.

8. $\begin{array}{r} 620 \\ \times 3.4 \\ \hline \end{array}$

9. $0.6\overline{)3.207}$

Add or subtract each pair of numbers below. Make sure your answers are fully reduced.

10. $7\dfrac{1}{2}+\dfrac{5}{6}$

11. $\dfrac{4}{9}-\dfrac{5}{12}$

Multiply or divide each pair of fractions below.

12. $\dfrac{2}{3}\times\dfrac{9}{14}$

13. $\dfrac{1}{2}\div\dfrac{1}{6}$

Convert each fraction below into decimal form. Round any repeating decimals to two digits (hundredths).

14. $\dfrac{1}{50}$

15. $\dfrac{7}{11}$

Answer each question below.

(a) 16. 52 yards 2 feet + 47 yards 1 foot (Put your answer in feet.)

(b) 17. How many centimeters are in 8 dekameters?

(c) 18. Convert 245 meters to kilometers.

(d) 19. How many hectometers are in 374 meters?

Translate the word problem below into math; then solve.

(e) 20. A man in Indonesia claims to have made the world's tallest wedding cake. His cake is 24 meters tall. How tall is this in centimeters?

Lesson 60—Conversions Between Common and Metric

In the last lesson, we learned to convert from one unit to another in the metric system. But what about converting between a metric unit and a common (English) unit, such as between inches and meters? Since a lot of people still use common units, especially in the U.S., it's important to be able to do that. The problem is that the common system is complicated, while the metric system is simple and based on the number 10. So the two systems don't fit well together, which makes the conversion factors between the two really messy.

Meters to Inches and Back

The common-metric unit conversion most often used is between the meter and the inch. It turns out that there are 39.37 inches in 1 meter.

$$39.37 \text{ inches} = 1 \text{ meter}$$

See what we mean about messy? This conversion factor isn't even a whole number. Let's go through a specific example, though, to show you how this factor is used.

How many inches are in 2 meters?

Since meters are larger than inches, we're going from larger to smaller units. That means we need to multiply. Specifically, we multiply 2 by 39.37.

$$2 \times 39.37 = 78.74$$

Multiply to convert meters to inches.

That gives us 78.74 inches, which is equal to 2 meters.

Let's do another example.

Convert 551 inches to meters.

Since we're going from smaller units (inches) to larger units (meters), this time we should divide. And we need to divide by 39.37, of course, since that's the conversion factor.

$$\frac{551}{39.37} = 14$$

Divide to convert inches to meters.

That leaves us with an answer of about 14 meters.

Amazingly, we only need this one conversion factor (39.37 inches = 1 meter) to do any other common-metric unit conversion we want. For example, what if we wanted to convert feet to meters, but didn't have that particular conversion factor? We could still do the calculation. All we would have to do is convert feet to inches first, and then we could use 39.37 inches = 1 meter to get the answer. And it would work the same way if we were going to convert between any other two units (common and metric). All it takes is 39.37 inches = 1 meter.

Other Conversion Factors

Even though technically we only need the meters to inch conversion factor, it speeds things up to know a few other ones. Below is a list of other common-metric conversions that are used pretty often.

Some Common-Metric Conversion Factors

1 inch (in) = 2.54 centimeters (cm)
1.0936 yards (yd) = 1 meter (m)
1 mile (mi) = 1.609 kilometers (km)

Let's do an example with one of these other conversion factors. Let's convert 18 inches to centimeters. Since there are 2.54 centimeters in 1 inch, we know that inches are larger than centimeters (because it takes more than 1 centimeter to make 1 inch). That means in converting 18 inches to centimeters, we're going from larger to smaller units. So we should multiply 18 by 2.54.

$$18 \times 2.54 = 45.72$$

Converting inches to centimeters.

The answer turns out to be 45.72 centimeters.

Let's do one more common-metric conversion.

Convert 5 yards to meters.

Since 1 meter = 1.0936 yards, a meter must be larger than a yard. That means in converting 5 yards to meters, we're going from smaller to larger units. We should therefore divide 5 by 1.0936.

$$\frac{5}{1.0936} = 4.57$$

Converting yards to meters.

We get about 4.57 meters.

Those are a few examples of how we convert between metric and common units.

Practice 60

 a. How many meters are in 380 centimeters?

b. Convert 5 meters to inches. (common-metric conversion factors: 39.37 inches = 1 meter; 1 inch = 2.54 centimeters; 1.0936 yards = 1 meter; 1 mile = 1.609 kilometer)

c. Convert 13 meters to yards. Round your answer to two digits (hundredths).

d. What percent of 180 is 126?

e. Translate the word problem below into math; then solve.

In 1988, a man from France "walked" across the Atlantic Ocean on skis that were almost fourteen feet long and could float. The trip took two months and he survived by eating plankton along the way. If the man walked a total distance of 5,636 km, how many miles did he walk? Round your answer to two digits (hundredths).

Problem Set 60

Add or subtract each group of numbers below.

1.
$$\begin{array}{r} 46.57 \\ +\,39.18 \\ \hline \end{array}$$

2.
$$\begin{array}{r} 502.8 \\ -\,364.5 \\ \hline \end{array}$$

Multiply or divide each pair of numbers below. Write any remainders in decimal form.

3.
$$\begin{array}{r} 48.9 \\ \times\,1.5 \\ \hline \end{array}$$

4. $15\overline{)10,080}$

Add or subtract each pair of fractions below. Make sure your answers are fully reduced.

5. $\dfrac{5}{18}+\dfrac{7}{18}$

6. $\dfrac{3}{4}-\dfrac{1}{6}$

Multiply or divide each pair of numbers below.

7. $\dfrac{3}{10}\times\dfrac{5}{4}$

8. $\dfrac{3}{14}\div 3$

Convert each decimal below into a common fraction. Make sure your answers are fully reduced.

9. 0.65   10. 0.004

Convert each percent below into decimal form.

11. $7\frac{2}{5}\%$ 12. 124%

Do each unit conversion below. (common system conversion factors: 12 inches = 1 foot; 3 feet = 1 yard; 1,760 yards = 1 mile.)

13. Convert 2 miles 327 yards to feet.

(a) 14. How many meters are in 420 centimeters?

Do each unit conversion below. (common-metric conversion factors: 39.37 inches = 1 meter; 1 inch = 2.54 centimeters; 1.0936 yards = 1 meter; 1 mile = 1.609 kilometer)

(b) 15. Convert 8 meters to inches.

(c) 16. Convert 17 meters to yards. Round your answer to two digits (hundredths).

Answer each question below.

17. What is $\frac{8}{9}$ of 45?

18. What is 25% of 78?

(d) 19. What percent of 140 is 112?

Translate the word problem below into math; then solve.

(e) 20. The longest distance that anyone has ever walked on their hands is 1,400 km. How far is this in miles? Round your answer to two digits (hundredths).

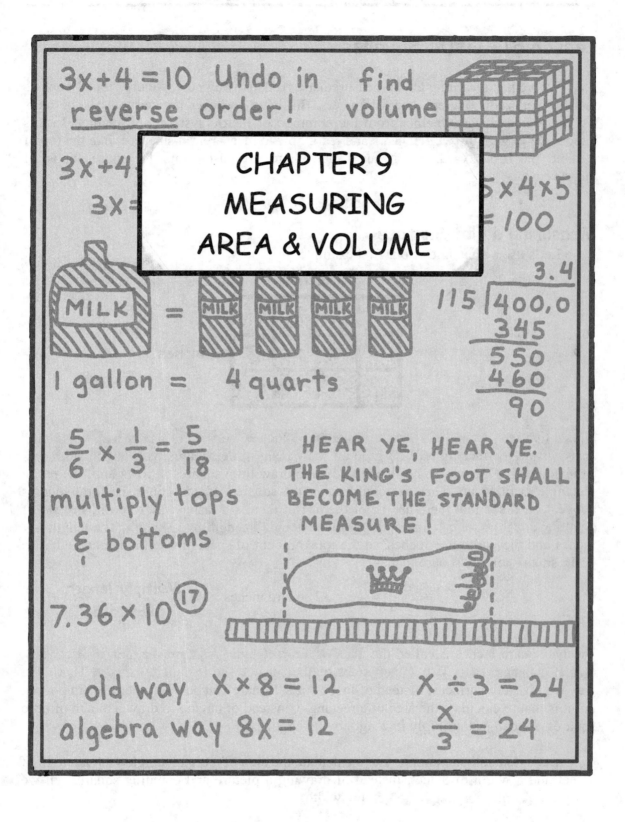

Lesson 61—Little Squares

We've been learning about measurement. And, as you know, we use "units" such as inches, feet, yards, meters, and kilometers. But have you ever noticed that all the units we've studied so far, whether from the common or metric system, are lengths? In this lesson, we're going to switch gears and learn how to measure flat surfaces, like the top of a table or a backyard. As it turns out, there are also units for those kinds of measurements.

Measuring a Flat Surface

Let's use a rectangle as our first example.

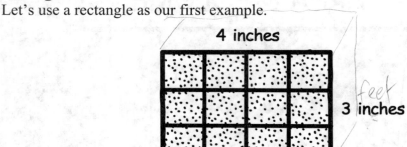

Notice that the rectangle is 4 inches long and 3 inches wide. Here's how we measure the space inside the rectangle. We figure out how many little squares with 1 inch sides will fit inside of it. One way to do this would be to draw little squares in rows until the entire rectangle is filled up. Then we could count the squares. If you count the little squares above, you'll see that there are 12 of them. But there's a faster way to do it. Instead of counting squares, we can just multiply the rectangle's length by its width. The length is 4 inches and the width is 3 inches, so the total amount of space inside the rectangle has to be 12 squares or 12 "square inches."

$$4 \times 3 = 12 \text{ square inches}$$

Multiply length by width.

Twelve square inches is called the **area** of the rectangle. And, once again, it just means that 12 squares, each with 1 inch sides, will fit inside the rectangle exactly. That's the way we measure surfaces. Instead of inches, it's "square" inches. But the other important point is that to calculate the area of a rectangle, instead of having to draw a bunch of little squares, we can just multiply its length by its width.

Let's do another example. Let's calculate the area of a big rectangle with a length of 7 feet and a width of 3 feet. Instead of drawing a picture and counting squares, all we have to do is multiply the length by the width.

$$7 \times 3 = 21 \text{ square feet}$$

This means that 21 squares with 1 foot sides will fit inside the rectangle exactly.

Larger Areas Need Larger Units

Notice that when the sides are measured in inches, the area is in square inches, and if the sides are measured in feet, the area is in square feet. So we can measure area in different units just as we measure length in different units. It's smart to always use the units that are the easiest. For smaller surfaces, like a piece of paper, units like square inches work better.[1] For bigger surfaces, like a backyard, square yards would work a whole lot better. To measure the area of an entire city, we would need square miles. For example, the city of Los Angeles has an area of 469 square miles, which means that 469 squares with sides 1 mile long could fit on the ground inside L.A.

To make sure we have enough square units to measure any size surface, we should take all four major units of length from the common system—inches, feet, yards, and miles—and turn them into square inches, square feet, square yards, and square miles.

Units of Length	Units of Area
inches	square inches
feet	square feet
yards	square yards
miles	square miles

There's also one other unit for measuring areas in the common system that is popular. You've probably heard of it. It's called an **acre**. The acre is a very old unit that was used for measuring land. It was originally the amount of land 1 yoke of oxen could plow in one morning. Because of tradition, we still use acres to measure land surfaces, even though not many of us plow fields with oxen anymore. An acre is smaller than a square mile by a fair amount. A large backyard might be about $\frac{1}{2}$ acre.

---

[1] By the way, a regular size sheet of paper turns out to have an area of over 93 square inches.

Converting Units to Find Area

There's something else we should mention. What if we want to calculate an area, but the length and width are in different units? For example, here's a rectangle with a length of 3 feet and a width of 24 inches.

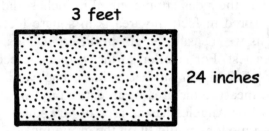

3 feet

24 inches

See, the length is in feet, but the width is in inches. And the problem is that we can't multiply when the units are different. But it's easy to see what to do. We can just convert one of the measurements into different units. We can either convert 3 feet to inches or 24 inches to feet. Let's convert 24 inches to feet by dividing by 12 to get 2 feet. And from there, we just multiply as usual.

$$3 \text{ feet} \times 2 \text{ feet} = 6 \text{ square feet}$$

Convert inches to feet and multiply.

Since both length and width are now in feet, the answer is 6 square feet.

So to calculate areas, the length and width have to be in the same units. It's no different from calculating lengths, really. Before we can add feet to inches, we have to convert so that the units are the same. But when calculating areas, the answer comes out to square units. And it could be square feet, square inches, square miles, or anything else, depending on the specific problem.

Practice 61

a. How many inches are in 11 yards? (common system conversion factors: 12 inches = 1 foot; 3 feet = 1 yard; 1,760 yards = 1 mile.)

b. How many centimeters are in 7.5 meters?

c. Convert 4 inches to centimeters. (common-metric conversion factors: 39.37 inches = 1 meter; 1 inch = 2.54 centimeters; 1.0936 yards = 1 meter; 1 mile = 1.609 kilometer)

d. Convert 4 yards to meters. Round your answer to two digits (hundredths).

e. Translate the word problem below into math; then solve.

Leeches are bloodsucking worms that live in water. Some are 8 inches long. How long is this in centimeters? (1 inch = 2.54 centimeters)

Problem Set 61

Tell whether each sentence below is True or False.

1. Flat surfaces or "areas" are measured by determining how many little squares will fit on them.

2. Several units used to measure area are square inches, square feet, square yards, square miles, and acres.

Complete each sentence below with the best of the choices given.

3. A dekameter is equal to 100 _____.

    A. kilometers   B. hectometers
    C. meters   D. decimeters
    E. centimeters

4. 10 decimeters equals 1 _____.

    A. kilometer   B. hectometer
    C. dekameter   D. meter
    E. centimeter

Add or subtract each group of numbers below.

5.
$$\begin{array}{r} 35{,}009 \\ +12{,}571 \\ \hline \end{array}$$

6.
$$\begin{array}{r} 7.5 \\ -3.875 \\ \hline \end{array}$$

Multiply or divide each pair of numbers below. Write any remainders in decimal form.

7.
$$\begin{array}{r} 0.42 \\ \times 3.1 \\ \hline \end{array}$$

8. $2.4\overline{)675}$

Add or subtract each pair of fractions below. Make sure your answers are fully reduced.

9. $\dfrac{1}{12} + \dfrac{7}{12}$

10. $\dfrac{2}{5} - \dfrac{1}{3}$

Multiply or divide each pair of fractions below.

11. $\dfrac{2}{9} \times \dfrac{3}{8}$

12. $\dfrac{4}{7} \div \dfrac{2}{14}$

Convert each percent below into decimal form.

13. $21\dfrac{1}{5}\%$

14. 375%

Do each unit conversion below. (common system conversion factors: 12 inches = 1 foot; 3 feet = 1 yard; 1,760 yards = 1 mile.)

(a) 15. How many inches are in 12 yards?

(b) 16. How many centimeters are in 8.6 meters?

Do each unit conversion below. (common-metric conversion factors: 39.37 inches = 1 meter; 1 inch = 2.54 centimeters; 1.0936 yards = 1 meter; 1 mile = 1.609 kilometer)

(c) 17. Convert 3 inches to centimeters.

(d) 18. Convert 5 yards to meters. Round your answer to two digits (hundredths).

Answer each question below.

19. What is 40% of 730?

20. What percent of 56 is 14?

Translate the word problem below into math; then solve.

(e) 21. The nightstand was 36 inches tall. How tall is this in centimeters? (1 inch = 2.54 centimeters)

Lesson 62—Area Unit Conversions

In the last lesson, we learned how to calculate area. Remember, that's just the way we measure a flat surface like a rectangle. The method we learned was to multiply the length by the width. And if you'll recall, we calculated the area of a rectangle that was 3 feet by 24 inches. Here it is again.

3 feet

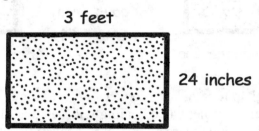

24 inches

To do the calculation, we converted 24 inches to 2 feet and then multiplied to get 6 square feet. But what if we wanted to know the area in square inches? One way to do this would be to go back to the rectangle and convert 3 feet to inches and then multiply length times width again in inches. Doing that would give us 36 inches, and then $36 \times 24 = 864$ square inches.

The Conversion Factor Multiplied Twice

That's quite a bit of work to go from square feet to square inches. Is there any way to convert from one to the other, without going back and multiplying again? Yes, there is. To see how it works let's look at a single square foot.

1 foot

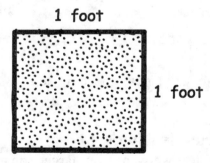

1 foot

This obviously has an area of 1 square foot, and we can get that answer by multiplying its length by its width ($1 \times 1 = 1$). But now let's convert the side lengths to inches. That gives us a 12 inch length and a 12 inch width. Next, let's calculate the area in square inches. We get 12 times 12 or 144 square inches. Notice that after converting from feet to inches, the side lengths went from 1 to 12, but the area went from 1 to 144. That's because in calculating area we multiply the length and width. So if both are 12 times bigger than they were before, the answer has to be 12×12 or 144 times bigger.

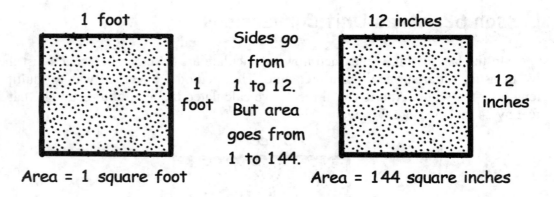

This always happens when converting area units. The conversion factor is multiplied twice. For example, when dealing with lengths, the conversion factor for going from yards to feet is 3 (since there are 3 feet in a yard). We have to multiply by 3 to make the conversion, in other words. But to convert from square yards to square feet, we have to multiply by 3 times 3, or 9. A picture will show why this is true. On the left is 1 square yard. But when we change the units from yards to feet (on the right), we get a length of 3 feet and a width of 3 feet.

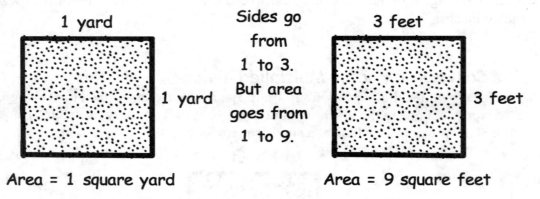

Since the sides go from 1 to 3, the areas go from 1 to 3×3 or 9 to get 9 square feet.

Smaller to Larger Means Divide

In both of our examples, we went from larger square units to smaller square units (from square feet to square inches and from square yards to square feet). What about going the other way, from smaller square units to larger square units? Well, then we would have to divide.

For example, if we want to convert 144 square inches into square feet, we should divide. But instead of dividing by 12, we divide by 12 times 12 or 144. Since 144÷144 equals 1, we end up with an answer of 1 square foot, which we know is right. And to go from 9 square feet to square yards, we divide by 3 times 3, or 9, to get 1 square yard.

314

More Examples

Let's do a few more examples to make sure you're getting it. Let's convert 7 square yards to square feet. Since we're going from larger to smaller units, we need to multiply. But instead of multiplying by 3, we multiply by 3 times 3, or 9. So we get $7 \times 9 = 63$ square feet.

How about converting 578 square inches to square feet? This is going from smaller to larger units, so we need to divide. But instead of dividing by 12, we need to divide by 12×12, or 144. Since $578 \div 144 = 4$, the answer is 4 square feet.

What about converting between square units that are far apart, like square yards to square inches? Let's convert 2 square yards to square inches. Since we're going from square yards all the way down to square inches, we need to do the conversion in steps. First, we convert square yards to square feet. Instead of multiplying by 3, though, we need to multiply by 3×3, or 9. Two times 9 equals 18, so we end up with 18 square feet. Next, we convert square feet to square inches by multiplying by 12×12, or 144, to get $18 \times 144 = 2{,}592$ square inches. That means 2 square yards equals 2,592 square inches. In other words, 2 squares with sides equaling 1 yard, take up the same amount of space as 2,592 squares with only 1 inch sides.

Practice 62

    a. 3 meters + 10 dekameters (Put your answer in meters.)

    b. Convert 9 square feet to square inches.

    c. Convert 63 square feet to square yards.

    d. 22 has how many $\frac{2}{7}$ s in it?

    e. Translate the word problem below into math; then solve.

        The world's largest T-shirt is approximately 7,470 square inches, how many square feet is this?

Problem Set 62

Tell whether each sentence below is True or False.

    1. To convert square feet to square inches, you should multiply by 144.

    2. To convert square feet to square yards, you should divide by 9.

Complete each sentence below with the best of the choices given.

3. 1 kilometer is equal to 10 _____.

    A. hectometers   B. dekameters   C. meters
    D. decimeters   E. centimeters

4. 10 millimeters equals 1 _____.

    A. kilometer   B. dekameter   C. meter
    D. decimeter   E. centimeter

Add or subtract each group of numbers below.

5.
$$\begin{array}{r} 2.875 \\ +\,3.104 \\ \hline \end{array}$$

6.
$$\begin{array}{r} 653 \\ -\,229 \\ \hline \end{array}$$

Multiply or divide each pair of numbers below. Write any remainders in decimal form.

7.
$$\begin{array}{r} 6.7 \\ \times\,5.4 \\ \hline \end{array}$$

8. $0.5\overline{)8.24}$

Add or subtract each pair of fractions below. Make sure your answers are fully reduced.

9. $\dfrac{5}{6}+\dfrac{4}{3}$

10. $\dfrac{2}{5}-\dfrac{4}{15}$

Multiply or divide each pair of numbers below.

11. $\dfrac{4}{7}\times 21$

12. $35\div\dfrac{5}{6}$

Convert each percent below into decimal form.

13. $3\dfrac{1}{2}\%$

14. 98%

Answer each question below.

    15.   17 feet 9 inches + 8 feet 9 inches (Put your answer in feet.)

(a) 16.   5 meters + 11 dekameters (Put your answer in meters.)

Do each unit conversion below.

(b) 17.   Convert 8 square feet to square inches.

(c) 18.   Convert 72 square feet to square yards.

Answer each question below.

    19.   What is 40% of 730?

(d) 20.   38 has how many $\frac{2}{5}$ s in it?

Translate the word problem below into math; then solve.

(e) 21.   The largest finger painting in the world is 141,120 square inches. How many square feet is this?

Lesson 63—Area in the Metric System

We've been learning how to calculate areas and convert them between different square units. But did you notice how complicated the conversions were? It's hard to remember that we have to multiply by 12×12, or 144, to go from square feet to square inches or that we have to multiply by 3×3, or 9, to go from square yards to square feet.

It's Easier with Metric

Why can't we do areas with metric units? They're all based on the number 10, which makes conversions much easier. The good news is we can, and to show you how it works, look at the square meter on the left.

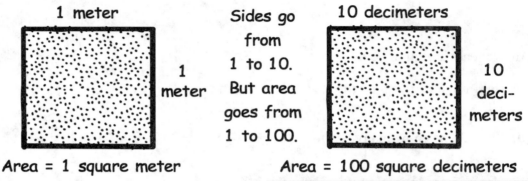

1 meter

1 meter

Area = 1 square meter

Sides go from 1 to 10. But area goes from 1 to 100.

10 decimeters

10 deci-meters

Area = 100 square decimeters

It has sides of 1 meter, of course. But when we convert the side lengths to decimeters (on the right), they're each 10 decimeters long (because 1 meter = 10 decimeters). Then look what happens to the area. Since 10×10 equals 100, the area is 100 square decimeters. So 1 square meter = 100 square decimeters. Here's the neat thing, though, about doing areas in metric. Since the units for length go up by 10s, all the square units (for area) go up by 10×10 or 100. So there's not as much to remember when doing area conversions in metric. Here are the major units for area in metric.

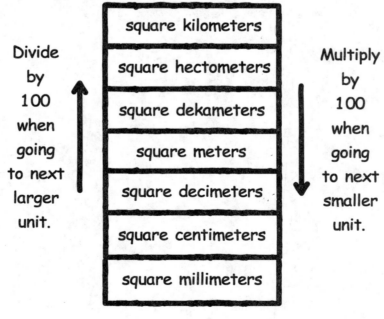

Divide by 100 when going to next larger unit.

| square kilometers |
| square hectometers |
| square dekameters |
| square meters |
| square decimeters |
| square centimeters |
| square millimeters |

Multiply by 100 when going to next smaller unit.

Just Move the Decimal Point

Now we'll do a few examples. Let's convert 3 square centimeters to square millimeters. We're going from larger units to smaller units, so we need to multiply, and there are 10 millimeters in 1 centimeter. However, since we're dealing with square units, we need to multiply not by 10 but by 10×10, or 100. That gives us this.

$$3 \times 100 = 300 \text{ square millimeters} \qquad \textbf{Multiply by 100}$$

So 3 square centimeters = 300 square millimeters. Notice how easy the multiplication was. All we really had to do was move the decimal point two places to the right (since we multiplied by 100).

What about converting 450 square hectometers (better known as hectares) to square kilometers? This time, we're going from smaller to larger units, so we need to divide. But since we're dealing with square units, we divide not by 10 but by 10×10, or 100. Rather than go through a complete division, we can just move the decimal point two places to the left to get 4.5 square kilometers.[2]

$$\frac{450}{100} = 4.5 \text{ square kilometers} \qquad \textbf{Divide by 100}$$

Finally, let's convert 17 square meters to square centimeters. What's different about this example is that we're skipping a unit (square decimeters). So what we have to do is multiply by 100 *twice*. The easiest way to do that is to move the decimal point 4 places to the right (2 places for each multiplication of 100). That gives us an answer of 170,000 square centimeters.

$$17 \times 100 \times 100 =$$
$$170,000 \text{ square centimeters} \qquad \textbf{Multiply by 100 twice}$$

Practice 63

a. Convert 2 square miles to square yards.

b. How many square decimeters are in 14 square meters?

c. Convert 3,888 square inches to square yards.

d. How many square meters are in 67,000 square centimeters?

---

[2] Remember, the decimal point goes to the right when multiplying and to the left when dividing.

e. Translate the word problem below into math; then solve.

A mosaic is a picture or design made with colored pieces, such as glass or tile, set in mortar. In 2000, a group of school children in New York City created a 29 square meter mosaic with jellybeans. How many square centimeters is this?

Problem Set 63

Tell whether each sentence below is True or False.

1. Converting from one square unit to another is easier in the metric system than it is in the common system.

2. To convert square millimeters to square centimeters, you divide by 100.

Complete each sentence below with the best of the choices given.

3. 1 dekameter is equal to 1,000 _____.

    A. kilometers   B. hectometers   C. meters
    D. decimeters   E. centimeters

4. 100,000 centimeters equals 1 _____.

    A. kilometer   B. dekameter   C. meter
    D. decimeter   E. centimeter

Add or subtract each group of numbers below.

5.
$$\begin{array}{r} 9.83 \\ + 7.06 \\ \hline \end{array}$$

6.
$$\begin{array}{r} 74,981 \\ - 35,026 \\ \hline \end{array}$$

Multiply or divide each pair of numbers below. Write any remainders in decimal form.

7.
$$\begin{array}{r} 0.551 \\ \times 0.7 \\ \hline \end{array}$$

8. $14\overline{)7,329}$

Add or subtract each pair of numbers below. Make sure your answers are fully reduced.

9. $\dfrac{7}{16} + \dfrac{5}{16}$

10. $3 - \dfrac{7}{6}$

Multiply or divide each pair of fractions below.

11. $\dfrac{1}{2} \times \dfrac{3}{11}$

12. $\dfrac{2}{9} \div \dfrac{3}{4}$

Convert each fraction below into decimal form. Round any repeating decimals to two digits (hundredths).

13. $\dfrac{1}{3}$

14. $\dfrac{21}{30}$

Answer each question below.

15. 3 miles 440 yards + 6 miles 880 yards (Put your answer in miles.)

16. 2.4 kilometers + 18 hectometers (Put your answer in hectometers.)

Do each unit conversion below.

(a) 17. Convert 3 square miles to square yards.

(b) 18. How many square decimeters are in 12 square meters?

(c) 19. Convert 5,184 square inches to square yards.

(d) 20. How many square meters are in 82,000 square centimeters?

Translate the word problem below into math; then solve.

(e) 21. In 1998, a company in Utah created the world's largest *Twister* mat—one big enough for hundreds of people to play the game. If the mat measured about 108 square meters, how many square centimeters is this?

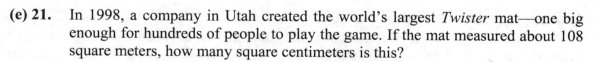

Lesson 64—Little Cubes

We've learned how to measure lengths and flat surfaces. But we haven't yet talked about measuring 3 dimensional (3-D) spaces, like the inside of a box.

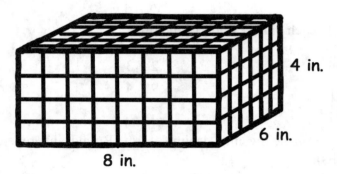

Lengths are measured with straight lines, like rulers, and flat surfaces are measured with little squares. What about 3-D spaces? As it turns out, they're measured with little cubes. In other words, if we want to know how big the box above is, we need to figure out how many little cubes will fit inside it.

Length x Width x Height

Fortunately, we don't have to count all the little cubes to come up with an answer. We can just multiply the box's length, width, and height. Notice how similar this is to the way we calculate the area of a rectangle. With areas, we multiply length and width.[3] With 3-D spaces, it's length, width, as well as height.

As you can see, our box has a length of 8 inches, a width of 6 inches, and a height of 4 inches, and since all the measurements are in the same units (inches), we can go ahead with the multiplication.

$$8 \times 6 \times 4 = 192 \text{ cubic inches}$$

Multiply length, width, and height.

The answer comes out to 192 cubic inches. "Cubic inches" means that 192 little cubes, each with 1 inch sides, will fit exactly inside our box. Actually, the technical term for 3-D space is **volume**. So we should say that the box has a volume of 192 cubic inches.

Choose Big Units for Big Stuff

Now we have inches, square inches, and cubic inches, depending on whether we're measuring a length, a flat surface (area), or a 3-D space (volume). So it shouldn't surprise you that it's also possible to have cubic feet, cubic yards, or even cubic miles. As always, we should choose the units based on the size of the space we're measuring. For example,

---

[3] That's because a flat surface is two-dimensional.

the space inside a refrigerator is usually measured in cubic feet.[4] Cubic miles, on the other hand, should only be used for really big spaces. An example would be the inside of the moon, which happens to be over 5 billion (5,273,994,240) cubic miles. That means that we could fit 5 billion cubes, each with 1 mile long sides, inside the moon. In fact, the moon's volume is so big that a unit even bigger than cubic miles might be better to use.

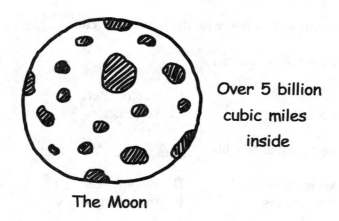

Over 5 billion cubic miles inside

The Moon

Practice 64

a. 60 hectometers – 5,400 meters (Put your answer in hectometers.)

b. How many centimeters are in 13 inches? (39.37 inches = 1 meter; 1 inch = 2.54 centimeters; 1.0936 yards = 1 meter; 1 mile = 1.609 kilometer)

c. Convert 360 square inches to square feet.

d. How many square kilometers are in 1,420,000 square meters?

e. Translate the word problem below into math; then solve.

Baby Gargantua's lunch box is 3 feet long, 2 feet wide, and 2 feet high. What is the lunch box's volume in cubic feet?

Problem Set 64

Tell whether each sentence below is True or False.

1. A three-dimensional space is measured by figuring out how many little cubes will fit inside of it.

---

[4] By the way, an average size refrigerator might have a volume of about 20 cubic feet.

2. The three-dimensional space inside a box is calculated by multiplying its length by its width.

3. The technical word for a three-dimensional space is "volume."

Complete each sentence below with the best of the choices given.

4. 10 hectometers equals 1 _____.

   A. kilometer   B. hectometer   C. meter
   D. decimeter   E. centimeter

5. 1 meter is equal to 1,000 _____.

   A. kilometers   B. dekameters   C. decimeters
   D. centimeters   E. millimeters

Add or subtract each group of numbers below.

6.
$$\begin{array}{r} 5.23 \\ 4.1 \\ +\,8.17 \\ \hline \end{array}$$

7.
$$\begin{array}{r} 13.6 \\ -\,9.04 \\ \hline \end{array}$$

Multiply or divide each pair of numbers below. Write any remainders in decimal form.

8.
$$\begin{array}{r} 43.5 \\ \times\,1.8 \\ \hline \end{array}$$

9. $0.9\overline{)52}$

Add or subtract each pair of numbers below. Make sure your answers are fully reduced.

10. $\dfrac{2}{3} + \dfrac{1}{5}$

11. $\dfrac{14}{2} - 4$

Multiply or divide each pair of numbers below.

12. $\dfrac{7}{8} \times \dfrac{2}{21}$

13. $18 \div \dfrac{3}{5}$

Convert each decimal below into a common fraction. Make sure your answers are fully reduced.

14. 0.6   **15.** 0.52

Answer each question below.

16. 7 feet − 54 inches (Put your answer in feet.)

(a) 17. 50 hectometers − 4,500 meters (Put your answer in hectometers.)

18. What is $\dfrac{3}{7}$ of 56?

Do each unit conversion below. (39.37 inches = 1 meter; 1 inch = 2.54 centimeters; 1.0936 yards = 1 meter; 1 mile = 1.609 kilometer)

(b) 19. How many centimeters are in 11 inches?

(c) 20. Convert 504 square inches to square feet.

(d) 21. How many square kilometers are in 1,750,000 square meters?

Translate the word problem below into math; then solve.

(e) 22. If a ballroom is 200 feet long, 140 feet wide, and 30 feet high, what is its volume in cubic feet?

Lesson 65—Volume Unit Conversions

In the last lesson, we learned how to calculate the volume (size) of a 3-D space like a box. All we do is multiply the length by the width by the height of the space and that gives us an answer in cubic inches, cubic feet, or whatever (depending on the units that are used for length, width, and height).

Not Once, Not Twice, but...

Sometimes, though, if an answer is in cubic feet, we might want to convert it to cubic inches. How is that done? Well, let's say we want to convert 32 cubic feet into cubic inches. We know that to convert a length from feet to inches, we multiply by 12, and to convert an area from square feet to square inches, we multiply by 12×12, or 144. What should we multiply by to convert cubic feet to cubic inches? If you guessed 12×12×12 which comes to 1,728, you're right! Here's why that works. Take a cube with 1 foot sides

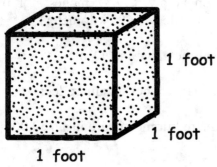

1 foot

1 foot

1 foot

Obviously, this has a volume of 1 cubic foot. If we wanted to waste time calculating it, we could just multiply its length, width, and height: 1×1×1 equals 1. But what if we were to convert those measurements into inches? Then the length, width, and height would each become 12. And multiplying length, width, and height would give us 12×12×12, or 1,728 cubic inches.

$$1\times1\times1 = 1 \text{ cubic foot} \qquad 12\times12\times12 = 1,728 \text{ cubic inches}$$

So 1 cubic foot equals 1,728 cubic inches. That's why we multiply by 1,728 to convert cubic feet to cubic inches. For every cube with 1 foot sides, there have to be 1,728 cubes with 1 inch sides.

The same thing happens if we convert cubic yards to cubic feet. Instead of multiplying by 3 or by 3×3, we have to multiply by 3×3×3, or 27. To do an actual example, let's convert 11 cubic yards to cubic feet. Even though 1 yard equals 3 feet, we don't multiply by 3, because we're not dealing with a length here. We don't multiply by 3×3, or 9, either, because we aren't dealing with an area. Since this is a volume (involving cubic units) we need to multiply by 3×3×3 or 27. That makes sense, because a cube with sides that are 1 yard long is the same as a cube with 3 feet sides, and 3 feet by 3 feet by 3 feet comes to a volume of 27 cubic feet.

$$11 \times 27 = 297 \text{ cubic feet}$$ **Multiply by 27**

We end up with 297 cubic feet. That's how many cubes with 1 foot sides will fit inside 11 cubic yards of space.

The basic rule, then, is that we multiply by the proper number three times when converting cubic units. Of course, if we're going from smaller to larger units we need to divide instead of multiply. The rules about when to multiply and divide work the same with cubic units as they do with lengths and areas.

From Smaller to Larger Units

Let's go through an actual example that requires dividing. This time let's convert 54 cubic feet to cubic yards. We have to divide here because we're going from smaller to larger units, but we don't divide by 3 or even by 9. Instead we have to divide by $3 \times 3 \times 3$, or 27 to get 2 cubic yards.

$$54 \div 27 = 2 \text{ cubic yards}$$ **Divide by 27**

Skipping Again

The last point we should make is that it's possible to convert between any two cubic units. For instance, we can convert 5 cubic yards all the way down to cubic inches. But when skipping units we do it in steps. The first step is to convert 5 cubic yards to cubic feet. To do that we multiply by $3 \times 3 \times 3$, or 27 square feet to get 5×27, or 135 cubic feet. The second step is to convert 135 cubic feet to cubic inches. To make that conversion, we multiply by $12 \times 12 \times 12$, or 1,728, to get $135 \times 1,728 = 233,280$ cubic inches. So 5 square yards is the same as 233,280 cubic inches.

Converting cubic yards to cubic inches in two steps.

$$5 \times 27 = 135 \text{ cubic feet} \qquad 135 \times 1,728 = 233,280 \text{ cubic inches}$$

That means 5 cubes with sides equaling 1 yard takes up the same amount of space as 233,280 one-inch-sided cubes.

Practice 65

a. What percent of 50 is 35?

b. How many cubic inches are in 6 cubic feet?

c. Convert 189 cubic feet to cubic yards.

d. How many square centimeters are in 4 square meters?

e. Translate the word problem below into math; then solve.

The owner of Carlisle Construction is a little overprotective of his brand new cement mixer, so each night, he parks it in a storage facility that is 120 feet long, 45 feet wide, and 45 feet high. What is the facility's volume in cubic yards?

Problem Set 65

Tell whether each sentence below is True or False.

1. To convert cubic feet to cubic inches, you should multiply by 1,728.

2. To convert cubic feet to cubic yards, you should divide by 27.

Complete each sentence below with the best of the choices given.

3. 1,000 decimeters equals 1 _____.

    A. kilometer   B. hectometer   C. dekameter
    D. meter   E. centimeter

4. 1 kilometer is equal to 100 _____.

    A. hectometers   B. dekameters   C. decimeters
    D. centimeters   E. millimeters

Add or subtract each group of numbers below.

5.
$$8,049$$
$$+657$$

6.
$$0.386$$
$$-0.097$$

Multiply or divide each pair of numbers below. Write any remainders in decimal form.

7.
$$250$$
$$\times 0.8$$

8. $2.5\overline{)453}$

Add or subtract each pair of fractions below. Make sure your answers are fully reduced.

9. $\dfrac{7}{20} + \dfrac{7}{20}$

10. $\dfrac{8}{9} - \dfrac{2}{3}$

Multiply or divide each pair of numbers below.

11. $64 \times \dfrac{5}{4}$

12. $\dfrac{4}{3} \div \dfrac{2}{7}$

Convert each percent below into decimal form.

13. 0.5%

14. 189%

Answer each question below.

15. $3\dfrac{1}{2}$ miles − 3,520 yards (Put your answer in miles.)

16. 7 kilometers − 2,000 meters (Put your answer in kilometers.)

(a) 17. What percent of 75 is 60?

Do each unit conversion below.

(b) 18. How many cubic inches are in 5 cubic feet?

(c) 19. Convert 216 cubic feet to cubic yards.

(d) 20. How many square centimeters are in 3 square meters?

Translate the word problem below into math; then solve.

(e) 21. Super entrepreneur Freddie Fandango thinks his latest product might set the world on fire (hopefully not literally). It's basically a giant microwave oven that cooks lots of whole hams and turkeys in just a few seconds (so Freddie claims). If the microwave is 9 feet long, 6 feet wide, and 3 feet high, what is its volume in cubic yards?

Freddie Fandango

Lesson 66—Liquid Measures of Volume

We've learned to measure volume in cubic feet, cubic inches, and so on. But here's some bad news. Cubic units aren't actually used much in the common system. In fact, about the only things measured in cubic feet are the insides of refrigerators and freezers. That's because there are other units of volume that were created long ago that are even more popular.

Just Weigh It

Before mathematical knowledge was very developed, people hadn't figured out how to calculate cubic units. Yet they still needed to measure volumes, so they found a nonmathematical way to do it. To measure the volume of a pot, for instance, they would just fill it to the brim with water.

Fill the pot to the brim.

Then they would pour the water back out and weigh it. The weight of the water served as a measure for what the pot could hold. The great thing about this approach is that water, or any other liquid, fills a container it's poured into completely, no matter what the shape of the container. And so with this approach, you never have to calculate anything. (But you do have to pour a lot of water!) Water measurement became so widespread that today most of our common units for volume are still based on water or "liquid" measurements.[5]

Gallon, Quart, Pint, and Ounce

The four best known liquid units for volume are the **gallon, quart, pint**, and **fluid ounce**. A gallon is a volume that (whatever the specific shape of the container) will hold 8.337 pounds of water. The gallon was first used in Britain, and it was equal to 10 pounds

---

[5] These are often called units of "capacity," because they're based on how much a container will hold instead of a direct calculation of a space.

of water. That's still the size of the gallon in Britain today. But the U.S. gallon is only 8.337 pounds.

To measure a U.S. gallon of volume, then, we just pour 8.337 pounds of water into a container and mark the water's height on the container's side. From that point down is equal to 1 gallon

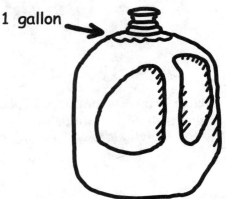

1 gallon

What about the other liquid units? Well, there are 4 quarts in a gallon, so 4 quarts = 1 gallon.[6] That means to convert between quarts and gallons, we multiply or divide by 4. The next smaller unit is the pint. There are two pints in a quart, so 2 pints = 1 quart. And the conversion factor between a pint and quart is 2. Then there are 16 fluid ounces in a pint: 16 fluid ounces = 1 pint. The conversion factor between a fluid ounce and a pint is therefore 16. Here is the list of the units and their relationships in a table.

Units of Liquid Measure

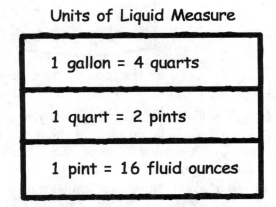

1 gallon = 4 quarts

1 quart = 2 pints

1 pint = 16 fluid ounces

These units probably look more familiar to you than cubic inches or cubic feet. That's because, as we said, these are used much more often (at least in English speaking countries) than cubic units for measuring volume. That's why you buy a gallon of milk at the grocery store instead of a cubic foot of milk!

---

[6] The word "quart" comes from a Latin word for 4.

Practice 66

a. How many inches are in 12 yards?

b. How many pints are in 14 quarts?

c. How many cubic feet are in 31 cubic yards?

d. Convert 3 miles to kilometers. (39.37 inches = 1 meter; 1 inch = 2.54 centimeters; 1.0936 yards = 1 meter; 1 mile = 1.609 kilometer)

e. Translate the word problem below into math; then solve.

Lucy, the health food fanatic, drinks 7 sixteen ounce glasses of raisin juice each day. How many pints (not ounces) of raisin juice does she consume each day?

Problem Set 66

Tell whether each sentence below is True or False.

1. People first measured the space inside a container (its volume) by pouring liquid inside of it and then weighing the liquid.

2. The most popular units for measuring volume in the common system are the gallon, quart, pint, and fluid ounce.

Complete each sentence below with the best of the choices given.

3. 1 *square* meter equals 100 _____.

    A. square kilometers
    B. square hectometers
    C. square dekameters
    D. square decimeters
    E. square centimeters

4. 100 *square* millimeters equals 1 _____.

    A. square kilometer
    B. square hectometer
    C. square dekameter
    D. square decimeter
    E. square centimeter

Add or subtract each group of numbers below.

5.
$$52.7$$
$$+3.59$$

6.
$$8.25$$
$$-4.178$$

Multiply or divide each pair of numbers below. Write any remainders in decimal form.

7.
$$46.1$$
$$\times 3.5$$

8. $0.3\overline{)759}$

Add or subtract each pair of numbers below. Make sure your answers are fully reduced.

9. $\dfrac{1}{8} + \dfrac{5}{4}$

10. $4 - 2\dfrac{2}{5}$

Multiply or divide each pair of fractions below.

11. $\dfrac{2}{6} \times \dfrac{3}{10}$

12. $\dfrac{1}{3} \div \dfrac{2}{9}$

Convert each fraction below into decimal form. Give exact answers (no rounding).

13. $\dfrac{7}{8}$

14. $\dfrac{6}{11}$

Answer each question below.

15. What is $\dfrac{2}{3}$ of 126?

16. What is 14% of 57?

Do each unit conversion below.

(a) 17. How many inches are in 15 yards?

(b) 18. How many pints are in 12 quarts? (1 gallon = 4 quarts; 1 quart = 2 pints; 1 pint = 16 fluid ounces)

(c) 19. How many cubic feet are in 28 cubic yards?

(d) 20. Convert 2 miles to kilometers. (39.37 inches = 1 meter; 1 inch = 2.54 centimeters; 1.0936 yards = 1 meter; 1 mile = 1.609 kilometer)

Translate the word problem below into math; then solve.

(e) 21. Mr. Le Grand owns a worldwide chain of European-style coffee shops. Every time he visits a shop, he purchases a 16 ounce café au lait (coffee with steamed milk). If Mr. Le Grand visits 5 stores each day, what is his daily consumption of café au laits in pints (not ounces)?

Lesson 67—Volume in the Metric System

We've learned about volume in the common system. What about volume in the metric system? Not surprisingly, doing volume with metric units is a lot easier. That's because everything in the metric system goes by 10s. Let's go over some of the details.

First of all, we know that the metric units for length (like meters and decimeters) all differ by 10 times. In other words, the next larger unit is always 10 times the previous one. That means to go from one to the next, all we have to do is multiply by 10 (if we're getting bigger) or divide by 10 (if we're getting smaller).

A meter is 10 times a decimeter in length.

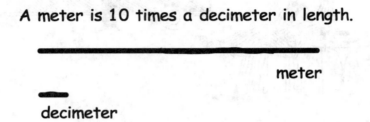

meter

decimeter

The metric units for area (like square meters and square decimeters) all differ by 100 times. In that case, to go up from one area unit to the next, we need to multiply by 100, and to go down we divide by 100.[7]

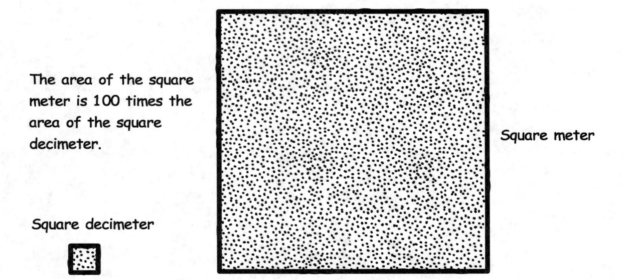

The area of the square meter is 100 times the area of the square decimeter.

Square meter

Square decimeter

What about cubic metric units like cubic meters and cubic decimeters? These units are used for measuring volume. A cubic meter has a volume the size of a cube with sides that are 1 meter long, and a cubic decimeter is the size of a cube with 1 decimeter sides. How do these volumes differ? Well, if lengths go up by 10 times and areas go up by 100

---

[7] Of course, these drawings aren't actual size.

times, it stands to reason that volumes would go up by 1,000 times (10×10×10). That means when converting from one cubic unit to the next larger one, we have to divide by 1,000. And when converting from a larger cubic unit to the next smaller one, we need to multiply by 1,000.

Converting in Metric

Let's do an example. We'll convert 4 cubic meters to cubic decimeters. Since these are cubic units, the conversion factor is 1,000. And since we're going from larger to smaller units, we need to multiply by 1,000.

$$4 \times 1,000 = 4,000$$

So we get 4,000 cubic decimeters.

Let's do another example. This time we'll convert 800 cubic meters to cubic dekameters. These are cubic units again, which means that our conversion factor is 1,000. But in this case we're going from smaller to larger units, so we should divide by 1,000.

$$800 \div 1,000 = 0.8$$

The answer to this one is 0.8 cubic dekameters.

Inventing the Liter

Actually, there is one change that's been made to volumes in the metric system. But unlike the changes that were made (through the years) to gallons, quarts, pints, and the other common units, this change is very logical.

It turns out there's a problem with cubic meters, cubic decimeters, and all the other cubic units in the metric system. They're too far apart. A cubic meter is 1,000 times as large as a cubic decimeter, and a cubic decimeter is 1,000 times as large as a cubic centimeter, and so on. That means even units that are right next to each other are incredibly far apart. It's like trying to cook a meal with measuring cups that all differ in size by 1,000 times.

Fortunately, the scientists who designed the metric system realized that it would be better if the units were closer together. That's why they created a new unit which is exactly the same size as the cubic decimeter (because it's a good size for everyday use). This new unit is called the liter. So 1 liter = 1 cubic decimeter. Then the scientists created larger and smaller units based on the liter, using the standard metric system prefixes (which are shown on the next page).

The key point, though, is that these units all differ only by 10s. A liter is 10 times the size of a deciliter, a deciliter is 10 times the size of a centiliter, and so on.

That makes the units for volume a lot closer in size and more convenient to use. With this change, metric units of volume are just as close together as metric units for length, which is really useful.

By the way, if you're having trouble picturing how large a liter is, just remember that soda is often sold in 2 liter bottles. So a liter is half a big bottle of soda.

Units based on the liter

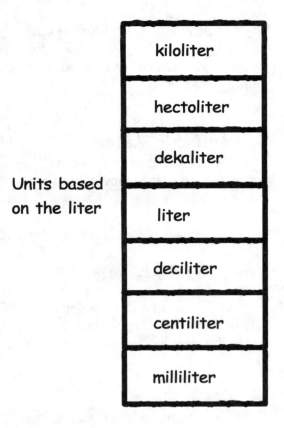

Converting with Liters

Finally, let's work a couple of examples with liters. Say we have a container that is 7.5 liters in size. How many deciliters is that?

How many deciliters?

Well, since we're going from larger to smaller units, we need to multiply. Also, since liters are 10 times the size of deciliters, we should multiply by 10.

$$7.5 \times 10 = 75$$

That gives us 75 deciliters. The main point is that we convert by multiplying only by 10, even though we're working with volume units.

Here's one more quick example. Let's convert 825 liters to hectoliters. Since we're going from smaller to larger units, we need to divide this time. But liters and hectoliters are two steps apart (look back at the table). So what we have to do is divide by 10 twice.

$$825 \div 10 = 82.5 \quad \text{and} \quad 82.5 \div 10 = 8.25$$

We could have done the calculation even faster by just moving the decimal point two places to the left. But whatever method you use, the answer is 8.25 hectoliters.

Practice 67

a. What percent of 120 is 30?

b. How many square yards are in 675 square feet?

c. Convert 26 liters to deciliters.

d. How many gallons are in 20 quarts? (1 gallon = 4 quarts; 1 quart = 2 pints; 1 pint = 16 fluid ounces)

e. Translate the word problem below into math; then solve.

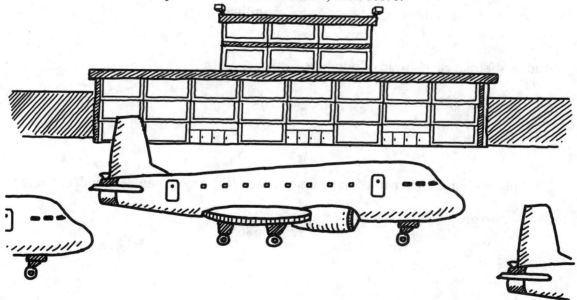

The largest cargo aircraft has a volume of 1,400 cubic meters. How many cubic decimeters is this?

Problem Set 67

Tell whether each sentence below is True or False.

1. To convert from cubic meters to cubic decimeters, you have to multiply by 10.

2. The designers of the metric system created a new unit called the liter to make the units of volume closer together in size.

Complete each sentence below with the best of the choices given.

3. 1 *cubic* kilometer equals 1,000 _____.

   A. cubic kilometers   B. cubic hectometers   C. cubic dekameters
   D. cubic decimeters   E. cubic centimeters

4. 1,000 *cubic* millimeters equals 1 _____.

   A. cubic kilometer   B. cubic hectometer   C. cubic dekameter
   D. cubic decimeter   E. cubic centimeter

5. 10 liters equals 1 _____.

   A. kiloliter   B. hectoliter   C. dekaliter
   D. deciliter   E. centiliter

Add or subtract each group of numbers below.

6. $\begin{array}{r} 12{,}053 \\ +\,14{,}780 \\ \hline \end{array}$

7. $\begin{array}{r} 0.782 \\ -\,0.54 \\ \hline \end{array}$

Multiply or divide each pair of numbers below. Write any remainders in decimal form.

8. $\begin{array}{r} 9.30 \\ \times\,6.1 \\ \hline \end{array}$

9. $8\overline{)586}$

Add or subtract each pair of fractions below. Make sure your answers are fully reduced.

10. $\dfrac{4}{15} + \dfrac{6}{15}$

11. $\dfrac{8}{5} - \dfrac{3}{4}$

Multiply or divide each pair of numbers below.

12. $\dfrac{5}{12} \times 60$

13. $14 \div \dfrac{7}{9}$

Convert each fraction below into decimal form. Give exact answers (no rounding).

14. $\dfrac{9}{20}$

15. $\dfrac{1}{18}$

Answer each question below.

16. What is $\dfrac{3}{4}$ of 80?

17. How many $\dfrac{1}{2}$ s are in 17?

(a) 18. What percent of 150 is 45?

Do each unit conversion below.

(b) 19. How many square yards are in 765 square feet?

(c) 20. Convert 24 liters to deciliters.

(d) 21. How many gallons are in 16 quarts? (1 gallon = 4 quarts; 1 quart = 2 pints; 1 pint = 16 fluid ounces)

Translate the word problem below into math; then solve.

(e) 22. The largest blimps ever built could carry 200,000 cubic meters of hydrogen gas. How many cubic decimeters is this?

CHAPTER 10
SIMPLE ALGEBRA
EQUATIONS

Lesson 68—Advanced Arithmetic

So far this book has been all about arithmetic, which is just basic math. But this is a pre-algebra book, after all, so let's move on to algebra.

Finding Missing Numbers

What is algebra, anyway? You've probably heard about it. In fact, a lot of people say it's difficult and mysterious, but what is it really? Well, despite the scary stories, algebra is actually not that different from arithmetic. You might even say that algebra is just a more advanced version of arithmetic. To explain, let's do a comparison. Here are several simple arithmetic problems.

$$19+42=\textbf{?} \qquad 23\times15=\textbf{?} \qquad 128\div4=\textbf{?}$$

To work these, we only need to find the missing numbers by doing the calculations. Putting in the missing numbers, we get this.

$$19+42=\textbf{61} \qquad 23\times15=\textbf{345} \qquad 128\div4=\textbf{32}$$

Now let's compare these arithmetic problems to three *algebra* problems.

$$19+\textbf{?}=61 \qquad 23\times\textbf{?}=345 \qquad 128\times\textbf{?}=32$$

To solve these, we just find the missing numbers again.

$$19+\textbf{42}=61 \qquad 23\times\textbf{15}=345 \qquad 128\times\textbf{4}=32$$

Do you see how similar arithmetic and algebra are? They're both about finding missing numbers. So what makes algebra harder? Well, notice that the arithmetic problems all have the missing number on one side by itself. That makes the answer easy to find. But algebra problems have the missing number mixed together with other numbers (through addition, subtraction, etc.). And that makes finding the answer more difficult.

Other Differences

Here are some other differences. Arithmetic problems usually have only one operation. Remember, addition, subtraction, multiplication, and division are called **operations**. With only one operation, arithmetic problems are usually fairly simple. Algebra problems, on the other hand, often involve several operations, which makes the process of finding the missing number quite a bit more complicated. Here's an example of an algebra problem with lots of operations.

$$4\times\textbf{?}+3-1=5\times2$$

The answer to this problem is still the number that makes the two sides equal when it's put in for the question mark. (It's 2, in case you're wondering.)

Another difference between algebra and arithmetic is that in arithmetic problems, the missing number appears only once. (There's just one question mark, in other words.) But in algebra problems, it can appear many times. Here is an example of an algebra problem that has several question marks.

$$?\times7+?-4=3\times?+11$$

The correct answer here is the number which makes the sides equal when put in for *all three* question marks. (This answer turns out to be 3.)

These last two examples may look tough, and finding the answers does require some skill. But notice that in each example, the name of the game is still finding the missing number. And that's why algebra and arithmetic are so much the same.

x's and y's

There's one other difference between algebra and arithmetic that's worth mentioning. Instead of using question marks to stand for missing numbers, algebra uses letters—especially the letters x, y, and z. That's why everybody talks about algebra being full of letters instead of numbers. But there's actually nothing strange about it if you realize that the letters are just missing numbers. The letter most commonly used is x, so here are the last two problems we showed with x's in place of the question marks.

$$4\times x+3-1=5\times2 \qquad x\times7+x-4=3\times x+11$$

Before reading this lesson, these problems might have seemed confusing. But now you know that algebra problems are just a more complicated game of finding the missing number—an advanced form of arithmetic.

Practice 68

a. Tell whether $x\times3-2+x=11+x-5$ is an algebra or arithmetic problem.

b. Find the missing number in the problem $x\times11=55$.

c. Find the missing number in the problem $13\div x=13$.

d. Find the missing number in the problem $x-\dfrac{1}{5}=\dfrac{2}{5}$.

e. Translate the word problem below into math; then solve.

Eric is homeschooled, and whenever he goes to the grocery store with his mom, she turns the trip into a math lesson. Today, one of the questions was "How many deciliters are in a 2 liter bottle of grape soda?" Eric got it right. What was his answer?

Problem Set 68

Tell whether each sentence below is True or False.

1. Algebra and arithmetic problems can be described as "games," where the goal is to find the missing number.

2. In arithmetic problems, the missing number appears by itself on one side of the equals sign.

3. In algebra problems, the missing number is mixed together with other numbers.

Complete each sentence below with the best of the choices given.

4. In algebra, letters are used in place of _____.

   A. missing numbers   B. operations   C. calculations
   D. words   E. people

5. Addition, subtraction, multiplication, and division are called _____.

   A. answers   B. operations   C. missing numbers
   D. calculations   E. letters

6. _____ problems usually contain only one operation.

   A. Algebra   B. Difficult   C. Medical
   D. Arithmetic   E. Geometry

7. _____ problems usually have several operations.

   A. Algebra   B. Arithmetic   C. Simple
   D. Medical   E. Subtraction

Add or subtract each group of numbers below.

8.
$$9.35$$
$$+7.18$$

9.
$$63.1$$
$$-52.9$$

Multiply or divide each pair of numbers below. Write any remainders in decimal form.

10.
$$8.02$$
$$\times 0.9$$

11. $1.4\overline{)124.6}$

Add or subtract each pair of fractions below. Make sure your answers are fully reduced.

12. $\dfrac{1}{3}+\dfrac{1}{5}$

13. $\dfrac{9}{14}-\dfrac{1}{2}$

Multiply or divide each pair of fractions below.

14. $\dfrac{4}{9}\times\dfrac{18}{20}$

15. $\dfrac{7}{3}\div\dfrac{5}{6}$

Tell whether these are arithmetic or algebra problems.

16. $x\div 7=3$

17. $4\times 9=x$

(a) 18. $x\times 4-6+x=5+x-2$

Find the missing number in each problem below.

(b) 19. $x\times 12=48$ **(c) 20.** $15\div x=15$ **(d) 21.** $x-\dfrac{1}{7}=\dfrac{2}{7}$

Translate the word problem below into math; then solve.

(e) 22. Super Duper Saver Mart is selling 5 liter jugs of a new item called *Tastes as Good as Maple Syrup*. How many deciliters are in the jug?

Lesson 69—What's it for Anyway?

Now you know that algebra is in many ways just a game of finding missing numbers. But if algebra were only a game, we wouldn't be forced to learn it. So what's the purpose of algebra?

Well, it turns out that algebra is used to find answers to real-life problems. That's what makes it really valuable. Here's a simple example.

> Mike Gleason is a football fanatic. Naturally, when Mike's hometown pro football team made it to the Super Bowl, he had to take his whole family to the game. If Mike took 11 people (his wife, Sherry, and their five kids along with Mike's Dad and his three brothers) and if the total bill for the tickets was $3,025, how much did each ticket cost?

Some Important Terms

Before we try to figure this out, you should realize that answering a real-life problem with algebra involves several steps. The most difficult one is translating the problem into a mathematical statement called an equation. All of the examples in the previous problem set were actually equations, even though we didn't use that word. An **equation** is just two groups of numbers (and maybe x's) with an equal sign between them. Here are a couple of the equations from the last problem set to refresh your memory.

$$15 \times x = 45 \qquad x - \frac{2}{3} = \frac{1}{3}$$

The equals signs say that what's on the left is supposed to equal what's on the right, when the proper number is put in for x. By the way, the groups of numbers and x's on either side of each equals sign are actually called **expressions**. So a more precise definition for an equation is two expressions that have an equals sign between them.

Setting Up the Equation

Now let's translate our Super Bowl problem into an equation. The first step is to make x represent the thing that we're trying to find. This is critical, so you should always write out what x means on paper. Since we're trying to find the price of each Super Bowl ticket, that's what we'll set equal to x.

$$x = \text{price of each Super Bowl ticket}$$

The next step is to pick out two things from the facts of the problem that are supposed to be equal. In this case, if you study the problem carefully, you may realize that the price of each ticket multiplied by the number of people in Mike's family should equal the total cost. This idea should be written out in a word equation like this.

$$\text{Price of each ticket} \quad \times \quad \text{Number in family} \quad = \quad \text{Total spent}$$

The third step is to turn the word equation into a math equation. We know that the price of each ticket is x, the number of people in the family is 11, and the total spent is $3,025. So next we'll replace the words with x's and numbers, like this.

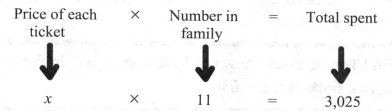

Here's the same equation, without the extra spaces.

$$x \times 11 = 3,025$$

Notice that the equation doesn't include dollar signs. That's because equations should have only numbers, never symbols like dollar signs, cent signs, inches, feet, minutes, etc.

Solving the Equation

After we've translated the problem into an equation, our fourth step is to find the missing number, which, of course, is the answer to the equation. That's the number that when put in for x makes both sides equal. You probably know that the formal name for answer is **solution**. Finding the answer to an equation is also called "solving" the equation. So to sound mathematical, we would say that by "solving the equation $x \times 11 = 3,025$, we found its solution to be 275."

Interpreting the Solution

The fifth and final step of the whole process is to interpret the meaning of the answer (solution). The equation itself doesn't tell us what the solution, 275, stands for. That's because equations just have numbers in them, nothing else. The 275 could be anything: 275 turnips, 275 potato chips, or 275 tennis balls. We need to look back to see what x means in this particular case. In our problem, the x represents the price of each Super Bowl ticket, so 275 means "275 dollars for each ticket," and this is the answer to our problem.[1]

Here, again, are all the steps for finding the answer to a problem using algebra.

---

[1] Of course, $275 is a lot of money to spend on a football game (way too much actually), but Mike felt he had to do it.

Solving a Problem with Algebra

1.	Make x stand for whatever you're trying to find.
2.	Study the facts to find two things that must be equal; then write a word equation.
3.	Turn the word equation into an algebra equation, with numbers and an x.
4.	Find the solution (answer) which when put in for x makes both sides equal.
5.	Interpret the meaning of the solution.

Practice 69

a. Convert 18 cubic centimeters to cubic millimeters.

b. How many miles are in 22,176 feet?

c. Write an equation to represent the problem below. Don't solve the problem.

The sum of 25 and what number is 62?

d. Write an equation to represent the problem below. Don't solve the problem.

What number minus 17 is equal to 34?

e. Translate the word problem below into math; then solve.

Karen likes to buy silly little gifts for her employees to cheer them up during especially hectic times. For example, yesterday she bought each of them a court jester hat with bells. If each hat costs $3.50, and she bought $63 worth of hats, how many employees does Karen have?

Problem Set 69

Tell whether each sentence below is True or False.

1. The main purpose of algebra is to find answers to real-life problems.

2. An equation is just two groups of numbers (and maybe x's) with an equal sign between them.

3. Addition, subtraction, multiplication, and division are called solutions.

Complete each sentence below with the best of the choices given.

4. A group of numbers and x's is called a (or an) _____.

    A. equation   B. solution   C. paragraph
    D. expression   E. multiplication

5. The answer to an equation is also called the _____.

    A. expression   B. tabulation   C. exception
    D. solution   E. sum

6. 1,000 centiliters equals 1 _____.

    A. kiloliter   B. hectoliter   C. dekaliter
    D. deciliter   E. centiliter

Multiply or divide each pair of numbers below. Write any remainders in decimal form.

7.
$$\begin{array}{r} 8{,}070 \\ \times 0.2 \\ \hline \end{array}$$

8. $6.2\overline{)522.35}$

Add or subtract each pair of numbers below. Make sure your answers are fully reduced.

9. $7\frac{1}{2} + 4\frac{7}{8}$

10. $3 - 1\frac{2}{3}$

Convert each fraction below into decimal form. Give exact answers (no rounding).

11. $\dfrac{1}{9}$

12. $\dfrac{3}{16}$

Do each unit conversion below.

(a) 13. Convert 14 cubic centimeters to cubic millimeters.

(b) 14. How many miles are in 20,064 feet?

15. Convert 68 square feet to square inches.

Write an equation to represent each problem below. Don't solve the problem.

(c) 16. The sum of 23 and what number is 51?

(d) 17. What number minus 19 is equal to 27?

18. $\dfrac{1}{2}$ multiplied by what number equals 14?

Find the solution (missing number) in each equation below.

19. $x + \dfrac{1}{4} = \dfrac{1}{2}$

20. $x \times 14 = 28$

21. $x - 39 = 72$

Translate the word problem below into math; then solve.

(e) 22. When Moose's mom saw that her butcher shop was having a sale on T-Bone steaks, she thought she'd better buy all she could with the money she had on her, which happened to be $27. If the steaks were on sale for $4.50 per pound, how many pounds did she buy?

Lesson 70—The Golden Rule of Algebra

We've learned about algebra equations and how they're used. But have you noticed that finding that missing number can be pretty hard? That's because, in the last two problem sets, you've had to solve all the equations in your head. Don't get stressed out, though, because algebra equations aren't really supposed to be solved that way. Algebra actually has step-by-step procedures for solving equations that are simple to learn and that give you the right answer every time. In fact, this is the first of many lessons where we show you how these methods work. And after you've had some practice, you'll be able to solve equations that would have been impossible to do in your head. To get started, let's compare the two equations below.

$$x = 63 - 25 \qquad\qquad x + 25 = 63$$

Which of these seems easier to you? Most people would say the one on the left is easier, because it's just an arithmetic problem. To find its solution (answer), we just subtract 25 from 63 to get 38. The equation on the right looks harder, even though it involves the same numbers. That's because it's in algebra form, where x is not already by itself on one side. If asked to find its solution, we might have to shuffle things around in our heads, like this:

"Let's see, if $x + 25$ is equal to 63, then x has to be $63 - 25$."

But notice something about this mental process. We ended up turning the algebra equation $x + 25 = 63$ into the arithmetic equation $x = 63 - 25$. That tells us two things. It tells us that both equations have the same answer, and more importantly, it tells us that we can get the answer to the harder equation by solving the easy equation.

Undoing Addition

As it turns out, that's how the equation-solving methods of algebra work. They help us turn a hard algebra equation into a simple arithmetic equation that has the same answer. But instead of having to do everything in your head, the process is done one step at a time on paper. Now let's actually go through the solving steps on another example.

$$x + 5.14 = 13.86$$

This is an algebra equation, and our goal is to turn it into an easy arithmetic equation, where x is by itself on the left side. The question is how can we get rid of the 5.14? Simple. We just *subtract* 5.14, like this.

$$x + 5.14 - 5.14$$

Here's why subtracting works. If we add 5.14 to any number, then take away 5.14, we end up with the original number again. It's as if your best friend gave you $5.14, but then, two seconds later, took the $5.14 back—you have the same amount of money you did before. So after subtracting 5.14, the left side of the equation is equal to just x, which is what we wanted.

$$x + 5.14 - 5.14 \quad \text{equals} \quad x$$

This process of subtracting a number to get rid of an addition is called **undoing**. By subtracting 5.14, we are reversing or "undoing" the addition of 5.14 to get x by itself. In fact, any addition can be undone by subtracting the very same number that was added.

The Golden Rule of Algebra

There's one catch, however. Subtracting a number from one side could spoil an equation entirely and give us a wrong answer.[2] To avoid this, we have to follow the most important rule of algebra—so important, in fact, that it's called the **golden rule of algebra**. The rule is that if we change the value of one side of an equation, we must change the other side by the same amount.

The golden rule is pretty obvious, really. If the two sides of an equation are supposed to be equal to start, then they should still be equal after changing the value of each side by the same amount. It's a little bit like a scale. If both sides are in balance to begin with, then they should still be in balance after we subtract the same amount from each side.

The sides are still in balance.

So getting back to our example, let's follow the golden rule and subtract 5.14 from *both sides* of the equation.

$$x + 5.14 - 5.14 = 13.86 - 5.14$$

The left side is now equal to just x.

$$x = 13.86 - 5.14$$

---

[2] The equation gets "spoiled" because the solution changes. For example, the equation $x + 5 = 8$ has an answer of 3. But if we subtract 2 from the left side, without doing anything to the right side, the equation becomes $x + 3 = 8$. This equation has been spoiled because it now has an answer of 5 instead of 3.

And notice what's happened. By undoing, we have turned our tough algebra equation into a simple arithmetic equation (with the x on one side by itself and the numbers on the other). And since we followed the golden rule in the process, the equation hasn't been spoiled. From here, we can find the solution by simply subtracting the numbers on the right.

$$x = 8.72$$

The solution (answer) is 8.72.

Checking the Answer

Now, it's important to point out that an answer can always be checked by putting it in for x in the original equation to see if the two sides are made equal. Let's try that with the equation we just solved. Remember, this is what it looked like originally.

$$x + 5.14 = 13.86$$

If we put in (or "substitute" as it's also called) 8.72 for x, we get this.

$$8.72 + 5.14 = 13.86$$

All that's left now is to do the calculation on the left side.

$$13.86 = 13.86$$

Since the sides are equal, our answer of 8.72 is correct.

Undoing Subtraction

Many equations have a number *subtracted* from x. How do we handle these? Take the equation $x - \dfrac{1}{4} = \dfrac{1}{2}$ as an example. To undo the subtraction, we *add* $\dfrac{1}{4}$ to each side.

$$x - \frac{1}{4} + \frac{1}{4} = \frac{1}{2} + \frac{1}{4}$$

The left side now has $\dfrac{1}{4}$ taken away from x, then another $\dfrac{1}{4}$ added back again. By the same logic we used before, this makes the left side equal to just x.

$$x = \frac{1}{2} + \frac{1}{4}$$

Again, by undoing we have turned our algebra equation into a far simpler arithmetic equation.

From here the solution can be found by adding on the right.

$$x = \frac{3}{4}$$

This answer can also be checked by putting in $\frac{3}{4}$ for x in the original equation. We won't bother showing the steps this time, but you can do them on your own if you like.

Inverse Operations

Notice that we eliminated the subtraction of $\frac{1}{4}$ by *adding* $\frac{1}{4}$. In fact, we can undo any subtraction by adding back the same number. So not only can subtraction undo addition, but addition can also undo subtraction. Two operations that undo each other are called **inverse operations**. Since addition and subtraction are inverse operations, we can solve any equation where a number is added to or subtracted from an x (even a really tough case like $x + 8.003067 = 17.432995$) by undoing.

Practice 70

a. How many fluid ounces are in 3 gallons? (1 gallon = 4 quarts; 1 quart = 2 pints; 1 pint = 16 fluid ounces)

b. Convert 370 square meters to square dekameters.

c. What must be done to the expression $x - 145$ to make it equal x?

d. Solve the equation $x + 49 = 75$ by undoing.

e. Translate the word problem below into an equation; then solve.

On a cold January afternoon, workers at a local charity distributed 12.7 gallons of beef vegetable soup. If they had 2.3 gallons leftover, how many gallons did they start with?

Problem Set 70

Tell whether each sentence below is True or False.

1. Any addition can be undone by subtracting the very same number.

2. Any subtraction can be undone by adding the very same number.

3. The golden rule of algebra says that if you change the value of one side of an equation the value of the other side must be changed by the same amount.

Complete each sentence below with the best of the choices given.

4. If the same number is added to both sides of an equation, the solution to the equation will _____.

    A. stay the same   B. increase   C. decrease
    D. equal zero   E. be spoiled

5. Algebra equations are solved by turning them into _____ that have the same answer.

    A. solutions   B. expressions   C. algebra equations
    D. inverse operations   E. arithmetic equations

6. Two operations that can undo each other are called _____ operations.

    A. solution   B. expression   C. algebra
    D. inverse   E. arithmetic

Add or subtract each group of numbers below.

7. $\begin{array}{r} 632 \\ 917 \\ +546 \\ \hline \end{array}$
           8. $\begin{array}{r} 635.1 \\ -98.6 \\ \hline \end{array}$

Add or subtract each pair of numbers below. Make sure your answers are fully reduced.

9. $1\frac{4}{5} + 1\frac{3}{5}$
          10. $\frac{4}{6} - \frac{2}{3}$

Multiply or divide each pair of numbers below.

11. $24 \times \frac{1}{6}$
          12. $\frac{4}{7} \div 2$

Convert each percent below into decimal form.

13. $82\frac{3}{4}\%$

14. 105%

Do each unit conversion below.

(a) 15. How many fluid ounces are in 2 gallons? (1 gallon = 4 quarts; 1 quart = 2 pints; 1 pint = 16 fluid ounces)

(b) 16. Convert 490 square meters to square dekameters.

Answer each question below.

17. What must be done to the expression $x+92$ to make it equal x?

(c) 18. What must be done to the expression $x-115$ to make it equal x?

Solve each equation below by undoing.

19. $x+5=28$

20. $x-13=36$

(d) 21. $x+57=81$

Translate the word problem below into an equation; then solve.

(e) 22. Clement lost the bet. Now he has to drink the entire jar of lukewarm milk. So far, he has drunk only 2.4 ounces. If he has 9.6 ounces to go, how many ounces were in the jar to begin with?

Lesson 71—Undoing Multiplication and Division

We just learned to undo addition and subtraction in an equation. In this lesson, we'll learn how to undo multiplication and division.

Undoing Multiplication

Let's start with a multiplication example.

$$x \times 6 = 84$$

Remember how this works. To solve here, we need to change the algebra equation into an easy arithmetic equation. So on this one, we have to get rid of (undo, in other words) the multiplication by 6 to get x by itself on the left.

The question is how do we undo multiplication? Well, let's do a little experiment. Say the number 2 is multiplied by 5 to get 10. What must be done to turn the result back into 2? Subtracting 5 doesn't work because $2 \times 5 - 5$ is equal to $10 - 5$ or 5, not 2. Adding 5 is no good either ($2 \times 5 + 5$ is $10 + 5$ or 15, not 2). To return to 2, we have to *divide* by 5. ($2 \times 5 \div 5$ equals $10 \div 5$, or 2). If you try this on other numbers, you'll find that a multiplication can always be undone by dividing by the very same number.

Now you can see how to undo the multiplication by 6 in the equation. We just divide by 6. But let's not forget the golden rule of algebra here. We have to divide the right side by 6 too.

$$x \times 6 \div 6 = 84 \div 6$$

This makes the left side equal to just x.

$$x = 84 \div 6$$

That turned the algebra equation into an arithmetic equation, which is exactly what we wanted. From here we can solve easily by just doing the division on the right.

$$x = 14$$

The Answer is a Fraction

Notice that the answer in this example is a whole number, but a lot of times, dividing both sides of an equation can give a fraction or decimal answer. For instance, look at this problem.

$$x \times 4 = 9$$

To solve it we have to divide both sides by 4.

$$x \times 4 \div 4 = 9 \div 4$$

Dividing by 4 after multiplying by 4 leaves just x on the left side.

$$x = 9 \div 4$$

But since 4 doesn't divide into 9 evenly, we end up with the fraction $\dfrac{9}{4}$ (or 2.25 in decimal form) on the right side.

$$x = \frac{9}{4} \qquad \text{or} \qquad x = 2.25$$

Undoing Division

What about undoing division? Take a look at this one.

$$x \div 7 = 15$$

We need to turn this algebra equation into an arithmetic equation by getting x by itself on one side of the equals sign. To do that, we have to undo the division by 7, and as you may have guessed, division is undone by multiplication. (For example, if we have $8 \div 2$ and want to undo the division to get back to 8, we multiply by 2. This gives us $8 \div 2 \times 2$, which is the same as 4×2, or 8.) So for $x \div 7 = 15$, to undo we multiply both sides by 7.

$$x \div 7 \times 7 = 15 \times 7$$

That leaves us with just x on the left side.

$$x = 15 \times 7$$

And once again we've changed our algebra equation into an arithmetic equation. To get the answer from here, all we have to do is multiply on the right.

$$x = 105$$

Since multiplication and division undo each other, they too are inverse operations, just like addition and subtraction. So every one of the four major operations of arithmetic—addition, subtraction, multiplication, and division—has an inverse operation that will undo it.

Practice 71

a. What must be done to the expression $x \times 14$ to make it equal x?

b. What must be done to the expression $x \div 25$ to make it equal x?

c. Solve the equation $x \times 6 = 186$ by undoing.

d. Solve the equation $x \div 5.5 = 7.3$ by undoing.

e. Translate the word problem below into math; then solve.

If a brick is 2 inches wide, 4 inches tall, and 8 inches long, what is its volume in cubic inches?

Problem Set 71

Tell whether each sentence below is True or False.

1. A multiplication can be undone by dividing by the very same number.

2. A division can be undone by dividing by the very same number.

Complete each sentence below with the best of the choices given.

3. 1 gallon equals 4 _____.

    A. quarts   B. pints   C. fluid ounces
    D. cubic inches   E. liters

4. 1 pint equals 16 _____.

    A. gallons   B. quarts   C. fluid ounces
    D. cubic inches   E. liters

5. 100 centimeters equals 1 _____.

    A. kilometer   B. hectometer   C. dekameter
    D. meter   E. millimeter

Add or subtract each group of numbers below.

6.
$$\begin{array}{r} 8.9 \\ 12.8 \\ +1.76 \\ \hline \end{array}$$

7.
$$\begin{array}{r} 300.5 \\ -231.8 \\ \hline \end{array}$$

Add or subtract each pair of fractions below. Make sure your answers are fully reduced.

8. $\dfrac{7}{12} - \dfrac{5}{12}$

9. $\dfrac{7}{9} + \dfrac{2}{3}$

Multiply or divide each pair of fractions below. Make sure your answers are fully reduced.

10. $\dfrac{2}{5} \times \dfrac{3}{8}$

11. $\dfrac{1}{7} \div \dfrac{11}{14}$

Do each unit conversion below.

12. How many millimeters are in 87 decimeters?

13. Convert 1,152 square inches to square feet.

Answer each question below.

(a) 14. What must be done to the expression $x \times 17$ to make it equal x?

(b) 15. What must be done to the expression $x \div 35$ to make it equal x?

Solve each equation below by undoing.

16. $x + 4.2 = 19$

17. $x - 38 = 65$

(c) 18. $x \times 7 = 161$

19. $x \div 9 = 21$

(d) 20. $x \div 6.5 = 8.2$

Translate the word problem below into math; then solve.

(e) 21. Concrete blocks are typically 8 inches wide, 8 inches tall, and 16 inches long. How many cubic inches is this?

Lesson 72—Changing Places

By now, you're probably getting better and better at solving equations. But take a look at this one.

$$4 + x = 25$$

We could figure out the answer in our heads, but what is the proper way to undo the addition? In all of the equations we've solved so far, x was on the outside. Here it's on the inside, next to the equals sign. Wouldn't it be easier to undo if we could make the 4 and the x change places? Is this allowed?

Flip 'Em Around

Yes, we can change these numbers around, because a basic rule of arithmetic says that two numbers can be added in any order, and their sum will be the same. It's called the commutative property of addition, and we talked about it way back in Chapter 1. This is the rule that says that $4 + 6$ equals $6 + 4$, $1 + 7$ equals $7 + 1$, and so on. But the important thing to know is that we can use this rule even when an x is involved. So in our example we can change $4 + x$ to $x + 4$.

$$x + 4 = 25$$

Now we can solve in the normal way.

$$x + 4 - 4 = 25 - 4$$

$$x = 25 - 4$$

$$x = 21$$

Next, let's take a look at another equation where it's helpful to make a number and an x change places.

$$8 \times x = 72$$

Here we want to switch the 8 and the x to make the undoing step easier. And this is legal, because there's another arithmetic rule which says that two numbers can be multiplied in any order, and their answer (product) will be the same. We already talked about this rule too. It's called the commutative property of multiplication, remember. It tells us that 8×5 is the same as 5×8. But the key point is that it can be used when an x is involved. So we can change $8 \times x$ to $x \times 8$.

$$x \times 8 = 72$$

Now it's easy to see how to undo. We just divide both sides by 8 like this.

$$x \times 8 \div 8 = 72 \div 8$$

The left side is equal to just x.

$$x = 72 \div 8$$

And doing the division on the right gives us the answer.

$$x = 9$$

These arithmetic rules work for all numbers. So anytime we have two numbers added or multiplied, no matter what they are—even if one of them is an x—we're free to switch their positions. When we change an expression around like this, we say that we are **rewriting** the expression. But make sure that you always follow one of the basic rules of arithmetic we talked about when rewriting.

It Won't Work for Subtraction and Division

One more thing. The rules about changing places only work for addition and multiplication. They do *not* work for subtraction or division. That means $5 - x$ cannot be changed to $x - 5$. And $4 \div x$ cannot be changed to $x \div 4$. Don't forget that.

Practice 72

a. Convert 2.3 liters to milliliters.

b. Tell whether the expressions $x - 9$ and $9 - x$ are equivalent.

c. Solve the equation $10.7 + x = 54.6$.

d. Solve the equation $53 \times x = 424$.

e. Translate the word problem below into an equation; then solve.

A whopping 3,289 people attended the power tool convention. Of these, 3,172 were men. How many were women?

Problem Set 72

Tell whether each sentence below is True or False.

1. Two numbers can be added in any order and their sum will be the same.

2. Two numbers can be divided in any order and their quotient will be the same.

Complete each sentence below with the best of the choices given.

3. 1 kilometer equals 10,000 _____ .

      A. hectometers   B. dekameters   C. meters
      D. decimeters   E. centimeters

4. 1 mile equals 5,280 _____ .

      A. yards   B. feet   C. inches
      D. kilometers   E. meters

Multiply or divide each pair of numbers below. Write any remainders in decimal form.

5. $\begin{array}{r} 345 \\ \times 1.7 \\ \hline \end{array}$ **6.** $0.12\overline{)5.61}$

Add or subtract each pair of numbers below. Make sure your answers are fully reduced.

7. $3\frac{1}{4} + 2\frac{1}{2}$ **8.** $\frac{11}{5} - 1\frac{3}{5}$

Convert each fraction below into decimal form. Give exact answers (no rounding).

9. $\frac{3}{8}$ **10.** $\frac{1}{6}$

Do each unit conversion below.

(a) 11. Convert 3.8 liters to milliliters.

12. How many yards are in 54 feet?

Tell whether each pair of expressions below is equivalent.

(b) 13. $x - 5$ and $5 - x$

14. $7 + x$ and $x + 7$

Solve each equation below by undoing.

(c) 15. $12.4 + x = 78.3$ **16.** $x - \dfrac{1}{5} = \dfrac{3}{5}$ **(d) 17.** $61 \times x = 549$

18. $x \div \dfrac{2}{7} = \dfrac{1}{2}$ **19.** $x \div 32 = 1.5$ **20.** $x \times \dfrac{1}{4} = \dfrac{1}{3}$

Translate the word problem below into an equation; then solve.

(e) 21. There were 5,642 participants in last year's antique and custom car show. Of these, 4,398 were from California. How many were *not* from California?

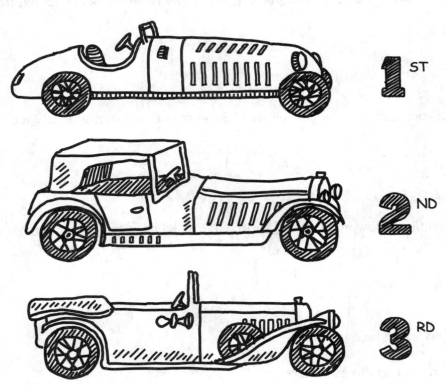

Lesson 73—New Symbols

You know that multiplication is shown with the × symbol and division with the ÷ symbol, but you may be surprised to find out that those symbols are really only used in arithmetic. In algebra and all the more advanced math subjects, multiplication and division are actually written differently.

Writing Multiplication the Algebra Way

Here's how it works. To write "2 multiplied by x" the algebra way, we just put the 2 and x right next to each other, like this.

$$2x$$

So in algebra we write the equation $2 \times x = 40$ as $2x = 40$. You may be wondering, what difference it makes. Well, there are several reasons for writing multiplication differently in algebra. Eliminating the × symbol and pushing the 2 and x up against each other takes up less space. And, as you know, algebra problems can be a lot longer than arithmetic problems. So extra space is helpful. Another reason is that the symbol × looks a lot like an x. And so getting rid of the × symbol avoids a lot of confusion.

Another thing to keep in mind is that the number is always shown first when writing a multiplication with an x. That means to write the equation $x \times 5 = 13$ correctly, the x and 5 should not only be pushed completely together, but the order should also be changed to get $5x = 13$. Of course, mathematically it doesn't matter which number is listed first in a multiplication. But everybody has gotten into the habit of always putting the number first, so you should too.

The only problem is that pushing together won't work when you're multiplying two numbers instead of a number and an x. For example, if we try to write 5×6 by taking out the × symbol and pushing the numbers together, we get 56, which looks just like the number "fifty–six." So when multiplying two numbers we put parentheses around each number. The algebra way to write 5×6, then, is like this.

$$(5)(6)$$

The numbers are still pushed together, but the parentheses show that 5 and 6 are actually two different numbers. Actually, we only need one set of parentheses to separate the 5 and 6. So 5×6 can also be written as $(5)6$ or $5(6)$.

There's even another way to show two numbers multiplied. We can use a dot. Here's 5 times 6 written with a dot.

$$5 \cdot 6$$

The dot can be used to show 5 multiplied by x too: $5 \cdot x$. But notice that the dot takes up some extra space, and since the 5 and x can be pushed completely together without causing any problems, the dot isn't usually used to show a number multiplied by an x.

Writing Division the Algebra Way

We said that division is also shown differently in algebra. What takes the place of the $\div$ symbol then? Actually, it's the fraction bar. This makes sense if you think about it, because the fraction bar is used to stand for division even in basic math. For example, $\frac{12}{2}$ is the same as $12 \div 2$. In arithmetic, the fraction bar isn't used nearly as often as the $\div$ sign. But in algebra, the fraction bar is used almost always. That means an algebra equation like $x \div 9 = 15$ is actually written as $\frac{x}{9} = 15$. The fraction bar not only saves space but also has some other advantages that we'll talk about later.

Practice 73

a. Write "x times 7" the algebra way.

b. Write "x divided by 3" the algebra way.

c. Convert 6 square meters to square decimeters.

d. Tell whether the expressions $\frac{x}{11}$ and $\frac{11}{x}$ are equivalent.

e. Translate the word problem below into an equation; then solve.

Today, alone, the cafeteria worker has dipped $1\frac{3}{5}$ gallons of Jell-O™. If there is still $\frac{9}{10}$ of a gallon left in her Jell-O™ tub, how many gallons were in the tub to start with? Write your answer as a fraction.

Problem Set 73

Tell whether each sentence below is True or False.

1. Multiplication is written differently in algebra than it is in basic math.

2. Division is written differently in algebra than it is in basic math.

Complete each sentence below with the best of the choices given.

3. 1,000 meters equals 1 _____ .

      A. kilometer   B. hectometer   C. dekameter
      D. meter   E. decimeter

4. 1 yard equals 36 _____ .

      A. miles   B. feet   C. inches
      D. decimeters   E. centimeters

Add or subtract each group of numbers below.

5. $\begin{array}{r} 8,467 \\ +\,4,320 \\ \hline \end{array}$ **6.** $\begin{array}{r} 2.875 \\ -\,1.309 \\ \hline \end{array}$

Add or subtract each pair of fractions below. Make sure your answers are fully reduced.

7. $\dfrac{12}{18} + \dfrac{3}{18}$ **8.** $\dfrac{2}{3} - \dfrac{1}{7}$

Convert each percent below into decimal form.

9. 78% $\dfrac{78}{100}$ .78   **10.** 103.75%

Answer each question below.

(a) 11. Write "x times 8" the algebra way.

(b) 12. Write "x divided by 2" the algebra way.

Do each unit conversion below.

(c) 13. Convert 4 square meters to square decimeters.

14. How many yards are in 720 inches?

Answer each question below.

15. What must be done to the expression $x + \dfrac{1}{3}$ to make it equal x?

16. What must be done to the expression $\dfrac{x}{4.5}$ to make it equal x?

Tell whether each pair of expressions below is equivalent.

(d) 17. $\dfrac{x}{12}$ and $\dfrac{12}{x}$

18. $x29$ and $29x$

Solve each equation below by undoing.

19. $0.8 + x = 1.5$ 　　　　20. $x - \dfrac{1}{9} = \dfrac{2}{3}$ 　　　　21. $x - 2{,}500 = 1{,}760$

Translate the word problem below into an equation; then solve.

(e) 22. Yesterday, the cafeteria worker dipped $1\dfrac{1}{4}$ gallons of potato salad. If she had $\dfrac{1}{2}$ of a gallon left, how many gallons did she start with? Write your answer as a fraction.

Lesson 74—Undoing the Algebra Way

Ever wondered what happens when we try to solve equations written in the new algebra style? Here's an example.

$$11x = 44$$

Undoing Multiplication

The 11 and x are pushed together, so this means 11 times x equals 44. So to solve the equation we need to undo the multiplication by 11. And, as you know, that's done by dividing both sides by 11. But since division is always shown with a fraction bar, we have to write the undoing step like this.

$$\frac{11x}{11} = \frac{44}{11}$$

Even though this may look funny, the left side is still saying that x is multiplied by 11 and then the result is divided by 11. So the left side is still equal to just x.

$$x = \frac{44}{11}$$

The last step is to divide 44 by 11 to get 4.

$$x = 4$$

Here's an example of an equation where x is multiplied by a fraction.

$$\frac{1}{3}x = 24$$

How can we show the undoing step on this one? It's pretty simple, really. We just draw a fraction bar underneath everything on each side and divide by $\frac{1}{3}$.

$$\frac{\frac{1}{3}x}{\frac{1}{3}} = \frac{24}{\frac{1}{3}}$$

On the left side, x is multiplied by $\frac{1}{3}$ and then this result is divided by $\frac{1}{3}$, which leaves just x.

$$x = \frac{24}{\frac{1}{3}}$$

Now, to get the answer, we still need to do the division on the right. To divide 24 by $\frac{1}{3}$, we invert the bottom fraction and multiply. Also, remember that the multiplication can be written with parentheses or with a dot. Here are both methods.

$$x = (24)\left(\frac{3}{1}\right) \qquad \text{or} \qquad x = 24 \cdot \frac{3}{1}$$

The answer is 72.

What About Division?

Let's do one where the x is divided by a number.

$$\frac{x}{8} = 17$$

There's nothing too complicated here. To undo the division, we multiply both sides by 8. Either the dot or parentheses can be used. (Putting $\frac{x}{8}$ and 8 right next to each other without a dot or parentheses is not allowed, because it might look like x divided by 88.)

$$\frac{x}{8} \cdot 8 = 17 \cdot 8 \qquad \text{or} \qquad \left(\frac{x}{8}\right)(8) = (17)(8)$$

Since we can multiply two numbers in any order, we also could have put the 8s on the left side like this.

$$8 \cdot \frac{x}{8} = 8 \cdot 17 \qquad \text{or} \qquad (8)\left(\frac{x}{8}\right) = (8)(17)$$

And since multiplication undoes division, we end up with this.

$$x = 8 \cdot 17 \qquad \text{or if you prefer} \qquad x = (8)(17)$$

The solution is 136.

A Messy One

Equations where x is divided by a fraction are handled in the same way. Take this example.

$$\frac{x}{\frac{2}{3}} = 9$$

We undo by multiplying both sides by $\frac{2}{3}$.

$$\frac{x}{\frac{2}{3}} \cdot \frac{2}{3} = 9 \cdot \frac{2}{3}$$

(We could have done this step with parentheses just as easily.)

The multiplication by $\frac{2}{3}$ undoes the division by $\frac{2}{3}$, leaving x by itself on the left.

$$x = 9 \cdot \frac{2}{3}$$

Carrying out the multiplication gives us 6.

Practice 74

a. Write "3 times 5" the algebra way.

b. Solve the equation $12x = 180$.

c. Solve the equation $\frac{x}{9} = 5.4$.

d. Solve the equation $\frac{x}{\frac{2}{5}} = 20$.

e. Translate the word problem below into an equation; then solve.

The largest elephants weigh 30.25 times as much as the largest gorillas, so if the largest elephants weigh 14,520 pounds, how much do the largest gorillas weigh?

Problem Set 74

x

Tell whether each sentence below is True or False.

1. To undo $3x = 12$ the algebra way, you write $3x \div 3 = 12 \div 3$.

2. To undo $\dfrac{x}{5} = 16$ the algebra way, you write $\dfrac{x}{5} \cdot 5 = 16 \cdot 5$.

Complete each sentence below with the best of the choices given.

3. 2 pints equal 1 _____ .

    A. gallon   B. quart   C. fluid ounce
    D. cubic inch   E. liter

4. 1,760 yards equals 1 _____ .

    A. mile   B. foot   C. inch
    D. kilometer   E. hectometer

Multiply or divide each pair of numbers below. Write any remainders in decimal form.

5. $\begin{array}{r} 0.64 \\ \times 0.23 \\ \hline \end{array}$

6. $9\overline{)2{,}856}$

374

Add or subtract each pair of numbers below. Make sure your answers are fully reduced.

7. $14 + \dfrac{8}{5}$

8. $9 - 7\dfrac{3}{4}$

Convert each fraction below into decimal form. Give exact answers (no rounding).

9. $\dfrac{7}{5}$

10. $\dfrac{1}{11}$

Do each unit conversion below.

11. How many centimeters are in 9 meters?

12. Convert 3,520 yards into miles.

Answer each question below.

(a) 13. Write "2 times 6" the algebra way.

14. What must be done to the expression $x - \dfrac{4}{9}$ to make it equal x?

15. What must be done to the expression $1,250x$ to make it equal x?

Solve each equation below by undoing.

(b) 16. $13x = 156$

(c) 17. $\dfrac{x}{6} = 7.5$

18. $\dfrac{1}{8} + x = \dfrac{1}{2}$

19. $\dfrac{1}{5}x = \dfrac{3}{10}$

(d) 20. $\dfrac{x}{\frac{3}{4}} = 24$

Translate the word problem below into an equation; then solve.

(e) 21. The longest tapeworms in the world are actually 1.65 times as long as the tallest giraffes. If the longest tapeworms measure 33 feet, how many feet tall are the tallest giraffes?

Lesson 75—Solving Percent Problems with Algebra

You already know how to find the percent of a number—we've been doing that for awhile. Take this problem, for example: What is 45% of 28? All we have to do is multiply 0.45 (which is 45% written as a decimal) and 28 to get 12.6.

Finding the Missing Number

But what if the question were asked backwards? What if it were "12.6 is 45% of what number?" Of course, we know the answer is 28, but it would be pretty hard to figure out if you didn't know that in advance.

The easiest way to find the answer to a backwards percent problem is to use an algebra equation. Let's start by letting x represent the missing number.

$$x = \text{missing number}$$

Then since 45% of x equals 12.6, our equation needs to be

$$0.45x = 12.6$$

This equation makes perfect sense when you think about it. We know that there is a missing number, and that 45% of it equals 12.6. If that's true, then when we multiply the missing number by 0.45, shouldn't we get 12.6? Yes. And that's exactly what this equation does.

Solving the equation from here should be easy. We just have to undo the multiplication by dividing both sides by 0.45.

$$\frac{0.45x}{0.45} = \frac{12.6}{0.45}$$

On the left we have x multiplied by 0.45 and then divided by 0.45, so that side becomes just x.

$$x = \frac{12.6}{0.45}$$

That's turned our algebra equation into a simple arithmetic problem, and now we can do the calculation on the right side to get the answer.

$$x = 28$$

Do you see the advantage of algebra? This example makes it clear. If we hadn't written an algebra equation, you probably wouldn't have known how to solve the problem because it was a pretty hard one. But by using our knowledge about how to find the percent of a number, we were able to set up an equation and get the answer just by undoing with division. We didn't have to know anything else.

Finding the Missing Percent

Let's try another example with percents.

What percent of 70 is 14?

We've done problems like this before. Do you remember how they work? We use division. The "of" number (70 in this case) goes on bottom and the "is" number (14) goes on top. That gives us this.

$$\frac{14}{70} = 0.2$$

We end up with 0.2. The last step is to change the decimal to a percent by moving the decimal two places to the right and putting the percent symbol back in.

$$\frac{14}{70} = 0.2 = 20\%$$

So the answer is 20%.

That's the way we learned to solve the problem with arithmetic. But this problem can also be solved with an algebra equation. Since we're looking for the missing percent, we'll let that be x.

$$x = \text{missing percent}$$

We know that the percent of a number can be found by multiplication, so since $x\%$ of 70 is 14, x times 70 should equal 14. When we write that out in an equation it looks like this.

$$x70 = 14$$

But since the number should always be to the left of the x, let's change the equation to

$$70x = 14.$$

From here all we have to do is solve normally. We undo the multiplication by dividing both sides by 70.

$$\frac{70x}{70} = \frac{14}{70}$$

On the left, x is multiplied by 70 and then divided by 70. That leaves just x (since the division undoes the multiplication).

$$x = \frac{14}{70}$$

Does this look familiar? It's the same calculation we got before when we solved the problem the arithmetic way. But this time we didn't have to remember to divide, or that the "of" number goes on bottom and the "is" number on top. All we had to know was the basic rule about multiplying to find a percent of a number. To finish solving our equation, we divide 14 by 70 on the right.

$$x = 0.2$$

Finally, we change the decimal back to a percent. But that raises an important point. Whenever percents are put in equations, they're always in decimal form. That means we have to change them back to a percent after we have the answer.

$$x = 0.2 = 20\%$$

We end up with 20%, which is the same answer we got doing the problem with arithmetic.

Once you get used to it, you'll probably think percent problems are easier to solve with algebra than they are with arithmetic, because you don't have to remember as much. And the harder the problem, the better it is to use algebra.

Practice 75

a. How many square meters are in 350 square centimeters?

b. Convert 2.6 liters to milliliters.

c. Solve the equation $\frac{5}{4}x = \frac{1}{8}$.

d. Solve the equation $\dfrac{x}{\frac{3}{2}} = \dfrac{4}{9}$.

e. Translate the word problem below into an equation; then solve.

Harold paid 5% in sales tax on his new "smart fabric" warm-ups. (Smart fabrics can, for example, be made of threads that automatically tighten to block a cold breeze or loosen to release body heat.) If Harold paid $37.25 in sales tax on the warm-ups, what was their pre-tax price?

Problem Set 75

Complete each sentence below with the best of the choices given.

1. 1 square kilometer equals 100 _____ .

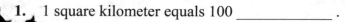

    A. square hectometers   B. square dekameters   C. square meters
    D. square decimeters   E. square centimeters

2. 1 square yard equals 9 _____ .

    A. square miles   B. square feet   C. square inches
    D. square kilometers   E. square meters

Add or subtract each group of numbers below.

3.
$$\begin{array}{r} 36.0 \\ 67.5 \\ +90.2 \\ \hline \end{array}$$

4.
$$\begin{array}{r} 98.5 \\ -79.1 \\ \hline \end{array}$$

Add or subtract each pair of fractions below. Make sure your answers are fully reduced.

5. $\dfrac{5}{6}+\dfrac{3}{6}$

6. $\dfrac{4}{7}-\dfrac{1}{2}$

Convert each percent below into decimal form.

7. $12\dfrac{1}{4}\%$

8. 150%

Do each unit conversion below.

(a) 9. How many square meters are in 280 square centimeters?

(b) 10. Convert 1.2 liters to milliliters.

Answer each question below.

11. Write "x times 15" the algebra way.

12. Write "x divided by 3" the algebra way.

Tell whether each pair of expressions below is equivalent.

13. $x + \dfrac{4}{7}$ and $\dfrac{4}{7} + x$

14. $x0.03$ and $0.03x$

Solve each equation below by undoing.

15. $x - 3.5 = 18.7$ **16.** $52x = 676$ **17.** $\dfrac{x}{21} = 0.5$

18. $x + \dfrac{2}{3} = \dfrac{4}{3}$ **(c) 19.** $\dfrac{6}{5}x = \dfrac{1}{10}$ **(d) 20.** $\dfrac{x}{\frac{4}{3}} = \dfrac{7}{8}$

Translate the word problem below into an equation; then solve.

(e) 21. Molly paid 8% in sales tax on her holophone, a phone that shows the person you're talking to in 3-D. If Molly paid $416 in sales tax on the phone, what was its pre-tax price?

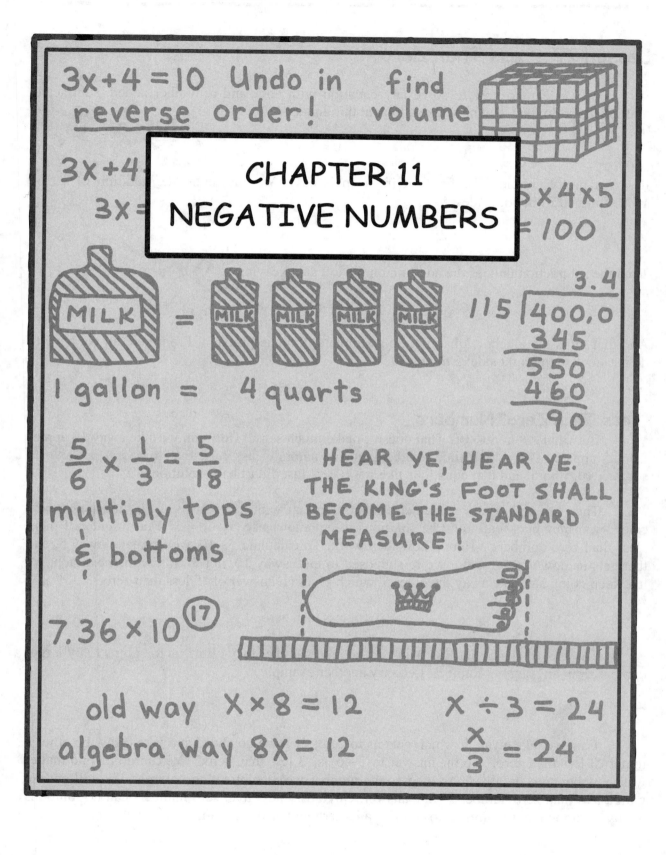

CHAPTER 11
NEGATIVE NUMBERS

Lesson 77—Less Than Zero

We've learned how to solve any equation with an x and a number added, subtracted, multiplied, or divided. But now take a look at this equation.

$$x + 10 = 5$$

It *seems* pretty simple. The first solving step is easy. We just undo the addition of 10 by subtracting 10 from both sides.

$$x + 10 - 10 = 5 - 10$$

Then the subtraction undoes the addition on the left side, leaving x.

$$x = 5 - 10$$

And that turns the algebra equation into a simple arithmetic problem. From here all we have to do is calculate the right side: 5 minus 10.

"Less Than Zero" Numbers

But what's 5 minus 10? That doesn't make much sense. How can we take away 10 apples from 5 apples? For a long time, mathematicians naturally assumed that it wasn't possible to subtract 10 from 5, and that equations like $x + 10 = 5$ just didn't have solutions.

Then one day a clever mathematician came up with a bright idea. He invented a new category of numbers that could be solutions to equations like $x + 10 = 5$. You might call them "less than zero numbers." Here's how they work. To calculate $5 - 10$ we first take away 5, and that gets us down to zero. But we're supposed to take away 10, not 5. So for the next step, we just keep going and take away the other 5, which gives an answer of "5 less than zero."

$$5 - 10 = 5 \text{ less than zero}$$

The great thing about less than zero numbers is that they allow us to subtract any larger number from any smaller number. Let's try another example.

$$3 - 6$$

First we take away 3, which gets us to zero; then we go ahead and take away the other 3 to get "3 less than zero." So the answer to $3 - 6$ is "3 less than zero." We can do this no matter what numbers are involved. As long as the number we're subtracting is larger, we will end up with a less than zero number for the answer. Obviously, less than zero numbers can be solutions to any equation that requires us to subtract a larger number from a smaller number.

Negative and Positive Numbers

You probably have heard of less than zero numbers before. They're actually called **negative numbers**, and instead of writing the words "less than zero" beside them, we use a little minus sign. So "5 less than zero" is actually called "negative 5." Written with the little minus sign, it looks like this: -5.

$$5 \text{ less than zero} = -5$$

Since this is a negative number, the little minus sign is called a "negative sign". From now on, the ordinary numbers that you've always used will be called **positive numbers**, just to avoid confusion. The only exception is zero, which isn't positive or negative.

When negatives are mixed together with positive (ordinary) numbers, a plus sign (or positive sign) is sometimes used in front of the positive numbers. So 2 can be written as +2. But since positives are used so much more often than negatives, the plus sign is usually left off. That means a number without a sign is assumed to be positive. If we see the number "2," we know it means positive 2, not negative 2. So if we want to use a negative number, we have to include the negative sign or it will be assumed to be positive.

Now that we have *both* positive numbers (the numbers we've been using all along) and negative numbers, we really can solve any equation with an x and a number added, subtracted, multiplied, or divided.

Practice 77

    a.   Convert 10 gallons to quarts.

    b.   How many miles are in 10,560 yards?

    c.   Tell whether the expressions $x \div \dfrac{1}{5}$ and $\dfrac{1}{5} \div x$ are equivalent.

    d.   Write the answer to $3 - 8$ as a negative number.

    e.   Translate the word problem below into an equation; then solve.

        Jenkins bought some driving moccasins at a 25% discount. If the discount saved him $17.50, what was the moccasins original price?

Problem Set 77

Tell whether each sentence below is True or False.

1. Numbers that are less than zero are called negative numbers

2. The ordinary numbers that you learned about in arithmetic, which are greater than zero, are called positive numbers.

Add or subtract each group of numbers below.

3. $\begin{array}{r} 8.9 \\ 12.8 \\ +1.76 \\ \hline \end{array}$

4. $\begin{array}{r} 300.5 \\ -231.8 \\ \hline \end{array}$

Multiply or divide each pair of fractions below. Make sure your answers are fully reduced.

5. $\dfrac{5}{2} \times \dfrac{2}{7}$

6. $\dfrac{4}{9} \div \dfrac{16}{3}$

Do each unit conversion below.

(a) 7. Convert 12 gallons to quarts.

(b) 8. How many miles are in 8,800 yards?

Tell whether each pair of expressions below is equivalent.

9. $x - \dfrac{3}{5}$ and $\dfrac{3}{5} - x$

(c) 10. $x \div \dfrac{1}{9}$ and $\dfrac{1}{9} \div x$

Answer each question below.

11. What must be done to the expression $x + 158$ to make it equal x?

12. How far will a go cart moving at 30 miles per hour travel in 3 hours?

13. How far will an exercise fanatic walking at 5 miles per hour travel in 4 hours?

Write the answer to each problem below as a negative number.

(d) 14. $4-7$ **15.** $1-9$ **16.** $3-15$

Solve each equation below by undoing.

17. $\dfrac{2}{5}+x=1$ **18.** $x-14.2=36.8$ **19.** $\dfrac{1}{3}x=\dfrac{1}{6}$

20. $\dfrac{x}{\frac{3}{8}}=24$

Translate the word problem below into an equation; then solve.

(e) 21. Raquel bought an insanely expensive espresso machine at a 60% discount. If the discount saved her $270, what was the machine's original price?

Lesson 78—The Number Line

One way to picture the negative numbers that we learned about in the last lesson is with a number line.

The number line is just a simple line with numbers on it. Notice that the positive numbers are on the right side and the negative numbers are on the left. Zero is right in the middle. The arrows on either end are meant to show that the number line goes on forever in both directions. Of course, we only use the arrows because there's not enough space on the page to keep going on and on.

And we really would have to go on forever in both directions, because there are an infinite number of positive numbers and an infinite number of negative numbers. We could keep going to the left, beyond -7 to -8, -9, and so on, all the way up to $-28,000,000$ if we wanted (or even higher)! You probably know that we show a number on the number line with a dot. For example, we can show the number -2 like this.

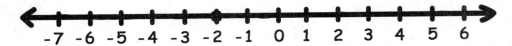

Which Negative is Greater?

The number line is really helpful for figuring out which of two negative numbers is greater. That can be confusing sometimes. For instance, which is greater, -2 or -7? At first, you might think it's -7 (since you're used to thinking that 7 is greater than 2) but it's not. Actually, -2 is greater because it's not as much "less than zero" as -7 is. All the confusion gets cleared up, though, when we put both numbers on the number line (using dots).

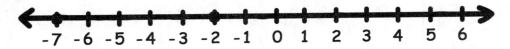

The greater number is always the one that's farther to the right on the number line. So since -2 is to the right of -7, we know that -2 has to be the greater number. This works because on the number line, the numbers always get larger as we move to the right and smaller as we move to the left. The positive numbers increase as they get farther and farther from zero, and the negative numbers increase as they get closer and closer to zero.

Negative Fractions and Decimals

So far we've only talked about negative whole numbers like $-1, -2, -3$, and so on. But there are also negative fractions and decimals, like $-\frac{1}{4}$, $-\frac{5}{8}$, $-7\frac{1}{2}$, -2.5, and -0.4. The negative fractions and decimals haven't been labeled on any of our number lines, but they're still there. We just didn't have enough room to put them in. Negative fractions and decimals lie in between the negative whole numbers. For example, the decimal -2.5 is between -2 and -3, and the fraction $-\frac{1}{4}$ is between 0 and -1.

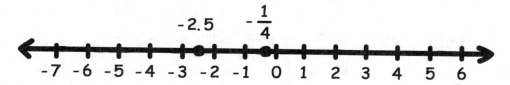

Positive fractions and decimals are also on the number line. The decimal 4.5, for example, is between the 4 and the 5.

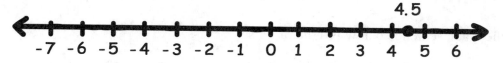

So the number line has positive and negative whole numbers, positive and negative fractions and decimals, and zero. There's also an important term that you should be aware of. Positive and negative whole numbers and zero are all called **integers**. People usually only label the integers on the number line because they don't have room for the fractions and decimals.

Opposites

Another interesting thing that a number line tells us is that every number has an **opposite**, which is the same number with an opposite sign. For example, 3 and -3 are opposites; so are 1.4 and -1.4 and $\frac{3}{8}$ and $-\frac{3}{8}$. And the interesting thing about opposites is that they're always the same distance from zero. We can see this if we look at the example of 3 and -3 below.

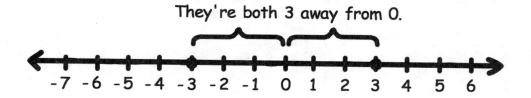

They're both 3 away from 0.

Practice 78

a. What is 35% of 240?

b. How far will a mouse running at 6 inches per second travel in 3 seconds?

c. Show -3.5 on the number line.

d. Solve the equation $\dfrac{2}{9}y = \dfrac{7}{18}$.

e. Translate the word problem below into an equation; then solve.

If a cyclist is traveling at 20 miles per hour, how many hours will it take him to travel 15 miles? Round your answer to the nearest hundredths place (two decimal places).

Problem Set 78

Tell whether each sentence below is True or False.

1. A number line can be used to show both positive and negative numbers.

2. The positive whole numbers, negative whole numbers, and zero are together called "integers."

3. The opposite of 5 is -5?

Multiply or divide each pair of numbers below. Write any remainders in decimal form.

4. $\begin{array}{r} 295 \\ \times 71 \\ \hline \end{array}$

5. $11\overline{)2{,}541}$

Add or subtract each pair of fractions below. Make sure your answers are fully reduced.

6. $\dfrac{6}{20} + \dfrac{4}{20}$

7. $\dfrac{7}{8} - \dfrac{5}{6}$

Answer each question below.

8. What is $\dfrac{3}{4}$ of 60?

(a) 9. What is 28% of 250?

10. How far will a jet flying at 550 miles per hour travel in 6 hours?

(b) 11. How far will an unidentified furry object running at 7 inches per second travel in 4 seconds?

Show each number below on a number line.

12. -3 **(c) 13.** -4.5

Write the answer to each problem below as a negative number.

14. $2-8$ **15.** $5-21$ **16.** $3-4$

Solve each equation below by undoing.

17. $x-\dfrac{1}{4}=\dfrac{3}{8}$ **18.** $7x=154$ **19.** $\dfrac{x}{6.5}=2.3$

(d) 20. $\dfrac{4}{9}y=\dfrac{5}{27}$

Translate the word problem below into an equation; then solve.

(e) 21. If a go-cart rider is traveling at 12 miles per hour, how many hours will it take him to travel 3 miles? Round your answer to the nearest hundredths place (two decimal places).

Lesson 79—How Negatives Are Used

We've been focusing a lot on negative numbers, but you may have been wondering whether they have any use in real life? Actually, negative numbers are very practical. If they weren't, they probably would never have become so popular.

In Business

Negatives are used all the time in business. Imagine you're a stock trader and need to keep track of all of your profits and losses. Say you made a $650 profit and a $320 loss. You could just write it down like this.

650 **profit**
320 **loss**

But there's a faster way: make profits be positive and losses negative. Then you just write them with positive and negative signs.

$$+650$$
$$-320$$

This not only takes up less space on the page, but it makes adding and subtracting the numbers easier too. Adding and subtracting negative numbers is something we'll learn more about later in the chapter.

In Lots of Other Places

Negatives are also used when measuring temperatures. For example, when somebody says "It's −15 degrees Fahrenheit," that just means 15 degrees below zero. A navigator of a ship could also use negative numbers too. He could make distances to the north positive and distances to the south negative. Then it would be easier to calculate the position and direction of the ship. Generally speaking, negative numbers are helpful in any situation that involves two opposite kinds of numbers, like profits and losses, temperatures above zero and below zero, and directions like north and south.

Practice 79

a. How many dekameters are in 59,000 centimeters?

b. How far could a cheetah running at 60 miles per hour travel in $\frac{1}{2}$ hour?

c. Use a positive or negative number to represent this quantity: A loss of 20 yards in football.

d. Solve the equation $\dfrac{x}{\frac{5}{8}} = \dfrac{4}{15}$.

e. Translate the word problem below into an equation; then solve.

Larry sells above ground swimming pools, and he receives a 15% commission on all the pools he sells. If Larry received $9,000 in commissions last year, how many dollars worth of pools did he sell?

Problem Set 79

Tell whether each sentence below is True or False.

1. Negative numbers are never used in business.

2. Negative numbers are useful in situations involving two opposite kinds of numbers, like north and south.

Add or subtract each group of numbers below.

3.
$$\begin{array}{r} 55{,}740 \\ +\,34{,}825 \\ \hline \end{array}$$

4.
$$\begin{array}{r} 7{,}923 \\ -\,4{,}296 \\ \hline \end{array}$$

Multiply or divide each pair of numbers below. Make sure your answers are fully reduced.

5. $18 \times \dfrac{5}{9}$

6. $\dfrac{20}{\frac{4}{5}}$

Do each unit conversion below.

7. Convert 12 yards to inches.

(a) 8. How many dekameters are in 75,000 centimeters?

Answer each question below.

9. What must be done to the expression $x - 5,924$ to make it equal x?

(b) 10. How far will a horse running at 20 miles per hour travel in $\frac{1}{2}$ hour?

11. How far will a blue shark swimming at 30 miles per hour travel in $1\frac{1}{2}$ hours?

Show each number below on a number line.

12. -5

13. $-\frac{1}{2}$

Tell which of each pair of numbers below is greater.

14. -9 and 6

15. -4 and -11

Use a positive or negative number to represent each quantity below.

(c) 16. A loss of 12 yards in football.

17. A temperature of 17 below zero.

18. A $2,000 profit in the stock market.

Solve each equation below by undoing.

19. $\frac{2}{5} + x = \frac{7}{10}$

20. $290x = 1,160$

21. $x - 72.5 = 28.4$

(d) 22. $\dfrac{x}{\frac{5}{6}} = \dfrac{3}{10}$

Translate the word problem below into an equation; then solve.

(e) 23. Larry has decided that the above ground swimming pools business is not the best way to earn a living (see practice problem e). He now thinks the big money is in rowing machines. If Larry switches jobs, he will earn a 12% commission on all the machines he sells. For Larry to receive $15,000 in commissions, how many dollars worth of machines must he sell?

Lesson 80—Addition with Negatives

Now that we know what negative numbers are and a little bit about how they're used, it's time to talk about how to actually add, subtract, multiply, and divide them. That's important, because if we can't do that, we won't be able to use negatives to solve practical problems. In this lesson, we'll start with adding negatives.

Adding Losses

Let's say we want to add -2 and -3. We can write it out to get

$$-2 + -3.$$

The easiest way to do this calculation is to think of the negatives as losses. With this approach, -2 is like a loss of 2, and -3 is like a loss of 3. If you lose \$2 and then \$3 more, how much have you lost in total? Obviously, you've lost \$5. So a loss of 2 plus a loss of 3 equals a loss of 5, which is another way of saying that $-2 + -3$ is -5.

$$-2 + -3 = -5$$

Another thing to keep in mind is that most people put parentheses around the second negative number like this.

$$-2 + (-3)$$

The parentheses show that the minus is actually a negative sign attached to the number 3. It prevents us from confusing the negative sign with the plus sign right before it. We don't need parentheses around the first number, because there's no other sign next to its negative sign.

Now let's try another example. This time we'll put the parentheses around the second number to show that the minus is actually a negative sign.

$$-8 + (-7)$$

Once again, we just need to think of negatives as losses. If we lose \$8 and then lose another \$7, we've lost \$15 in total. So -8 plus -7 has to equal -15.

$$-8 + (-7) = -15$$

Finally, let's try adding -4 and -5.

$$-4 + (-5)$$

Thinking of the negatives as losses again, we have a loss of 4 added to another loss of 5, which equals a loss of 9. That gives us this.

$$-4 + (-5) = -9$$

Are you starting to get the idea? One negative plus another negative equals an even bigger (in magnitude) negative.

Adding on the Number Line

We can also show addition of negatives on the number line. Let's try this with our first example, $-2 + (-3)$. To show -2 we draw an arrow that starts at 0 and goes two places to the left.

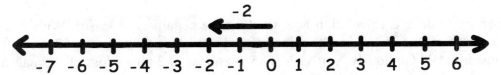

To add -3 we draw another arrow. This one starts where the first arrow ended, and goes three units to the left.

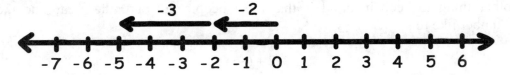

Combining the two, we end up with an arrow to the left that's 5 places long, or -5.

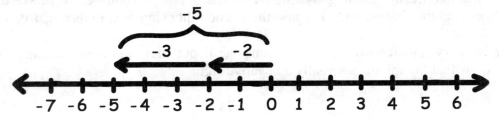

So the answer to $-2 + (-3)$ is -5.

Negative + Positive

We've covered adding a negative to a negative. Now let's add a negative to a positive number. We'll start by adding -3 and $+7$.

$$-3 + 7$$

Notice that there is no positive sign in front of the 7. Remember we don't have to include a positive sign, because everybody assumes a number is positive unless it has a negative sign. But we could have shown the positive sign like this: $-3 + (+7)$.

The best way to add a negative and a positive is to think of the negative as a loss (as usual) and the positive as a gain. So $-3 + 7$ is a loss of 3 plus a gain of 7. Now imagine that you lose \$3 but then find \$7. How much better off are you? You're \$4 better off. That means -3 plus $+7$ has to equal $+4$ (since a gain is positive).

$$-3 + 7 = 4$$

Here's another example of a negative added to a positive.

$$-11 + 3$$

We should think of this as a loss of 11 added to a gain of 3. If you lost \$11 and then gained \$3, are you better off or worse off? You're \$8 worse off. That's a loss of 8, which is -8.

$$-11 + 3 = -8$$

On the Number Line Again

It's also possible to show a positive added to a negative on a number line. For $-3 + 7$, we just show -3 as an arrow starting at 0 and going three places to the left. (Remember, negatives always have an arrow going to the left.)

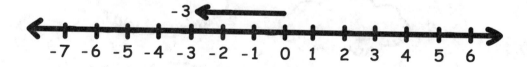

But the next step is a little tricky. Since 7 is positive, its arrow needs to go to the right. So we start the second arrow at the tip of the first arrow, and stretch it seven places to the right.

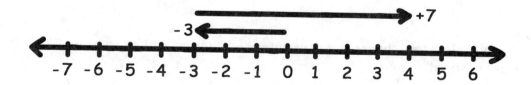

What's our final answer then? Well, we started at 0 and now we find ourselves four places to the right at +4. That means the answer is +4, which is what we got before.

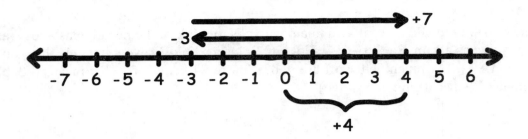

Some people like to use number lines when adding negatives. But you don't have to use them. Just remember to think of negatives as losses and positives as gains and you can usually figure out the answer in your head.

Practice 80

a. Add $-2+(-6)$.

b. Add $8+(-3)$.

c. Show $-4+(-1)$ on a number line.

d. Show $4+(-2)$ on a number line.

e. Translate the word problem below into an equation; then solve.

If a bird flew for 2 hours at a constant speed and traveled a distance of 74 miles, what was her speed?

Problem Set 80

Tell whether each sentence below is True or False.

1. When adding a negative number to a negative number, the answer is always negative.

2. When adding a negative number to a positive number, the answer is always positive.

Multiply or divide each pair of numbers below. Write any remainders in decimal form.

3.
$$\begin{array}{r} 0.85 \\ \times 2.1 \\ \hline \end{array}$$

4. $0.14\overline{)9.24}$

Add or subtract each pair of numbers below. Make sure your answers are fully reduced.

5. $8\frac{2}{9}+2\frac{1}{9}$

6. $6-4\frac{1}{5}$

Convert each fraction below into decimal form. Give exact answers (no rounding).

7. $\frac{3}{10}$

8. $\frac{8}{9}$

Answer each question below.

9. What is $\frac{2}{7}$ of 112?

10. What is $14\frac{1}{2}\%$ of 80?

Use a positive or negative number to represent each quantity below.

11. A gain of 35 yards in football.

12. 3 miles to the south. (Assume north is positive and south negative.)

Tell which of each pair of numbers below is *smaller*.

13. -1 and 0

14. -3.2 and -5.7

Add each pair of numbers below.

(a) 15. $-2+(-4)$ **(b) 16.** $9+(-2)$ **17.** $5+(-14)$

Show each addition below on a number line (using arrows).

(c) 18. $-3+(-1)$ **(d) 19.** $5+(-3)$

Solve each equation below by undoing.

20. $x+83=95$ **21.** $7.5x=51$ **22.** $\dfrac{x}{6.4}=13$

Translate the word problem below into an equation; then solve.

(e) 23. If a bird flew for 4 hours at a constant speed and traveled a distance of 76 miles, what was his speed?

Lesson 81—Subtraction with Negatives

In the last lesson, we learned how to add with negatives. But what about subtracting with negatives? How do we do that? Let's look at an example.

$$8-(-3)$$

First, we'll go through the calculation, and then we'll talk about why it works. It's going to seem pretty strange at first, but just stay with us.

Adding the Opposite

Here's what we do. First we change the subtraction to an addition. So instead of 8 minus something we have 8 plus something. Next, we change -3 to its opposite, which is $+3$.

$$8+(+3)$$

Since we don't have to write the positive sign in front of the 3, we can shorten the expression to this.

$$8+3$$

Now all we have to do is add 8 and 3 to get positive 11.

$$8+3=11$$

So 11 is the answer to our original problem.

$$8-(-3)=11$$

This method works every time. All we have to do when subtracting a negative is change the subtraction to addition, and then change the negative number to its opposite. From there we just add normally.

Let's do another one. We'll do another positive minus a negative.

$$9-(-5)$$

The process is exactly the same. We change the subtraction to addition; then we change -5 to its opposite, $+5$.

$$9+5$$

Now we add normally to get 14.

$$9+5=14$$

When the First Number Is Negative

It turns out that our method also works when the first number is negative. Let's try one like that.

$$-7-(-2)$$

Again, we change subtraction to addition and then change the second number, -2, to its opposite, $+2$.

$$-7+2$$

Now, as always, we add normally. Remember from the last lesson that to add a negative and a positive, we should think of the negative as a loss and the positive as a gain. So in this example we have a loss of 7 added to a gain of 2. That equals a loss of 5, or -5.

$$-7+2=-5$$

It Works with Positives Too

Here's something that may surprise you. We can even use our new method to subtract positive numbers. Look at this example.

$$12-8$$

The answer is 4, of course, because all we have to do is subtract the numbers as they are. But what if we wanted to get fancy? We could change subtraction to addition and then change $+8$ to its opposite, which is -8.

$$12+(-8)$$

Next, we just add: a gain of 12 added to a loss of 8 equals a gain of 4. Our answer, then, is 4, which is right! Of course, we would never want to use this method on such a simple problem. The only time it makes sense to change a subtraction to an addition of the opposite is when negative numbers are involved.

So to review, the basic rule is that we change subtraction to addition, and then change the second number—the one that was being subtracted—to its opposite. If the second number is negative, change it to a positive, and if the second number is positive, change it to a negative.

Taking Away a Loss

Now let's talk about why this rule works. We know that adding a negative is like adding a loss. So subtracting a negative should be the same as subtracting or taking away a loss. But if a loss is taken away, are you worse off or better off? If you had a loss of $5, but then that loss was eliminated, you're better off aren't you? After all, you got your $5 back. It's as if you owed a friend some money and then he said "Don't worry about it. You don't have to pay me back." That would make you better off. So subtracting, or taking away, a loss (a negative) is the same as adding a gain (a positive). And that's why we can subtract a negative by adding the opposite, which is a positive. And that's the easiest way to subtract with negatives. So any time you have to do a subtraction which involves negative numbers, immediately change the subtraction to addition of the opposite of the second number. And it may seem weird at first, but after some practice it will start to sink in.

Practice 81

a. How many miles are in 18,480 feet?

b. Tell which of the following numbers is greater: $-\dfrac{1}{5}$ and $-\dfrac{1}{2}$.

c. Subtract $-3-(-4)$.   d. Subtract $-6-17$.

e. Translate the word problem below into an equation; then solve.

Mr. and Mrs. Simmons are trying to save enough money to buy a Steinway™ grand piano. They have already saved $15,000 but that is nowhere close to enough. If their $15,000 in savings is sitting in a bank account that pays 6% in yearly interest.

i.) How much will Mr. and Mrs. Simmons have earned in interest one year from now?

ii.) If they leave their money *and* interest in the bank for another year, how much interest will they earn for the 2nd year?

Problem Set 81

Tell whether each sentence below is True or False.

1. $10 - (-4)$ is the same as $10 + 4$.

2. The way we subtract negative numbers is to change the subtraction to an addition.

Add or subtract each group of numbers below.

3.
$$\begin{array}{r} 25.31 \\ +\,9.248 \\ \hline \end{array}$$

4.
$$\begin{array}{r} 21.7 \\ -\,13.54 \\ \hline \end{array}$$

Multiply or divide each pair of fractions below. Make sure your answers are fully reduced.

5. $\dfrac{5}{2} \cdot \dfrac{4}{25}$

6. $\dfrac{\frac{1}{12}}{\frac{2}{3}}$

Do each unit conversion below.

7. Convert 5.4 meters to millimeters.

(a) 8. How many miles are in 13,200 feet?

Answer each question below.

9. How far will a speed boat going 64 miles per hour travel in $2\frac{1}{2}$ hours?

10. How far will a spider crawling at 2 inches per second travel in 25 seconds?

Tell which of each pair of numbers below is greater.

11. 3 and -4

(b) 12. $-\dfrac{1}{4}$ and $-\dfrac{1}{2}$

Add each pair of numbers below.

13. $-7+(-4)$ 14. $6+(-13)$ 15. $-3+(-3)+(-3)$

Subtract each pair of numbers below.

16. $6-(-2)$ (c) 17. $-2-(-5)$ (d) 18. $-4-15$

Solve each equation below by undoing.

19. $\dfrac{1}{2}+x=1\dfrac{1}{2}$ 20. $13x=351$ 21. $x-91.8=125.4$

Translate the word problem below into an equation; then solve.

(e) 22. Mr. Noonan opened up a college savings account for his daughter at the local bank. He put $8,000 in the account, which pays 5% in yearly interest.

     i.) How much will Mr. Noonan have earned in interest one year from now?

     ii.) If he leaves his money and interest in the bank for another year, how much interest will he earn for the 2nd year?

Lesson 82—Multiplication with Negatives

Now that we've covered addition and subtraction with negatives, it's time to talk about multiplication. Just like in the last lesson, we'll learn the rules first; then we'll look at why they work.

Signs are Different

Here's our first example.

$$(2)(-5)$$

The important thing to notice here is that we have a positive times a negative. The signs of the numbers being multiplied are different, in other words. Here's how we handle problems like this. The first step is to multiply the numbers without paying any attention to the signs. So for our example of $(2)(-5)$, we forget for a minute that the 5 is negative and just multiply 2 and 5.

$$(2)(5) = 10$$

This isn't the final answer, though. We still have one more step. Since the numbers being multiplied have opposite signs, we make the answer negative.

$$(2)(-5) = -10$$

Our answer, then, is -10.

Let's do another one.

$$(-4)(3)$$

We have a negative times a positive, which means the two numbers have different signs again. So our first step is to multiply not paying attention to the signs.

$$(4)(3) = 12$$

Next, since the signs are opposite, we make the answer negative.

$$(-4)(3) = -12$$

The answer to this one is -12. Are you getting the idea? When the signs of the two numbers being multiplied are different, the answer will *always* be negative.

Signs are the Same

What about when the signs are the same? Here's an example like that.

$$(-2)(-7)$$

Even though this time, two negatives are being multiplied, the first step is still to multiply the numbers not paying attention to the signs.

$$(2)(7) = 14$$

But since the signs are the same, we have to make the answer positive.

$$(-2)(-7) = 14$$

In fact, it turns out, that the answer to a multiplication where both signs are the same will *always* be positive.

There's one last case we should show you, even though it's an obvious one. When both numbers are positive, the answer is always positive. For instance, in 5×6 both the 5 and 6 are positive, which is why the answer is positive 30 (but you already knew that!)

$$(5)(6) = 30$$

The main point is that even this simple example fits with our rules for multiplying with negatives. When the signs are different, the answer is always negative. And when the signs are the same, the answer is always positive. And that's true even in a simple case like 5×6.

Here are the official rules for multiplication with negatives.

Multiplying with Negatives

negative × positive = negative
positive × negative = negative
negative × negative = positive
positive × positive = positive

Why It Works: Positive x Negative

Now that we've covered the rules, let's talk about why they work. Let's go back to the example $(2)(-5)$. Think for a second about what multiplication really means. When we multiply two positive numbers in arithmetic, like $(2)(5)$, that's the same as adding 5 two times.

$$(2)(5) = 5 + 5$$

Since $5 + 5$ equals 10, $(2)(5)$ also equals 10. So multiplication is just a short way to write a number added to itself several times. If the example had been $(3)(5)$, the answer would have been $5 + 5 + 5$, or 15.

But now it's easy to see why $(2)(-5)$ has to equal -10. It's because $(2)(-5)$ is just -5 added two times, or $-5 + -5$ and we know that equals -10.

$$(2)(-5) = -5 + -5 = -10$$

The same thing happens anytime we have a positive times a negative, no matter what numbers are involved. It's always like adding a negative number to itself several times (a loss plus a loss plus a loss, and so on). Take the example of $(3)(-2)$. That's the same as $-2 + (-2) + (-2)$, and we know that adds up to -6.

Or look at the example of $(-8)(2)$. The negative comes first this time, but don't let that throw you off. Remember, we can always switch the order of numbers that are multiplied. So let's think of $(-8)(2)$ as $(2)(-8)$. That tells us that $(-8)(2) = -8 + (-8)$, which equals -16.

Finally, let's look at one more problem: $(4)(-6)$. This is the same as -6 added 4 times, or $-6 + -6 + -6 + -6$, and that comes out to -24.

So a negative times a positive (or a positive times a negative) must always have a negative answer, because it's really just a negative added to itself over and over again. And that always has to come out negative.

Why It Works: Negative x Negative

What about a negative times a negative? Why does that rule work? This one's a little more difficult to explain. We can think of a negative times a negative as taking away a negative number several times. Take the example $(-2)(-7)$. We can't think of this as adding -7 two times because -2 isn't the same as 2. But we can think of it as taking away -7 twice. If we take away a loss of 7 twice, we're 14 better off. That's why a negative times a negative equals a positive. That may not be a very satisfying explanation, but it's the best one there is.

Practice 82

a. Add $-\dfrac{2}{3} + \left(-\dfrac{1}{3}\right)$.

b. Subtract $29 - (-33)$.

c. Multiply $(-4)(8)$.

d. Multiply $(-2)(-6)$.

e. Translate the word problem below into an equation; then solve.

Dave wants to buy a classic leather flight jacket that is being sold for $60 less than the normal price. If the jacket normally costs $300, by what percent is it being discounted? (The answer to your equation will be a decimal. Don't forget to convert it to a percent.)

Problem Set 82

Tell whether each sentence below is True or False.

1. When multiplying with negatives, if the signs are different, the answer is always negative.

2. When multiplying with negatives, if the signs are the same, the answer is always positive.

Multiply or divide each pair of numbers below. Write any remainders in decimal form.

3. $\begin{array}{r} 3.9 \\ \times 7.5 \\ \hline \end{array}$

4. $0.6\overline{)83.5}$

Add or subtract each pair of fractions below. Make sure your answers are fully reduced.

5. $\dfrac{4}{12} + \dfrac{3}{4}$

6. $\dfrac{2}{3} - \dfrac{1}{7}$

Convert each percent below into decimal form.

7. 32%

8. $54\dfrac{1}{8}\%$

Answer each question below.

9. What is $\dfrac{5}{9}$ of 351?   **10.** What is $\dfrac{1}{2}$ of $\dfrac{1}{4}$?

Add each pair of numbers below.

11. $-17+(-25)$ **12.** $-11+15$ **(a) 13.** $-\dfrac{3}{4}+\left(-\dfrac{1}{4}\right)$

Subtract each pair of numbers below.

14. $-9-7$ **15.** $-12-(-6)$ **(b) 16.** $32-(-41)$

Multiply each pair of numbers below.

17. $(+6)(-4)$ **(c) 18.** $(-5)(7)$ **(d) 19.** $(-3)(-9)$

Solve each equation below by undoing.

20. $x+4.7=16.3$ **21.** $31x=589$ **22.** $\dfrac{x}{\frac{2}{5}}=\dfrac{10}{11}$

Translate the word problem below into an equation; then solve.

(e) 23. Suzy wants to buy a Navy pea coat that is being sold for $30 less than the normal price. If the coat normally costs $75, by what percent is it being discounted? (The answer to your equation will be a decimal. Don't forget to convert it to a percent.)

Lesson 83—Division with Negatives

So far, we've talked about addition, subtraction, and multiplication with negatives. But we still have division left. The good news is that dividing with negatives is incredibly easy, once you know how to multiply with negatives. That's because the rules are exactly the same. Specifically, when dividing with negatives, if the signs of the numbers are different, the answer is negative, and if the signs of the numbers are the same, the answer is positive.

Some people actually write the division rules this way, as fractions.

Dividing with Negatives

$\dfrac{negative}{positive}$ = negative	$\dfrac{positive}{negative}$ = negative
$\dfrac{negative}{negative}$ = positive	$\dfrac{positive}{positive}$ = positive

Signs are Different

Now let's go through some examples to make sure you can actually use these rules. We'll start with -25 divided by $+5$.

$$\frac{-25}{+5}$$

Here we have a negative divided by a positive, and since the signs are different, we know that the answer has to be negative. The first step, though, is to divide the numbers not paying attention to their signs.

$$\frac{25}{5} = 5$$

Now we make the answer negative, which gives us a final answer of -5.

$$\frac{-25}{+5} = -5$$

Let's try another one.

$$\frac{18}{-6}$$

415

This time, the negative is on the bottom and the positive is on the top. But the signs are still different, so we know the answer has to be negative again. To do the calculation, we first divide the numbers not paying attention to their signs.

$$\frac{18}{6} = 3$$

Then we make the answer negative.

$$\frac{18}{-6} = -3$$

That's all there is to it.

Signs are the Same

Now let's do a negative divided by another negative.

$$\frac{-42}{-7}$$

Notice that the signs are the same, which means that the answer has to be positive. But, as always, we start by dividing the numbers not paying attention to their signs.

$$\frac{42}{7} = 6$$

Now since the signs are the same, we make sure the answer is positive, which leaves us with 6.

$$\frac{-42}{-7} = 6$$

We don't need to go through an example of a positive divided by a positive. That's just basic arithmetic. But following our rules, the answer has to be positive because the signs are the same.

Why It Works

Now let's talk about why these rules for division work. Think about how we come up with the answer to a simple division problem, like $\frac{72}{9}$. What we usually do is ask ourselves, "9 times what number equals 72?" Since 9×8 equals 72, then $\dfrac{72}{9} = 8$. In other words, we often figure out division problems using our knowledge of multiplication.

But now let's go through the same process on a division with a negative. Here's one.

$$\frac{-24}{8}$$

We start by asking, "8 times what number equals -24?" Since a positive times a negative equals a negative, 8 has to be multiplied by a *negative* number to get -24, and that number turns out to be -3.

$$\frac{-24}{8} = -3$$

This also works when the negative is on bottom. Let's do one like that.

$$\frac{14}{-7}$$

First, we ask the question, "-7 times what number equals $+14$?" Since a negative times a negative equals a positive, -7 has to be multiplied by *negative* 2 to get $+14$. So -2 is the answer.

$$\frac{14}{-7} = -2$$

This way of thinking will also explain why a negative divided by a negative has to be positive. Here's an example.

$$\frac{-15}{-3}$$

Again, we start with the question, "-3 times what number equals -15?" Since a negative times a positive equals a negative, -3 has to be multiplied by *positive* 5 to get -15. So that explains why 5 is the answer.

$$\frac{-15}{-3} = 5$$

The main point of the lesson is that the rules for dividing with negatives are the same as those for multiplying with negatives: If the signs are different the answer is negative, and if the signs are the same, the answer is positive.

Practice 83

a. How many square yards are in 2,700 square feet?

b. Subtract $\dfrac{5}{7} - \left(-\dfrac{1}{7}\right)$.

c. Divide $\dfrac{63}{-7}$.

d. Divide $\dfrac{-30}{-5}$.

e. Translate the word problem below into an equation; then solve.

Mr. Morris would probably be the most boring man on Earth were it not for his eclectic collection of tweed driving caps, which he usually purchases on his trips to England. On his last trip, he bought 8 caps, spending a total of $167.60. What was the average price of each cap?

Problem Set 83

Tell whether each sentence below is True or False.

1. When dividing with negatives, if the signs are different, the answer is always negative.

2. When dividing with negatives, if the signs are the same, the answer is always positive.

Add or subtract each group of numbers below.

3.
$$\begin{array}{r} 8,060 \\ +\,9,127 \\ \hline \end{array}$$

4.
$$\begin{array}{r} 659.25 \\ -\,296.75 \\ \hline \end{array}$$

Multiply or divide each pair of numbers below. Make sure your answers are fully reduced.

5. $24 \cdot \dfrac{7}{8}$

6. $\dfrac{8}{9} \div 16$

Do each unit conversion below.

7. Convert 8 kilometers to hectometers.

(a) 8. How many square yards are in 1,800 square feet?

Add each pair of numbers below.

9. $-9+(-14)$

10. $82+(-57)$

Subtract each pair of numbers below.

11. $7-(-7)$

12. $-13-5$

(b) 13. $\dfrac{3}{5}-\left(-\dfrac{1}{5}\right)$

Multiply each pair of numbers below.

14. $(6)(-9)$

15. $(-12)(+5)$

16. $(-7)(-4)$

Divide each pair of numbers below.

17. $\dfrac{-36}{+6}$

(c) 18. $\dfrac{56}{-7}$

(d) 19. $\dfrac{-40}{-8}$

Solve each equation below by undoing.

20. $\dfrac{3}{5}+x=1\dfrac{1}{5}$

21. $9x=2{,}052$

22. $\dfrac{x}{21.8}=5.3$

Translate the word problem below into an equation; then solve.

(e) 23. Katy loves shoes, especially velvet slippers with embroidered patterns. On her last trip to Paris, she bought 5 pairs of these slippers, spending a total of $328.75. What was the average price of each pair of slippers?

Lesson 84—Undoing Equations with Negatives—Part 1

Now that we've learned how to add, subtract, multiply, and divide with negatives, it's time to talk about how to handle negatives in equations. This is important, because after all, if we're going to use negatives to solve real problems, they're bound to pop up in equations. We'll start by learning how to undo some simple equations that have negatives in them.

Undoing a Subtracted Negative

Here's our first example.

$$x - (-3) = 8$$

Notice that a negative number is being subtracted from x. How do we undo this? There are actually two methods. One method is just to add the very same number, in this case -3, to both sides.

$$x - (-3) + (-3) = 8 + (-3)$$

The addition undoes the subtraction on the left side, leaving x.

$$x = 8 + (-3)$$

That's turned our algebra equation into a simple arithmetic equation. From here, all we have to do is add on the right. A gain of 8 added to a loss of 3 is equal to a gain of 5.

$$x = 5$$

So our answer is 5.

A Faster Method

But there's another, easier method for undoing $x - (-3) = 8$. Remember that subtraction is the same as adding the opposite. For instance, $10 - (-3)$ is the same as $10 + 3$, That's how we always subtract negatives. But we can use this fact to change the left side of the equation *before* undoing. Since subtracting is the same as adding the opposite, we can change the subtraction of -3 to an addition of $+3$. In other words, $x - (-3) = 8$ can be changed to $x + (+3) = 8$, which is just the same as $x + 3 = 8$.

$$x - (-3) = 8 \quad \Longrightarrow \quad x + (+3) = 8 \quad \Longrightarrow \quad x + 3 = 8$$

Now the equation is really easy to undo. No more negatives to worry about. We just have to subtract 3 from both sides.

$$x + 3 - 3 = 8 - 3$$

The left side equals x, because the subtraction undoes the addition, leaving us with

$$x = 8 - 3.$$

Finally, we subtract on the right to get the answer.

$$x = 5$$

And it's the same answer we got before. But it was much simpler to undo because we didn't have to mess with negatives. So an easier method for undoing the subtraction of a negative is just to change the subtraction to an addition of the opposite (a positive) first. Then undo normally. You can use this method every time.

Undoing an Added Negative

Here's another example of a negative in an equation.

$$x + (-5) = 7$$

This time, we have a negative number added to x. How do we undo this one? Again, there are two methods. The first one is just to undo the addition by subtracting the same number, -5, from both sides.

$$x + (-5) - (-5) = 7 - (-5)$$

The equation looks pretty messy now, but it's really not that hard. The subtraction of -5 undoes the addition of -5, leaving just x on the left.

$$x = 7 - (-5)$$

To do the calculation on the right, we can change subtraction to addition of the opposite (Remember, we always subtract with negatives this way.) That gives us this.

$$x = 7 + 5$$

Now, all that's left is to add 7 and 5 on the right side.

$$x = 12$$

So the first method is the same one we've always used to undo addition: just subtract the very same number from both sides.

The Simpler Approach

But there's another, easier method for undoing $x+(-5)=7$. Instead of subtracting negative 5 from both sides, we add a positive 5 to both sides. This may seem weird, but just watch.

$$x+(-5)+5=7+5$$

On the left side, we have $-5+5$. Think about it. That just equals 0, doesn't it? So the left side becomes $x+0$ or just x.

$$x+0=7+5 \quad \longrightarrow \quad x=7+5$$

Now x is by itself, which is exactly what we wanted! We undid the addition of -5 with the addition of $+5$. In other words, instead of undoing the addition with a subtraction, we were able to undo it with another addition. From here, all we have left is to add 7 and 5 on the right.

$$x=12$$

That gives us 12 for the answer, which is exactly what we got before.

Why Adding the Opposite Works

Let's talk about why adding $+5$ to both sides worked. Here's the original equation again.

$$x+(-5)=7$$

Remember that subtraction and adding the opposite are the same thing. So instead of subtracting -5 from both sides, it's legal to add the opposite of -5 ($+5$) to both sides. Mathematically, the two are the same.

$$x+(-5)+5=7+5$$

The only difference is that adding 5 is easier, because notice that on the right side all we have to do is add 7 and 5, which is really simple. Doing it the other way forces us to subtract a negative on the right, which is a little harder. And the great thing is that any addition can be undone this way. Instead of subtracting the same number, we can always undo by adding the opposite.

Let's look at another example.

$$x+(-7)=3$$

We could undo this by subtracting -7 from both sides, but subtracting a negative is messy (and can even seem a little confusing). So instead, let's add $+7$ to both sides, like this.

$$x+(-7)+7=3+7$$

Since $-7+7$ equals 0, x is now by itself on the left side.

$$x = 3 + 7$$

Now all we need to do is add on the right, which leaves us with

$$x = 10.$$

Let's finish with one more example.

$$x + (-2) = 11$$

Again, we could undo the addition by subtracting -2 from both sides. But since that would involve subtracting a negative, it's easier to add $+2$ to both sides instead.

$$x + (-2) + 2 = 11 + 2$$

Because $-2 + 2$ is 0, we end up with x all by itself on the left.

$$x = 11 + 2$$

Next, we just add 11 and 2 to get an answer of 13.

$$x = 13$$

Get into the Habit

We can undo *any* addition by adding the opposite instead of subtracting, but there's no reason to get fancy when x just has a positive number added to it. For example, in an equation like $x + 3 = 9$, we could undo by adding -3 to both sides. But why bother? It's easier to subtract 3 from both sides instead. However, when a negative number is added to x, it is easier to undo by adding the opposite to both sides. So get in the habit of using the second method when x has a negative number added to it.

Practice 84

   a. Multiply $(-2.5)(8)$.
   b. Divide $\dfrac{-171}{-3}$.

   c. Solve the equation $x - (-6) = 22$.

   d. Solve the equation $x + (-12) = 15$.

e.   Translate the word problem below into an equation; then solve.

The young newlyweds decided to explore the countryside together on a two-seater bike. If they traveled 7 hours for a total of 98 miles, how fast did they go in miles per hour?

Problem Set 84

Tell whether each sentence below is True or False.

1.   It is easier to undo in the equation $x-(-5)=11$ if you change the subtraction of -5 to addition of $+5$ first.

2.   Another method for undoing addition in the equation $x+(-4)=9$ is to add $+4$ to both sides.

Multiply or divide each pair of numbers below. Write any remainders in decimal form.

3.
$$\begin{array}{r} 9.24 \\ \times 3.7 \\ \hline \end{array}$$

4. $5\overline{)2,596}$

Add or subtract each pair of fractions below. Make sure your answers are fully reduced.

5. $\dfrac{2}{10}+\dfrac{3}{5}$

6. $\dfrac{5}{6}-\dfrac{1}{9}$

Convert each fraction below into decimal form. Give exact answers (no rounding).

7. $\dfrac{1}{18}$

8. $\dfrac{2}{15}$

Add each pair of numbers below.

9. $-12+(-37)$

10. $26+(-26)$

Subtract each pair of numbers below.

11. $19-(-52)$

12. $-31-(-29)$

Multiply each pair of numbers below.

13. $(10)(-8)$

14. $(-1)(-14)$

(a) 15. $(-3.5)(6)$

Divide each pair of numbers below.

16. $\dfrac{-50}{5}$

17. $\dfrac{60}{-12}$

(b) 18. $\dfrac{-118}{-2}$

Solve each equation below by undoing.

19. $35x = 420$

20. $\dfrac{x}{3} = \dfrac{7}{9}$

(c) 21. $x - (-9) = 24$

(d) 22. $x + (-11) = 13$

Translate the word problem below into an equation; then solve.

(e) 23. The lonely hitchhiker has walked 187 hours for a total of 374 miles, how fast is he going in miles per hour?

Lesson 85—Undoing Equations with Negatives—Part 2

In the last lesson, we learned how to undo equations where negative numbers were added to and subtracted from x. In this lesson, we'll learn how to undo when x has been multiplied or divided by a negative.

x Divided by a Negative

We'll start with a division example.

$$\frac{x}{-3} = 7$$

This one is probably easier than you think. There are no new rules or shortcuts to learn, and there's just one method. All we have to do is multiply both sides by -3, like this.

$$(-3)\left(\frac{x}{-3}\right) = (7)(-3)$$

The multiplication undoes the division on the left, leaving x by itself on one side.

$$x = (7)(-3)$$

The last step is to do the multiplication on the right. Since a positive times a negative is a negative, we know the answer has to be -21.

$$x = -21$$

Believe it or not, that's all there is to know about undoing division by a negative.

x Multiplied by a Negative

Now let's go through an example where x is multiplied by a negative.

$$-2x = -12$$

The good news is that there's really nothing new to learn here either. We just undo the multiplication by dividing both sides by -2.

$$\frac{-2x}{-2} = \frac{-12}{-2}$$

It's the same thing we've always done when undoing multiplication. The division undoes the multiplication on the left, leaving us with this.

$$x = \frac{-12}{-2}$$

Now we divide on the right. Since a negative divided by a negative is a positive, the answer is 6.

$$x = 6$$

So when it comes to undoing equations where x is multiplied or divided by a negative number, we use exactly the same methods we covered earlier (for positive numbers).

Practice 85

a. Divide $\dfrac{-72}{-6}$.

b. Solve the equation $x - (-13) = -14$.

c. Solve the equation $-7x = 91$.

d. Solve the equation $\dfrac{x}{-3} = -15$.

e. Translate the word problem below into an equation; then solve.

In a recent poll, 28% of the lifeguards who were surveyed said they thought body surfing should be an Olympic sport. If 126 lifeguards gave this response, how many were surveyed in total?

Problem Set 85

Add or subtract each group of numbers below.

1.
$$\begin{array}{r} 0.465 \\ + 0.829 \\ \hline \end{array}$$

2.
$$\begin{array}{r} 18.54 \\ - 9.92 \\ \hline \end{array}$$

Multiply or divide each pair of fractions below. Make sure your answers are fully reduced.

3. $\dfrac{2}{3} \cdot \dfrac{9}{24}$

4. $\dfrac{10}{12} \div \dfrac{5}{8}$

Answer each question below.

5. How far will a tank moving at 18 miles per hour travel in 6 hours?

6. How far will a satellite orbiting at 1,000 miles per hour travel in 12 hours?

Add each pair of numbers below.

7. $-11+(-29)$ **8.** $0+(-100)$

Subtract each pair of numbers below.

9. $7-(-3)$ **10.** $-9-13$

Multiply each pair of numbers below.

11. $(1)(-94)$ **12.** $(-6)(13)$ **13.** $(-2)(-52)$

Divide each pair of numbers below.

14. $\dfrac{-27}{9}$ **15.** $\dfrac{112}{-8}$ **(a) 16.** $\dfrac{-84}{-4}$

Solve each equation below by undoing.

17. $x+(-2)=9$ **(b) 18.** $x-(-17)=-18$ **(c) 19.** $-5x=95$

(d) 20. $\dfrac{x}{-4}=-12$

Translate the word problem below into an equation; then solve.

(e) 21. In a recent poll, 32% of the referees who were surveyed said that ejecting angry coaches was their favorite thing to do. If 152 referees gave this response, how many were surveyed in total?

Lesson 86—Negatives and Fractions

In the last lesson, we learned how to undo equations where x is multiplied by a negative number. Our example was $-2x = -12$. And, remember, after undoing we ended up with $x = \dfrac{-12}{-2}$. That made things pretty easy, since -12 can be divided evenly by -2 (to get 6). But sometimes, when undoing a multiplication of a negative, we end up with a division that doesn't come out even. In this lesson we'll learn how to deal with that.

Converting to a Decimal

For starters, take a look at this example.

$$-5x = 3$$

We know how to undo the multiplication by -5: we just divide both sides by -5.

$$\frac{-5x}{-5} = \frac{3}{-5}$$

The division undoes the multiplication on the left side, leaving x by itself.

$$x = \frac{3}{-5}$$

But this is where it gets a little tricky. On the right side, -5 won't go into 3 evenly. How should we write the answer? There are actually two ways we could go about it. The first is to convert the answer into a decimal. To do that we ignore the signs and divide 5 into 3 with long division to get 0.6. Then, to figure out the sign of the answer, we use the rule that says a positive divided by a negative equals a negative. That gives us an answer of -0.6.

$$x = \frac{3}{-5} = -0.6$$

That's how we convert fractions with negatives into decimals. We first use long division (which is the normal way of converting fractions to decimals), and then apply the rules for dividing negatives to figure out the sign of the decimal answer.

Leaving it as a Fraction

The second way of dealing with $\dfrac{3}{-5}$ is to leave it as a fraction. But we have to do something about that negative sign in the bottom. If we want the answer to be a fraction, we have to figure out the sign of the *entire* fraction. And that requires us to use the rules for dividing negative numbers again. The fraction $\dfrac{3}{-5}$ is a positive divided by a negative, which we know must equal a negative. So we write the answer like this.

$$x = -\frac{3}{5}$$

Positive divided by negative equals negative

In other words, we take the negative sign from the 5 and put it in front of the entire fraction, since we know that a positive divided by a negative equals a negative.

In fact, any time you have a fraction with a negative number in either the top or the bottom, you should figure out the sign of the entire fraction. For example, what if the answer to our equation had been $\dfrac{-3}{5}$? Now there's a negative on top and a positive on bottom. Again we just need to use the rules for dividing negatives. A negative divided by a positive equals a negative. So, just as in the last example, we should put the negative sign out in front of the entire fraction.

$$\frac{-3}{5} = -\frac{3}{5}$$

Negative divided by positive equals negative

What if the fraction had a negative in both the top *and* the bottom?

$$\frac{-3}{-5}$$

We still need to find the sign of the entire fraction. Applying the rules for dividing negatives, we know that a negative divided by a negative equals a positive. That means $\dfrac{-3}{-5}$ is actually equal to $+\dfrac{3}{5}$. But we really don't need the positive sign in front, because everybody knows that $+\dfrac{3}{5}$ is the same as $\dfrac{3}{5}$.

$$\frac{-3}{-5} = \frac{3}{5}$$

Negative divided by negative equals positive

Let's quickly go back over all the different possibilities for signs in fractions, so you won't forget them. Actually, we never went over the first case—a positive divided by a positive—because you already know that it equals a positive. Here are all four possibilities.

Negatives in Fractions

$$\frac{+3}{+5} = +\frac{3}{5} \qquad \frac{+3}{-5} = -\frac{3}{5}$$

$$\frac{-3}{+5} = -\frac{3}{5} \qquad \frac{-3}{-5} = +\frac{3}{5}$$

The main point is that when the answer to an equation is a division that doesn't come out even, you have two options. You can convert the answer into a decimal and then use the rules for dividing with negatives to figure out what the sign of the decimal should be. Or you can leave the answer as a fraction. But you'll still need to figure out the sign of the entire fraction by using the rules for dividing with negatives.

Practice 86

a. How many cubic inches are in 16 cubic feet?

b. Tell whether $\frac{-5}{8}$ and $-\frac{5}{8}$ are equivalent.

c. Solve the equation $x - (-5) = -11.2$.

d. Solve the equation $x + (-81) = -157$.

e. Translate the word problem below into an equation; then solve.

Phil and Leslie spent all of Saturday on their new motorboat. If they traveled 9 hours for a total of 144 miles, how fast did they go in miles per hour?

Problem Set 86

Multiply or divide each pair of numbers below. Write any remainders in decimal form.

1. $\begin{array}{r} 58.2 \\ \times\,4.9 \\ \hline \end{array}$

2. $15\overline{)38{,}925}$

Add or subtract each pair of fractions below. Make sure your answers are fully reduced.

3. $\dfrac{7}{8}+\dfrac{3}{4}$

4. $\dfrac{6}{5}-\dfrac{2}{3}$

Do each unit conversion below.

5. Convert 14 gallons to quarts.

(a) 6. How many cubic inches are in 14 cubic feet?

Add each pair of numbers below.

7. $-92+(-37)$

8. $-11+75$

Subtract each pair of numbers below.

9. $-13-8$

10. $24-(-16)$

Multiply each pair of numbers below.

11. $(-7)(13)$

12. $(-5)(-19)$

Divide each pair of numbers below.

13. $\dfrac{21}{-7}$

14. $\dfrac{-84}{-12}$

Tell whether each of the following pairs of fractions is equivalent.

(b) 15. $\dfrac{-7}{9}$ and $-\dfrac{7}{9}$ **16.** $\dfrac{-2}{-3}$ and $\dfrac{2}{3}$

Solve each equation below by undoing.

(c) 17. $x - (-8) = -15.6$ **18.** $\dfrac{x}{-12} = 34$ **19.** $19x = 209$

(d) 20. $x + (-73) = -141$

Translate the word problem below into an equation; then solve.

(e) 21. Bill lost his bet with his buddy Tom. As a result, Bill now has to drive all the way back from the stadium to his house with the score of the game emblazoned in shoe polish on his back windshield. If Bill drives 11 hours for a total of 715 miles, how fast will he be traveling in miles per hour?

Lesson 87—Handling a -x

Here's an equation that we learned how to solve a while ago.

$$5.8 + x = 26.3$$

Notice that the x isn't in its usual place on the far left. Remember, we've been handling these situations by switching $5.8 + x$ to $x + 5.8$.

$$x + 5.8 = 26.3$$

That's perfectly legal, of course. There's a basic rule of arithmetic (the commutative property of addition), which allows us to add two numbers in any order. But by moving the x to the far left, where we're used to seeing it, the equation is easier to undo.

Now check out this equation.

$$8.1 - x = 13.7$$

The x is on the inside again. And it would be nice to move it to the left to make this equation easier to undo. The problem is that we can't switch the order of numbers that are subtracted. Switching only works for addition and multiplication, remember.

Flipping Around a Subtraction

So what do we do in a case like this? We just use our knowledge of negative numbers. Since any subtraction can be changed to an addition of the opposite, and the opposite of x is $-x$, we can change $8.1 - x$ to $8.1 + (-x)$.

$$8.1 - x = 13.7 \qquad \longrightarrow \qquad 8.1 + (-x) = 13.7$$

Now the left side is an addition, which means that the order *can* be switched to get $-x$ on the far left.

$$-x + 8.1 = 13.7$$

From here, we can undo the addition in the usual way, by subtracting 8.1 from both sides.

$$-x + 8.1 - 8.1 = 13.7 - 8.1$$

That makes the left side equal to $-x$.

$$-x = 13.7 - 8.1$$

Next, we subtract on the right.

$$-x = 5.6$$

Changing a -x to x

Are we done? No, not yet. We have $-x$ on the left, but that's not what we're looking for. We need the value of plain old x. So we have to get rid of the negative sign on the x. It's not as hard as it might seem. All we have to do is multiply $-x$ by -1. To see why this works, take a close look at these multiplications.

$$(-1)(-2) = +2 \qquad (-1)(+8) = -8$$

$$(-1)(-4) = +4 \qquad (-1)(+10) = -10$$

See the pattern? A -1 multiplied by any number equals the number's opposite. That's always true, because of the rules for multiplying with negatives. So using this rule, we can change $-x$ to its opposite, which is just x. But we have to remember to avoid violating the golden rule. In other words, if we multiply one side of the equation by -1 we have to multiply the other side by -1 too.

$$(-1)(-x) = (-1)(5.6)$$

The left side is now a plain x, which is exactly what we wanted. The right side is -5.6, which is our final answer.

$$x = -5.6$$

The main thing to remember is that we can get rid of a $-x$ in an equation by multiplying both sides by -1.

Checking a Negative Answer

There's one more important point we need to cover: how to check a negative answer to an equation. To show you how it works, let's check -5.6. We need to put -5.6 back in for x in the original equation. Here's the original equation again.

$$8.1 - x = 13.7$$

But the best way to put a negative answer back in is to put parentheses around it, like this.

$$8.1 - (-5.6) = 13.7$$

The parentheses help us to remember the negative sign on the 5.6. Without the parentheses, it's easy to confuse the minus sign and the negative sign. We might end up leaving out the negative sign and just writing $8.1 - 5.6 = 13.7$, which is wrong. That's putting positive 5.6 in for x. So always put parentheses around a negative number when putting it in for x to check an answer. To finish the checking process, though, we just calculate the value of the left side by changing the subtraction to addition of the opposite and then adding. Since both sides end up equal, -5.6 is correct.

$$8.1 - (-5.6) = 13.7$$

$$8.1 + 5.6 = 13.7$$

$$13.7 = 13.7$$

Practice 87

a. Tell whether $9 - x$ and $-x + 9$ are equivalent.

b. Tell whether $(-1)(-y)$ and y are equivalent.

c. Solve the equation $3.5 - x = 17.6$.

d. Solve the equation $-4 - x = 16$.

e. Translate the word problem below into an equation; then solve.

John just bought the woman of his dreams an engagement ring for $720 less than the normal price. If the ring normally costs $2,400, by what percent is it being discounted? (The answer to your equation will be a decimal. Don't forget to convert it to a percent.)

Problem Set 87

Tell whether each sentence below is True or False.

1. To change a $-x$ to x in an equation, multiply both sides by -1.

2. It's best to put parentheses around a negative number when putting it in for an x in an equation.

Add or subtract each group of numbers below.

3. $\begin{array}{r} 82,216 \\ + 29,253 \\ \hline \end{array}$

4. $\begin{array}{r} 4,073 \\ - 2,869 \\ \hline \end{array}$

Multiply or divide each pair of numbers below. Make sure your answers are fully reduced.

5. $\dfrac{3}{14} \cdot \dfrac{7}{9}$

6. $24 \div \dfrac{3}{5}$

Add each pair of numbers below.

7. $-107 + (-113)$ **8.** $25 + (-94)$

Subtract each pair of numbers below.

9. $-28 - (-17)$ **10.** $-32 - 9$

Multiply each pair of numbers below.

11. $(-1)(10)$ **12.** $(47)(-8)$

Divide each pair of numbers below.

13. $\dfrac{-140}{70}$ **14.** $\dfrac{-36}{-4}$

Tell whether each pair of expressions below is equivalent.

(a) 15. $7 - x$ and $-x + 7$ **(b) 16.** $(-1)(-x)$ and x

Solve each equation below by undoing.

17. $\dfrac{3}{5}x = \dfrac{7}{10}$ **(c) 18.** $2.5 - x = 19.3$ **19.** $\dfrac{x}{4.1} = -6$

(d) 20. $-3 - x = 12$ **21.** $\dfrac{x}{\frac{3}{4}} = 12$

Translate the word problem below into an equation; then solve.

(e) 22. John thought that after he bought the woman of his dreams that beautiful engagement ring (see practice problem e) she would surely say "Yes." She didn't. Now John plans (mistakenly) to win her charms by buying her a diamond necklace too! If the necklace is being sold for $600 less than the normal price of $1,500, by what percent is it being discounted? (The answer to your equation will be a decimal. Don't forget to convert it to a percent.)

Lesson 88—Dealing with –x in a Fraction

We can change $-x$ to x by multiplying both sides of an equation by -1. But what if $-x$ is inside a fraction in an equation? Here's a problem like that.

$$\frac{-x}{7.9} = -1.5$$

There are two basic ways to handle this situation.

Multiplying by -1

The first method is just to undo the division by multiplying both sides by 7.9.

$$(7.9)\left(\frac{-x}{7.9}\right) = (7.9)(-1.5)$$

That leaves $-x$ on the left.

$$-x = (7.9)(-1.5)$$

On the right side, we have a positive multiplied by a negative, which equals a negative. So the right side becomes -11.85.

$$-x = -11.85$$

But -11.85 isn't the answer to the equation. We're not trying to find $-x$; we need just plain x. As we learned in the last lesson, though, $-x$ can be changed to x by multiplying both sides by -1.

$$(-1)(-x) = (-1)(-11.85)$$

That makes the left side plain x and the right side turns out to be 11.85, which is our final answer.

$$x = 11.85$$

So the first method for dealing with a $-x$ in a fraction is to undo normally. We'll end up with a $-x$ on one side, which we can get rid of by multiplying both sides by -1 at the end.

Moving the Sign

The other method for eliminating a $-x$ inside a fraction is to use the rules for dividing negatives. To show you how it works, let's go back to our original equation.

$$\frac{-x}{7.9} = -1.5$$

The fraction is a negative divided by a positive, which means that the whole fraction has to be negative. We could put a negative sign out in front of the entire fraction, if we wanted. But wouldn't a positive divided by a negative make the whole fraction negative too? Yes, it would. So why can't we move the negative sign from the x on top to the 7.9 on bottom?

$$\frac{x}{-7.9}$$

This is perfectly legal, because both $\frac{-x}{7.9}$ and $\frac{x}{-7.9}$ are the same as $-\frac{x}{7.9}$. Whether the negative is on the top or on the bottom, the value of the whole fraction is the same.

$$\frac{-x}{7.9} = \frac{x}{-7.9} = -\frac{x}{7.9}$$

Moving the negative sign to the bottom helps us because it gets rid of the $-x$. Now our equation looks like this.

$$\frac{x}{-7.9} = -1.5$$

From here, we can undo the division by multiplying both sides by -7.9.

$$(-7.9)\left(\frac{x}{-7.9}\right) = (-7.9)(-1.5)$$

That leaves us with just plain x on the left side, which is what we wanted.

$$x = (-7.9)(-1.5)$$

Finally, since a negative times a negative equals a positive, the answer comes out to 11.85. And that's the same thing we got using our first method.

$$x = 11.85$$

The main point is that there are two ways to undo an equation that has a $-x$ in a fraction. We can undo normally and then multiply both sides by -1, or we can move the negative sign to the other half of the fraction. Most people like the second method better, because you don't have to multiply both sides by -1.

Practice 88

a. Tell whether $\dfrac{-1}{-5}$ and $-\dfrac{1}{5}$ are equivalent.

b. Tell whether $\dfrac{-x}{3}$ and $\dfrac{x}{-3}$ are equivalent.

c. Solve the equation $\dfrac{-x}{15} = -8$.   **d.** Solve the equation $17 - x = -31$.

e. Translate the word problem below into an equation; then solve.

Mr. and Mrs. Thompson are trying to save enough money to go on an extended island vacation. They have already saved $800 but that is still not enough. If their $800 in savings is sitting in a bank account that pays 6% in yearly interest.

   i.) How much will Mr. and Mrs. Thompson have earned in interest one year from now?

   ii.) If they leave their money <u>and</u> interest in the bank for another year, how much interest will they earn for the 2nd year?

Problem Set 88

Multiply or divide each pair of numbers below. Write any remainders in decimal form.

1. $\begin{array}{r} 0.839 \\ \times 5.3 \\ \hline \end{array}$

2. $0.4\overline{)12.62}$

Add or subtract each pair of numbers below. Make sure your answers are fully reduced.

3. $\dfrac{3}{16} + \dfrac{7}{16}$

4. $2\dfrac{1}{5} - \dfrac{4}{5}$

Convert each percent below into decimal form.

5. 2.25%

6. $46\dfrac{1}{5}\%$

Add each pair of numbers below.

7. $-22+(-15)$ **8.** $-7+9$

Subtract each pair of numbers below.

9. $0-(-4)$ **10.** $-16-(-12)$

Multiply each pair of numbers below.

11. $(30)(-6)$ **12.** $(-14)(-19)$

Divide each pair of numbers below.

13. $\dfrac{33}{-3}$ **14.** $\dfrac{-56}{8}$

Tell whether each of the following pairs of expressions is equivalent.

(a) 15. $\dfrac{-1}{-4}$ and $-\dfrac{1}{4}$ **(b) 16.** $\dfrac{-x}{5}$ and $\dfrac{x}{-5}$

Solve each equation below by undoing.

17. $x+(-72)=-49$ **(c) 18.** $\dfrac{-x}{23}=-7$ **19.** $\dfrac{3}{7}x=27$

(d) 20. $14-x=-28$ **21.** $10.5x=131.25$

Translate the word problem below into an equation; then solve.

(e) 22. Mr. Macmillan opened up a college savings account for his son at the local bank. He put \$12,100 in the account, which pays 5% in yearly interest.

     i.) How much will Mr. Macmillan have earned in interest one year from now?

     ii.) If he leaves his money <u>and</u> interest in the bank for another year, how much interest will he earn for the 2nd year?

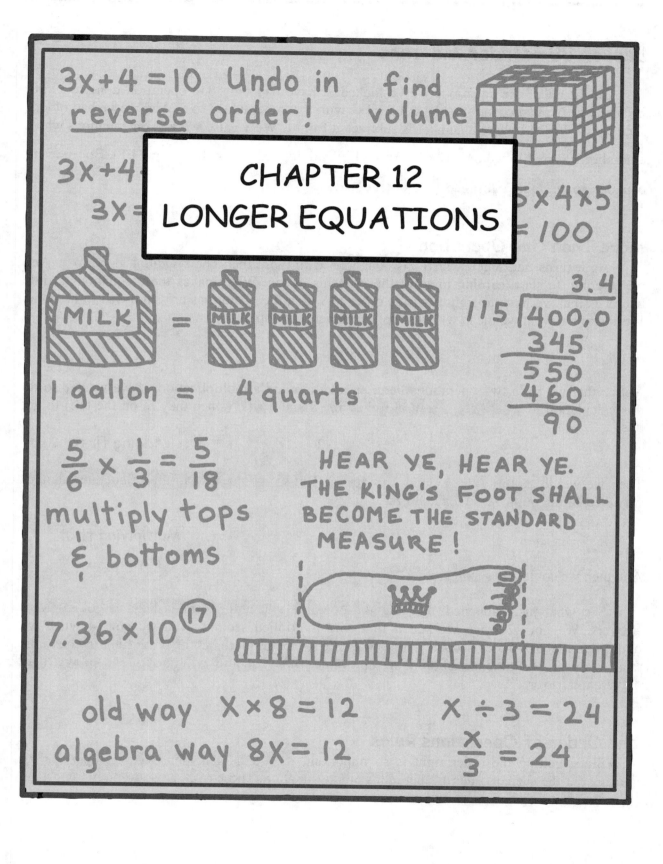

Lesson 89—Order Matters

So far all of the equations we've looked at have had only one operation done to x. For instance, we've had equations like $x+5=18$, with a number added to x. And we've had others, such as $x-7=29$, where a number is subtracted from x. We've also worked on equations where a number was multiplied by x (like $-3x=-12$) and divided into x (like $\frac{x}{6}=-4.1$). But in every equation so far, there's just been one operation done to x.

More Than One Operation

As it turns out, algebra also has equations with more than one operation done to x. And we're going to start learning to solve those in this lesson. What makes these equations a little harder is that we have to figure out the order in which the operations are supposed to be done. We'll explain what we mean with a simple arithmetic example.

$$8+3\cdot2$$

Notice that we have two operations here: an addition and a multiplication. If we wanted to do this calculation, it would seem natural to add the 8 and 3 first (since they're on the left) to get this.

$$11\cdot2 \qquad \textbf{Adding first}$$

Then we would multiply the 11 and 2 to get 22. But we could also do the calculation another way. We could multiply the 3 and 2 first.

$$8+6 \qquad \textbf{Multiplying first}$$

And then we could add second to get 14.

See what just happened? We did the operations in a different order and got different answers. We got 22 when we added first, and multiplied second. And we got 14 when we multiplied first and added second. This is why it's so important to get the order right in equations that have more than one operation. If we don't, the whole equation will be spoiled, and we'll get the wrong answer.

The Order of Operations Rules

Since getting the order right is so important, the mathematicians have set up rules for figuring out the correct order of operations in any situation. These rules are extremely important, so be sure to memorize them. Here they are.

Order of Operations Rules

1.	All multiplications and divisions are done first.
2.	All additions and subtractions are done second.
3.	If a different order is needed, the operations that are supposed to be done first must be put in parentheses.

Basically, here's what these rules mean. If we have a calculation that mixes multiplication and addition (like in our example) the multiplication should be done first. So according to the rules, the right way to calculate $8 + 3 \cdot 2$ is to multiply first, even though the multiplication is to the right of the addition, and it might feel unnatural. Doing this gives us $8 + 6$. The second step is to add the 8 and 6 to get 14. So 14 is the one and only correct answer, because of the rules for the order of operations. If we wanted to describe the meaning of $8 + 3 \cdot 2$ in words, we would say "multiply 3 and 2 *first*, and add the result to 8 *second*." The order of operations has to be included.

Using Parentheses

But what if we want the addition to be done first? Does multiplication always have to come before addition? Let's look again at our example.

$$8 + 3 \cdot 2$$

What do the order of operations rules tell us? Rule 3 says that if we want to change the usual order of multiplication first, addition second, we have to put parentheses around the addition. So if we want our problem to show that 8 and 3 should be added first, we would have to write it like this.

$$(8 + 3) \cdot 2 \qquad \textbf{Parentheses mean add first.}$$

The proper way to calculate $(8 + 3) \cdot 2$ is to add 8 and 3 first to get 11. Then we multiply 11 and 2 second to get 22. That's the only correct answer to this one. Those parentheses tell us that the addition has to be first. The meaning of $(8 + 3) \cdot 2$ in words is "add 8 and 3 first, and multiply the result by 2 second."

Subtraction Too

Here's an example with subtraction. Let's multiply 2 and 4, then subtract the total from 9. In this case multiplication is supposed to be first and subtraction second. To show the correct order, we should write it like this.

$$9 - 2 \cdot 4$$

According to the rules, unless there are parentheses, multiplication is always done before subtraction. So $9 - 2 \cdot 4$ means "multiply 2 and 4 first, then subtract the total from 9." Here's the actual calculation, which has an answer of 1.

$$9 - 2 \cdot 4 \quad \longrightarrow \quad 9 - 8 \quad \longrightarrow \quad 1$$

Let's do one more. Let's subtract 7 from 12 and then multiply that total by 5. The order of operations rules tell us that without parentheses we always do multiplication first. So to show that subtraction should be done before multiplication, we need to use rule 3 and put parentheses around the subtraction, like this.

$$(12 - 7) \cdot 5$$

Parentheses mean subtract first.

This means "do 12 − 7 first, then multiply the total by 5." Here's the complete calculation.

$$(12 - 7) \cdot 5 \quad \longrightarrow \quad 5 \cdot 5 \quad \longrightarrow \quad 25$$

The main point of this lesson is that when we're working with more than one operation, we have to make sure to do those operations in the correct order. And the mathematicians created rules for writing the order correctly. Once again, the rules are that multiplication and division are always done before addition and subtraction, unless the addition or subtraction is put inside parentheses.

Practice 89

a. Calculate the value of the expression $5 \cdot 3 + 6$.

b. Calculate the value of the expression $3(5 + 1)$.

c. Translate the following phrase into a mathematical expression: 5 and 6 multiplied together first, and then 4 added to that total. (Don't calculate the answer.)

d. Translate the following phrase into a mathematical expression: 2 and 7 added first, and that total multiplied by 4. (Don't calculate the answer.)

e. Translate the word problem below into an equation; then solve.

$$\frac{x}{100} = \frac{67}{80}$$

If Randy is driving at 25 miles per hour, how many hours will it take him to travel 20 miles? Round your answer to the nearest tenths place (one decimal place).

Problem Set 89

Tell whether each sentence below is True or False.

1. The first order of operations rule states: All multiplications and divisions are done first.

2. The second order of operations rule states: All additions and subtractions are done second.

3. The third order of operations rule states: If a different order is needed, the operations that are supposed to be first must be put inside parentheses.

Add or subtract each group of numbers below.

4.
$$\begin{array}{r} 68.24 \\ + 35.17 \\ \hline \end{array}$$

5.
$$\begin{array}{r} 53.49 \\ - 26.03 \\ \hline \end{array}$$

Do each unit conversion below.

6. Convert 28 yards to inches.

7. How many meters are in 125 decimeters?

Add each pair of numbers below.

8. $-\dfrac{1}{2} + \left(-\dfrac{1}{2}\right)$

9. $84 + (-49)$

Subtract each pair of numbers below.

10. $7 - (-15)$

11. $-63 - 71$

447

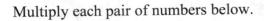

Multiply each pair of numbers below.

12. $(-21)(4)$ **13.** $(-7)(-5)$

Divide each pair of numbers below.

14. $\dfrac{-24}{8}$ **15.** $\dfrac{-63}{-9}$

Calculate the value of each expression below. (Make sure to do the operations in the correct order.)

(a) 16. $6 \cdot 2 + 7$ **(b) 17.** $2(3+4)$

Translate each of the following phrases into a mathematical expression. (Don't calculate the answer.)

(c) 18. 3 and 2 multiplied together first and then 5 added to that total.

(d) 19. 5 and 9 added first, and that total multiplied by 3.

Solve each equation below by undoing.

20. $x + (-10) = 24$ **21.** $\dfrac{5}{6}x = 20$ **22.** $\dfrac{-x}{12} = 9$

23. $-5 - x = -3$

Translate the word problem below into an equation; then solve.

(a) 24. If Brett is riding his mountain bike at 15 miles per hour, how many hours will it take him to travel 9 miles? Round your answer to the nearest tenths place (one decimal place).

Lesson 90—Writing Equations in Order

In the last lesson, we learned rules for the order of operations. But we kept things pretty simple and only worked with arithmetic problems, like $(12-7) \cdot 5$. Now we're going to apply the order of operations rules to real algebra equations.

Multiplication First

Here's our first example.

> There's some number that if we multiply it by 2 first, and then add 5 to the total we get 27. What's the number?

We need to translate this into an equation, and since we're trying to find the missing number, that's what x has to represent.

$$x = \text{missing number}$$

Notice the problem involves *two* operations—multiplication and addition—and that the multiplication is supposed to be done first. So we have to make the equation show that order. Let's start by just putting in the numbers and x. Then we'll figure out the right order of operations.

$$2x + 5 = 27$$

We have x multiplied by 2 and we have 5 added for a result of 27. Now what about the order? Is it right? Well, remember the rules. They say that multiplication is done before addition unless there are parentheses around the addition. Here we want multiplication to be first, because that's what the problem says. So there shouldn't be any parentheses in this equation. We've got it exactly right: $2x + 5 = 27$ means what we want it to mean. It says "If the missing number x is multiplied by 2 first and then 5 is added second, the result is equal to 27."

So when writing an equation for a problem with more than one operation, we have more to worry about than just getting the numbers and the x right. We have to get the order of operations right too. Otherwise the equation won't really represent the problem, and the answer will turn out wrong (even if we undo everything correctly).

Addition or Subtraction First

Let's try another one.

> There's some number that if we subtract 22 from it and then multiply that total by 7, the result is -42. What's the number?

To write the equation, we first let x stand for the missing number:

$x = $ missing number.

Since there are two operations (subtraction and multiplication), we have to make sure to get the order right. According to the problem, the subtraction is supposed to be done first. You may be wondering, though, how we were able to tell. Well, we had to read the problem carefully. It says "subtract 22 and *then* multiply." That little word "then" is what told us the subtraction comes first and the multiplication second. Another clue was the phrase "multiply *that total*." If we're supposed to multiply the total from the subtraction, then obviously we have to do the subtraction first.

Let's start by putting in the numbers and x.

$$x - 22 \cdot 7 = -42$$

Next, we need to make sure that the correct order of operations is shown. With the way the equation is written now, the order is wrong. Remember, our rules tell us to do multiplication first unless there are parentheses. So this equation says to multiply 22 and 7 first, and subtract that total from x second. But our original problem told us we're supposed to subtract 22 first, and then that total should be multiplied by 7 second. So we need to put parentheses in like this.

$$(x - 22) \cdot 7 = -42$$

Now the equation says "there's a missing number x and if we subtract 22 from it first and multiply that total by 7 second, the result is -42." That's exactly what we want.

Write It Right

One last thing. There's actually no reason to use the dot to show multiplication in this equation. Remember, we can show multiplication with parentheses too. Since $x - 22$ already has parentheses around it, we could write the equation as $(x - 22)7 = -42$. But since everybody puts the 7 first, the proper way to write it is actually like this.

$$7(x - 22) = -42$$

Mathematically, it doesn't make any difference whether the 7 goes before or after the $x - 22$, because multiplication can be done in any order. But everybody always puts the number before the parentheses. It's like writing $3x$ instead of $x3$.

Practice 90

a.   Calculate the value of the expression $-5(3 - 6)$.

b. Translate the following phrase into a mathematical expression: 5 and 6 multiplied together first and then -9 subtracted from that total. (Don't calculate the answer.)

c. Translate the following word problem into an equation: There's some number that if you multiply it by 5 first, and then add 4 to the total you get 24. (Don't solve.)

d. Translate the following word problem into an equation: There's some number that if you subtract 7 from it and then multiply that total by 3, the result is -15. (Don't solve.)

e. Translate the word problem below into an equation; then solve.

Maggie bought a designer cotton vest at a 30% discount. If the discount saved her $27, what did the vest cost originally?

Problem Set 90

Multiply or divide each pair of fractions below. Make sure your answers are fully reduced.

1. $\dfrac{4}{14} \cdot \dfrac{7}{8}$

2. $\dfrac{6}{10} \div \dfrac{2}{5}$

Convert each fraction below into decimal form. Give exact answers (no rounding).

3. $\dfrac{6}{5}$

4. $\dfrac{9}{11}$

Add each pair of numbers below.

5. $-45+(-17)$

6. $-23+19$

Subtract each pair of numbers below.

7. $2.5-(-1)$

8. $-8-13$

Multiply each pair of numbers below.

9. $(6)(-7)$

10. $(-9)(-9)$

Divide each pair of numbers below.

11. $\dfrac{52}{-13}$ **12.** $\dfrac{-45}{-5}$

Tell whether each of the following pairs of expressions is equivalent.

13. $\dfrac{-9}{10}$ and $-\dfrac{9}{10}$ **14.** $(-1)(-x)$ and $-x$

Calculate the value of each expression below. (Make sure to do the operations in the correct order.)

15. $9-5\cdot3$ **(a) 16.** $-4(2-8)$

Translate each of the following phrases into a mathematical expression. (Don't calculate the answer.)

(b) 17. 7 and 4 multiplied together first and then -3 subtracted from that total.

18. 4 minus 12 first, and that total multiplied by 2.

Translate each of the following word problems into an equation. (Don't solve.)

(c) 19. There's some number that if you multiply it by 3 first, and then add 7 to the total you get 31.

(d) 20. There's some number that if you subtract 9 from it and then multiply that total by 4, the result is -20.

Solve each equation below by undoing.

21. $\dfrac{1}{2}+x=\dfrac{3}{5}$ **22.** $\dfrac{x}{-7}=-14$ **23.** $25-x=-39$

Translate the word problem below into an equation; then solve.

(e) 24. Stephanie bought some Nappa leather boots at a 20% discount. If the discount saved her $23, what did the boots cost originally?

Lesson 91—Order and the Fraction Bar

In the last couple of lessons we've been learning about the order of operations. But so far we've only done problems that mix multiplication with addition or subtraction. What about division?

Mixing Operations with Division

To see how to handle division, let's go back to the rules.

1.	All multiplications and divisions are done first.
2.	All additions and subtractions are done second.
3.	If a different order is needed, the operations that are supposed to be done first must be put in parentheses.

Take a look at rule 1. It says that "all multiplications and *divisions* are done first." So the rules say that division is just like multiplication: it's supposed to be done before addition or subtraction. That means in an expression like $8 + \dfrac{12}{4}$, we should do the division first and the addition second. So to actually do the calculation, we would divide 12 by 4 first to get $8 + 3$. Then we would add 8 and 3 to get 11.

The Fraction Bar Clears Things Up

Now it should be clearer why we almost always use the fraction bar in algebra instead of the old arithmetic division symbol. Writing 12 divided by 4 as a fraction makes it easy to see that the division is supposed to be done first. Take a close look at our example.

$$8 + \frac{12}{4}$$

With the problem written this way, nobody would try to add 8 and 12 first. They would have to take the 12 out of the numerator of the fraction, and almost nobody would even think of doing that. So writing the division as a fraction helps us see how to do the operations in the correct order.

But if we had used the old division symbol, the problem would have been a lot more confusing.

$$8 + 12 \div 4$$

With the problem written this way, it seems natural to add 8 and 12 first (because we naturally do things from left to right). But that would be wrong, according to the order of operations rules. The fraction bar clears up the confusion.

Using the Fraction Bar to Change the Order

But what if the addition is supposed to come before the division? How should that be written? With parentheses? Actually, no. We use the fraction bar again. If we want to write the problem so that it means "add 8 to 12 first and then divide that total by 4," this is how we write it.

$$\frac{8 + 12}{4}$$

See, we just put the entire addition in the fraction. Doing it like this makes it really easy to get the order right again. Think about it. Nobody would try to divide 4 into just 12. They would add on top to figure out how big the numerator is first. Then they would divide. So by putting the addition inside the fraction, everybody naturally does the operations in the correct order. That's why we use the fraction bar, instead of parentheses, to show addition before division.

The only problem is that our rules don't mention using the fraction bar to show a change in the order of operations, so we need to change rule 3. Instead of saying that to change the order we have to put an operation inside parentheses, we should say that the operation needs to go inside parentheses *or* inside a fraction.

1.	All multiplications and divisions are done first.
2.	All additions and subtractions are done second.
3.	If a different order is needed, the operations that are supposed to be done first must be put in parentheses or *inside a fraction.*

Now the rules cover both multiplication and division.

Mixing Division and Subtraction

When division is mixed with subtraction everything works the same way. Here's an example.

$$14 - \frac{10}{2}$$

In this one, we're supposed to divide first, since the subtraction isn't inside the fraction. So to calculate this correctly, we divide first.

$$14 - 5$$

Then we subtract to get an answer of 9.

Here's another one.

$$\frac{18}{9-3}$$

This time, the subtraction is in the bottom of the fraction. That means we need to subtract 9 and 3 first and divide second. (Putting the subtraction inside the fraction makes that easy to see.) So we'll subtract on bottom first.

$$\frac{18}{6}$$

Next, we'll divide to get the answer, which is 3.

Practice 91

a. Calculate the value of the expression $\frac{4+8}{2}$. (Make sure to do the operations in the correct order.)

b. Translate the following phrase into a mathematical expression: 20 divided by 4 first and then 3 subtracted from that total. (Don't calculate the answer.)

c. Translate the following phrase into a mathematical expression: 7 added to 8 first and then that total divided by 5. (Don't calculate the answer.)

d. Translate the following word problem into an equation: There's some number that if you subtract 11 from it first and then multiply that total by 7, the result is 56. (Don't solve.)

e. Translate the word problem below into an equation; then solve.

Terry spent $15.40 on gasoline. If each gallon cost $1.40, how many gallons of gas did he purchase?

Problem Set 91

Tell whether each sentence below is True or False.

1. The fraction bar can be used to show the order of operations.

2. To show that an addition should be done before a division, the addition should be put inside a fraction.

Answer each question below.

3. How far will a mole digging at 3 feet per hour dig in 2 hours?

4. How far will a train moving at 42 miles per hour travel in $3\frac{1}{2}$ hours?

Add each pair of numbers below.

5. $-51+(-49)$ **6.** $14+(-72)$

Subtract each pair of numbers below.

7. $-7-(-18)$ **8.** $-20-40$

Multiply each pair of numbers below.

9. $(-4)(11)$ **10.** $(-28)(0)$

Divide each pair of numbers below.

11. $\dfrac{-30}{3}$ **12.** $\dfrac{-63}{-9}$

Calculate the value of each expression below. (Make sure to do the operations in the correct order.)

13. $9 + \dfrac{15}{3}$

14. $12 - 2 \cdot 4$

(a) 15. $\dfrac{3+7}{2}$

Translate each of the following phrases into a mathematical expression. (Don't calculate the answer.)

16. 3 and 6 multiplied together first and then 8 subtracted from that total.

(b) 17. 14 divided by 2 first and then 5 subtracted from that total.

(c) 18. 5 added to 11 first and then that total divided by 8.

Translate each of the following word problems into an equation. (Don't solve.)

19. There's some number that if you multiply it by 5 first, and then add 3 to the total, the result is 18.

(d) 20. There's some number that if you subtract 6 from it first and then multiply that total by 3, the result is 45.

Solve each equation below by undoing.

21. $-5x = -7$

22. $\dfrac{\frac{x}{2}}{5} = \dfrac{1}{8}$

(d) 23. $x + (-28) = -96$

Translate the word problem below into an equation; then solve.

(e) 24. Mike spent \$4.55 on Snickers™ bars for him and his road trip buddies. If each Snickers™ bar costs \$0.65, how many did Mike purchase?

Lesson 92—Using the Fraction Bar in Equations

In the last lesson we learned to show the order of operations using the fraction bar. We only did arithmetic problems in the examples, but we can also use the fraction bar to show order in equations.

Let's say we want to write an equation for this problem.

There's some number that if we divide it by 3 first, and then add 7 to that total, we get 14. What's the number?

We're trying to find the missing number, so we should make it x.

$$x = \text{missing number}$$

Notice that the problem says this missing number is divided by 3 first, and then 7 is added second. So the order is division first and addition second. That means we don't need to put the addition inside the fraction. To show that division should come first and addition second, we should write the equation like this.

$$\frac{x}{3} + 7 = 14$$

According to the order of operations rules, division is before addition unless the addition is inside a fraction. The addition is not inside the fraction here, so this equation says exactly what we want it to.

Addition First, Division Second

Let's try another one.

There's some number that if we add 4 to it first, and then divide that total by 2, we get 18. What's the number?

We'll go through the same process on this one. We'll let x represent the number we're trying to find.

$$x = \text{missing number}$$

Now take another look at the problem. Notice it says "if you add 4 to it *first*." That means the addition is before the division. So we're going to have to put the addition inside the fraction, like this.

$$\frac{x+4}{2} = 18$$

The equation means "x and 4 are added first, and then the total is divided by 2 to get 18." That's what we want.

Division First, Subtraction Second

Here's an example with subtraction.

> If we divide some number by 5 first, and then subtract that total from 39, the total is 22. What's the number?

In this problem the division is first, so the subtraction doesn't need to be inside the fraction. We divide x and 5 first and then subtract the result from 39.

$$39 - \frac{x}{5} = 22$$

According to the rules, this equation is telling us to divide first (because the subtraction is not inside the fraction) and subtract second. That's exactly what we want. Notice that the x divided by 5 comes after the 39. That's because our problem says to divide those first and then subtract the result *from* 39. If the problem had said take x divided by 5 and subtract 39 from *it*, then we would have had to write it like this: $\frac{x}{5} - 39$. So you have to be really careful when reading a problem to make sure you've translated it into an equation correctly.

See why the order of operations rules are so important? We have to know them to turn a real problem into an equation. And if we can't do that, then we can't really use algebra. But it takes practice, so don't get frustrated if you're having trouble. It takes a long time to master the process of turning a word problem into an equation. Just keep working at it.

Practice 92

a. Translate the following phrase into a mathematical expression: 8 and 3 multiplied together first and then that total subtracted from 14. (Don't calculate the answer.)

b. Translate the following word problem into an equation: There's some number that if you divide it by 4 first, and then subtract 11 from that total, the result is 32. (Don't solve.)

c. Translate the following word problem into an equation: There's some number that if you add 8 to it first and then divide that total by 3, the result is 27. (Don't solve.)

d. Solve the equation $-10 - x = -4$.

e. Translate the word problem below into an equation; then solve.

There were 1,500 natural food items in the health food store, but only 6 of them were blue. What percent of the natural foods were blue? (The answer to your equation will be in decimal form. Make sure your final answer is written as a percent.)

Problem Set 92

Add or subtract each pair of fractions below. Make sure your answers are fully reduced.

1. $\dfrac{1}{7} + \dfrac{3}{7}$ **2.** $\dfrac{5}{6} - \dfrac{2}{3}$

Convert each percent below into decimal form.

3. 57%   **4.** 132%

Add each pair of numbers below.

5. $-15 + (-27)$ **6.** $61 + (-48)$

Subtract each pair of numbers below.

7. $35 - (-11)$ **8.** $-83 - (-16)$

Multiply each pair of numbers below.

9. $(-12)(3)$ **10.** $(-9)(-11)$

Divide each pair of numbers below.

11. $\dfrac{-75}{25}$ **12.** $\dfrac{-24}{-6}$

Calculate the value of each expression below. (Make sure to do the operations in the correct order.)

13. $\dfrac{45}{4+5}$

14. $-3(9+2)$

Translate each of the following phrases into a mathematical expression. (Don't calculate the answer.)

15. -5 added to 13 first and that total multiplied by 4.

16. 14 minus 2 first and then that total divided by 3.

(a) 17. 7 and 6 multiplied together first and then that total subtracted from 21.

Translate each of the following word problems into an equation. (Don't solve.)

18. There's some number that if you multiply it by 2 first, and then subtract 6 from the total, the result is 16.

(b) 19. There's some number that if you divide it by 5 first, and then subtract 14 from that total, the result is 21.

(c) 20. There's some number that if you add 9 to it first and then divide that total by 2, the result is 30.

Solve each equation below by undoing.

21. $\dfrac{1}{3}+x=\dfrac{6}{7}$

22. $\dfrac{x}{-9}=17$

(d) 23. $-9-x=-5$

Translate the word problem below into an equation; then solve.

(e) 24. There were 1,800 different kinds of suits in the men's store, but only 9 of them were yellowish. What percent of the suits were yellowish? (The answer to your equation will be in decimal form. Make sure your final answer is written as a percent.)

PRE-ALGEBRA: A TEACHING TEXTBOOK

Lesson 93—Undoing in Reverse—Part 1

We've been learning how to write equations with two operations. But so far, we haven't actually solved any of them. In this lesson, we're going to take that next step and actually learn how to solve some two operation equations.

Undoing Addition First

Let's start with an equation that mixes multiplication and addition.

$$2x + 6 = 10$$

To get x by itself here, we have to undo *both* of the operations: the multiplication by 2 and the addition of 6. But which operation should we undo first? It makes a big difference. The rule (and it's a very important one) is that the operations are always undone in reverse order. That means whatever is done to x last, we undo it first. According to the order of operations rules, x is multiplied by 2 first and 6 is added second.[1] To solve the equation, then, we need to undo in reverse, which means addition should be undone first and multiplication second.

$$2x + 6 = 10$$

We undo the addition of 6 in the usual way: by subtracting 6 from both sides.

$$2x + 6 - 6 = 10 - 6 \qquad \textbf{Undoing addition first}$$

The left side looks a little messy, but it just means there's some quantity $2x$ that has 6 added to it, and then 6 subtracted again. That means the left side now equals just $2x$. (If someone gave you $6 but then took $6 back again, you'd have the same amount of money you started with, right?)

$$2x = 10 - 6$$

We can go ahead and subtract on the right too.

$$2x = 4$$

Now that the addition has been undone first, we're ready to undo the multiplication second. To undo the multiplication by 2, we just divide both sides by 2.

$$\frac{2x}{2} = \frac{4}{2} \qquad \textbf{Undoing multiplication second}$$

The left side is now just equal to x.

$$x = \frac{4}{2}$$

---

[1] That's because multiplication is always supposed to be done before addition unless there are parentheses, and this equation doesn't have any.

And notice that we've turned our hard algebra equation with two operations into a simple arithmetic problem. The last step is to divide on the right to get an answer of 2.

$$x = 2$$

So to solve $2x + 6 = 10$ we had to undo both of the operations. But the important thing was that we had to undo the addition first and the multiplication second. That's in reverse order.

Checking the Answer

Let's check our answer to make sure it's right. We need to put 2 in for x in the original equation.

$$2x + 6 = 10$$

$$2(2) + 6 = 10 \qquad \text{putting 2 in for } x$$

Next, we calculate the left side. But since we're just calculating and not undoing, we have to do the operations in the correct order (not in reverse). Reverse order is *only* for undoing. (Don't get confused about that.) There are no additions or subtractions inside parentheses, so the multiplication should be done first and the addition second.[2] Multiplying 2 and 2 gives us this.

$$4 + 6 = 10$$

Now we do the addition by adding 4 and 6 to get

$$10 = 10.$$

Since the sides are equal, 2 is correct.

Undoing Multiplication First

Let's look at another example where the x has two operations done to it.

$$3(x - 5) = 9$$

This equation has both a subtraction and a multiplication. The first step is to figure out the order in which the operations are done to x. The subtraction is in parentheses, so subtraction is first and multiplication is second. So the equation is telling us that there is a missing number, and if we subtract 5 from it first, and multiply the result by 3 second, we'll get 9. To solve the equation, we need to undo those operations in reverse order. That means we undo the multiplication first and the subtraction second. We can undo the multiplication by 3 by dividing both sides by 3. That

---

[2] Actually, the equation does have parentheses. But they're just showing us that 2 and 2 are multiplied. There aren't any operations inside parentheses.

might seem hard, but it's actually no big deal. All we have to do is put a fraction bar under everything on both sides, like this.

$$\frac{3(x-5)}{3}=\frac{9}{3}\qquad \text{Undoing multiplication first}$$

The left side has some quantity, $x-5$, multiplied by 3 and divided by 3. Since the division undoes the multiplication, we end up with only $x-5$ on that side.

$$x-5=\frac{9}{3}$$

Now we'll go ahead and divide on the right side to get 3.

$$x-5=3$$

Since we undid the multiplication first, we can now undo the subtraction second, by adding 5 to both sides.

$$x-5+5=3+5\qquad \text{Undoing addition second}$$

That leaves just x on the left.

$$x=3+5$$

Finally, we've turned the algebra equation into an arithmetic problem. The last step is to add on the right to get an answer of 8.

$$x=8$$

To solve $3(x-5)=9$, then, all we did was undo the multiplication first and the subtraction second. You can check the answer yourself, if you want, by putting 8 back in for x in the original equation and doing the operations in the correct order.

Practice 93

a. Translate the following word problem into an equation: There's some number that if you divide it by -6 first, and then add 24 to that total, the result is 15. (Don't solve.)

b. Translate the following word problem into an equation: There's some number that if you subtract 3 from it first, and then multiply that total by 14, the result is 70. (Don't solve.)

c. Solve the equation $4x+5=33$.

d. Solve the equation $5(x-2)=45$.

e. Translate the word problem below into an equation; then solve.

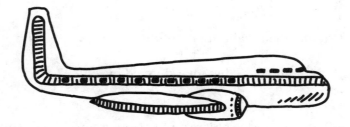

The jet flew for 3 hours, traveling a total of 1,740 miles. How fast did the jet travel in miles per hour?

Problem Set 93

Tell whether each sentence below is True or False.

1. When solving an equation with two operations, you should undo the operations in reverse order.

2. In the equation $2(x-7)=16$, the subtraction should be undone first.

Add or subtract (as indicated) each pair of numbers below.

3. $-29+(-43)$ 4. $-17-(-8)$ 5. $-20+51$

Multiply each pair of numbers below.

6. $(46)(-2)$ 7. $(-5)(-13)$

Divide each pair of numbers below.

8. $\dfrac{-7}{3.5}$ 9. $\dfrac{-140}{-20}$

Calculate the value of each expression below. (Make sure to do the operations in the correct order.)

10. $19-\dfrac{15}{3}$ 11. $5\cdot 2+6$ 12. $\dfrac{8+12}{5}$

Translate each of the following phrases into a mathematical expression. (Don't calculate the answer.)

13. 7 minus 25 first, and then that total multiplied by -6.

14. 28 added to 17 first, and then that total divided by -9.

Translate each of the following word problems into an equation. (Don't solve.)

(a) 15. There's some number that if you divide it by -8 first, and then add 22 to that total, the result is 13.

(b) 16. There's some number that if you subtract 4 from it first, and then multiply that total by 12, the result is 60.

Solve each equation below by undoing.

17. $-8x = 3$

18. $\dfrac{-x}{11} = 2$

19. $x - (-5) = -12$

20. $\dfrac{x}{2.5} = -4$

(c) 21. $3x + 4 = 22$

(d) 22. $2(x - 3) = 30$

Translate the word problem below into an equation; then solve.

(a) 23. The jalopy sputtered across the desert for 6 hours, traveling a total of 168 miles before it finally broke down. How fast did the jalopy travel in miles per hour?

Lesson 94—Undoing in Reverse—Part 2

In the last lesson, we learned one of the most important rules in all of algebra. It's that equations with more than one operation are solved by undoing in reverse order. Let's use that rule to solve this equation.

$$\frac{x}{2} + 5 = 8$$

The first step is to figure out the order in which the operations are done to x. Here x is divided by 2 first and 5 is added second (because division is before addition unless the addition is inside a fraction, remember).

Undoing Division

To solve, all we have to do is undo those operations in reverse order. That means we need to undo the addition first, and the division second. Undoing the addition is easy. We just subtract 5 from both sides.

$$\frac{x}{2} + 5 - 5 = 8 - 5 \qquad \textbf{Undoing addition first}$$

On the left we have $\frac{x}{2}$ with 5 added and then 5 subtracted. That's just equal to $\frac{x}{2}$.

$$\frac{x}{2} = 8 - 5$$

On the right we can subtract 8 minus 5.

$$\frac{x}{2} = 3$$

Next, we undo the division by multiplying both sides by 2.

$$2 \cdot \frac{x}{2} = 3 \cdot 2 \qquad \textbf{Undoing division second}$$

On the left side multiplication by 2 undoes division by 2, which leaves just x. And that turns the algebra equation into an arithmetic problem.

$$x = 3 \cdot 2$$

To get the answer, we just multiply on the right.

$$x = 6$$

The answer turns out to be 6. So to solve $\dfrac{x}{2}+5=8$, we just undid the addition first and the division second, which is undoing in reverse. That's all we have to do. The main point is that undoing in reverse works on equations with division too.

Undoing When x is Inside a Fraction

Let's try another example.

$$\frac{x-9}{4}=7$$

First, we have to figure out the order in which the operations are done to x. Since the subtraction is inside the fraction, we know from the rules that it's done first and division is done second. To solve, we need to undo in reverse order. That means the division is undone first, by multiplying both sides by 4.

$$4\cdot\frac{x-9}{4}=7\cdot4 \qquad \textbf{Undoing division first}$$

The left side looks complicated, but it just means that the quantity $x-9$ is divided by 4 and multiplied by 4. The multiplication undoes the division, so the left side becomes $x-9$.

$$x-9=7\cdot4$$

On the right, we multiply 7 and 4 to get 28.

$$x-9=28$$

Next, we undo the subtraction by adding 9 to both sides.

$$x-9+9=28+9 \qquad \textbf{Undoing subtraction second}$$

That makes the left side x.

$$x=28+9$$

We've turned the algebra equation into an arithmetic problem, and all we have to do now is to add 28 and 9 on the right to get 37.

$$x=37$$

So to solve harder equations with two operations, we just need to undo in reverse. It doesn't matter if we're mixing multiplication with addition or subtraction, or division with addition or subtraction. Undoing in reverse works in both cases.

Practice 94

a. Translate the following phrase into a mathematical expression: 20 divided by -4 first, and then that total subtracted from 90. (Don't calculate the answer.)

b. Translate the following word problem into an equation: There's some number that if you add 17 to it first, and then divide that total by 3, the result is 49. (Don't solve.)

c. Solve the equation $\dfrac{x}{4} + 3 = 16$.

d. Solve the equation $\dfrac{x-2}{5} = 18$.

e. Translate the word problem below into an equation; then solve.

Wayne was not only foolish enough to waste good money on a pair of camouflage house slippers, he also agreed to pay a 15% shipping and handling charge. If Wayne paid $2.40 in shipping and handling, how much must the house slippers have cost?

Problem Set 94

Multiply or divide each pair of numbers below. Write any remainders in decimal form.

1. $\begin{array}{r} 7.2 \\ \times 6.4 \\ \hline \end{array}$

2. $9\overline{)8,033}$

Add or subtract (as indicated) each pair of numbers below.

3. $-6 - (-9)$

4. $59 - (-27)$

5. $94 + (-73)$

Multiply or divide (as indicated) each pair of numbers below.

6. $(-8)(14)$

7. $\dfrac{-64}{8}$

8. $\left(-\dfrac{1}{4}\right)(-4)$

Tell whether each of the following pairs of expressions is equivalent.

9. $\dfrac{7}{-8}$ and $-\dfrac{7}{8}$

10. $x-(-4)$ and $x+4$

Calculate the value of each expression below. (Make sure to do the operations in the correct order.)

11. $7(-4+2)$

12. $\dfrac{35}{5}-4$

13. $\dfrac{12}{3-9}$

Translate each of the following phrases into a mathematical expression. (Don't calculate the answer.)

14. -4 multiplied by 8 first, and then 18 added to that total.

(a) 15. 36 divided by -6 first, and then that total subtracted from 100.

Translate each of the following word problems into an equation. (Don't solve.)

16. There's some number that if you multiply it by 2 first, and then subtract 25 from that total, the result is 38.

(b) 17. There's some number that if you add 13 to it first, and then divide that total by 9, the result is 54.

Solve each equation below by undoing.

18. $\dfrac{3}{2}x=15$

19. $8-x=23$

20. $x+\left(-\dfrac{1}{2}\right)=4$

21. $\dfrac{x}{-20}=4.5$

(c) 22. $\dfrac{x}{3}+7=19$

(d) 23. $\dfrac{x-9}{2}=11$

Translate the word problem below into an equation; then solve.

(e) 24. Sally went souvenir crazy on her trip to Mexico. She not only wasted good money on a sombrero that had blinking lights on it, she also agreed to pay a special 20% export tax. If Sally paid $9.60 in tax, how much must the sombrero have cost?

Lesson 95—Simplifying First

We've been learning how to solve equations with more than one operation. Here's the longest one yet.

$$3x + 5 + 7 = 18$$

Look at how long this equation is! It actually has three operations. Here's what this equation means: "There's a missing number, x, that if we multiply it by 3 first, then add 5 to that, and then add 7 to that, we get 18. What's the number?"

Making Less to Undo

There are two ways to solve this. One way is just to undo everything in reverse order. We could undo the addition of 7 by subtracting 7 from both sides. Then we could undo the addition of 5 by subtracting 5 from both sides, and so on. But there's another method which is faster. What we do is make the equation simpler first. And it's really easy to do. We just add the 5 and 7 first.

$$3x + 12 = 18 \qquad \textbf{Add 5 and 7 first}$$

This is called **simplifying**. We simplified the expression $3x + 5 + 7$ by rewriting it as $3x + 12$. The important thing is that now the equation is easier to undo, since there are only two operations instead of three.

Now to solve, we just undo in reverse order. The multiplication by 3 is done first (since the addition isn't in parentheses), and the addition of 12 is second. So we undo the addition first by subtracting 12 from both sides.

$$3x + 12 - 12 = 18 - 12$$

The subtraction undoes the addition on the left side, so it's just equal to $3x$.

$$3x = 18 - 12$$

We can subtract on the right to get

$$3x = 6.$$

Next, we undo the multiplication by dividing both sides by 3.

$$\frac{3x}{3} = \frac{6}{3}$$

The division undoes the multiplication on the left side, which leaves just x.

$$x = \frac{6}{3}$$

The last step is to do the arithmetic on the right for an answer of 2.

$$x = 2$$

Simplifying is a really smart thing to do on longer equations because it reduces the number of operations you have to undo.

Another Example

Let's try another long equation.

$$4x + 3 + 8 = 23$$

We could start undoing in reverse right away, but this equation is so long that it will be easier if we simplify first. All we have to do is add the 3 and 8.

$$4x + 11 = 23 \qquad \textbf{Add 3 and 8 first}$$

Now the equation is easier to undo, because there are only two operations. As usual, we undo in reverse order. Here the multiplication of x is first and the addition is second (because the addition isn't in parentheses). So to undo in reverse, we should undo the addition first by subtracting 11 from both sides.

$$4x + 11 - 11 = 23 - 11$$

Subtraction undoes addition on the left, so it just equals $4x$. And the right side just equals 12.

$$4x = 12$$

Now we undo the multiplication by dividing both sides by 4.

$$\frac{4x}{4} = \frac{12}{4}$$

Division undoes multiplication, making the left side equal x.

$$x = \frac{12}{4}$$

That turns our algebra equation into an arithmetic problem. The last step is to divide on the right to get an answer of 3.

$$x = 3$$

Practice 95

a. How many feet are in 5 meters? (There are approximately 39 inches in 1 meter.)

b. Translate the following phrase into a mathematical expression: 8 subtracted from 14 first, and then that total divided by 3. (Don't calculate the answer.)

c. Translate the following word problem into an equation: There's some number that if you subtract 14 from it first, and then multiply that total by 22, the result is 88. (Don't solve.)

d. Solve the equation $2x + 6 + 7 = 19$.

e. Translate the word problem below into an equation; then solve.

There is a number that if you add 5 to it first, and then divide that total by 3, you get 8. What's the number?

Problem Set 95

Tell whether each sentence below is True or False.

1. Longer equations are easier to solve if you simplify them first before undoing.

2. Simplifying first reduces the number of operations you have to undo.

Add or subtract each group of numbers below.

3.
$$\begin{array}{r} 62.81 \\ + 47.59 \\ \hline \end{array}$$

4.
$$\begin{array}{r} 56.95 \\ - 39.88 \\ \hline \end{array}$$

Do each unit conversion below.

5. Convert 216 inches to yards.

(a) 6. How many feet are in 4 meters? (There are approximately 39 inches in 1 meter.)

Add or subtract (as indicated) each pair of numbers below.

7. $21 + (-22)$

8. $-16 - (-33)$

Multiply or divide (as indicated) each pair of numbers below.

9. $\dfrac{-99}{-9}$ **10.** $(6)(-12)$ **11.** $\dfrac{65}{-13}$

Calculate the value of each expression below. (Make sure to do the operations in the correct order.)

12. $40 - 8 \cdot 4$ **13.** $\dfrac{-2 + 16}{7}$ **14.** $10(5 - 9)$

Translate each of the following phrases into a mathematical expression. (Don't calculate the answer.)

15. 6 added to 9 first, and then that total multiplied by 3.

(b) 16. 7 subtracted from 12 first, and then that total divided 5.

Translate each of the following word problems into an equation. (Don't solve.)

17. There's some number that if you divide it by -12 first, and then add 3 to that total, the result is 4.

(c) 18. There's some number that if you subtract 18 from it first, and then multiply that total by 24, the result is 72.

Solve each equation below by undoing.

19. $-9x = 108$ **20.** $2x + 8 = 26$ **21.** $\dfrac{x + 4}{7} = 3$

22. $3x + 4 + 2 = 21$ **(d) 23.** $4x + 3 + 8 = 35$

Translate the word problem below into an equation; then solve.

(e) 24. There is a number that if you add 7 to it first, and then divide that total by 4, you get 10. What's the number?

Lesson 96—More Simplifying First

In the last lesson, we learned to simplify a longer equation first before solving it by undoing. Now take a look at this long equation.

$$8 + 2x + 1 = 19$$

See what's different? The numbers aren't next to each other. There's a $2x$ between them. Does that change anything? Can we still simplify by adding the numbers first before undoing? Yes, we can.

Adding In Any Order

Remember the commutative property of addition and the associative property of addition? Those are basic rules about adding numbers in any order. The commutative property applies to two numbers. It's what tells us that $3 + 4$ is the same as $4 + 3$. The associative property applies to more than two numbers. Even though we covered this at the very beginning of the book, here's a quick example: $2 + 7 + 6 + 9$. We can add these in any order we want, and the answer will come out to be 24 every time. That's because of the associative property of addition.

Now back to our equation.

$$8 + 2x + 1 = 19$$

Because of the associative property, we know that the three quantities on the left side (8, $2x$, and 1) can be added in any order. So we can go ahead and add the 8 and 1, even though they aren't next to each other. That will give us this.

$$2x + 9 = 19 \qquad \textbf{Adding 8 and 1 first}$$

See, now there are only two operations to undo. The equation has been simplified, and next we just need to undo the addition first by subtracting 9 from both sides.

$$2x + 9 - 9 = 19 - 9$$

Since we've added 9 and then taken 9 away on the left side, it will become $2x$. And if we do the subtraction on the right side we come up with 10.

$$2x = 10$$

Next, we undo the multiplication by dividing both sides by 2.

$$\frac{2x}{2} = \frac{10}{2}$$

Because the division undoes the multiplication, the left side becomes x.

$$x = \frac{10}{2}$$

And now we've turned the algebra equation into an arithmetic problem, so all that's left to do is to divide on the right to get this.

$$x = 5$$

The answer is 5.

The main point, then, is that even when the numbers aren't right next to each other, we can simplify first by adding. And we can do this because of the associative property of addition, which tells us that the order doesn't matter when adding numbers.

Simplifying With a Subtraction

Let's try another example that's a little harder.

$$1 + 3x - 7 = -16$$

This is another long equation with three operations. The x is multiplied by 3, 1 is added to that, and then 7 is subtracted. It would be nice if we could simplify before beginning to undo, and it's really tempting to add 1 and 7 right away, but that would be wrong. Take another look. The 7 is subtracted. We can *add* in any order but we can't *subtract* in any order. So that won't work.

Is there still a way to simplify? Yes, there is. We just have to use our knowledge of negative numbers. Remember we learned that subtraction can be changed to addition of the opposite. So for our example, we can change the subtraction of 7 to addition of -7. It will look like this.

$$1 + 3x + (-7) = -16 \qquad \textbf{Change 7 to -7}$$

Now 1 and -7 are both added, and addition can be done in any order. So there's no problem in adding 1 and -7 on the left to get -6.

$$3x + (-6) = -16 \qquad \textbf{Add 1 and -7 first}$$

We've simplified the equation. From here, we can just undo in reverse order as usual. In this equation the multiplication by 3 is first, and the addition of -6 is second. That's because, as we know, multiplication is always done first unless the addition is in parentheses. (And don't get confused by the parentheses around the -6. There's no addition or subtraction inside. The parentheses are just there to show us that the negative sign is attached to the 6.)

477

We could undo the addition of -6 by subtracting -6, but that would be kind of messy. The easiest way to undo the addition of a negative number is to add the opposite to both sides. So here we'll add 6 to both sides of the equation.

$$3x + (-6) + 6 = -16 + 6$$

That makes the left side $3x$, and if we do the addition on the right side we get -10.

$$3x = -10$$

Now let's undo the multiplication by dividing both sides by 3.

$$\frac{3x}{3} = \frac{-10}{3}$$

The division undoes the multiplication on the left, leaving just x.

$$x = \frac{-10}{3}$$

The fraction on the right can't be reduced. So the only thing we need to do is figure out the sign of the entire fraction. Since a negative divided by a positive is a negative, this is the same as negative $\frac{10}{3}$. We show that by just putting the negative sign out in front of the entire fraction.

$$x = -\frac{10}{3}$$

So we end up with an answer of $-\frac{10}{3}$.

The main point is that our rules about adding numbers in any order can help us simplify equations. Even when one of the numbers is subtracted, we can still simplify by changing the subtraction to addition first.

Practice 96

    a. Simplify the expression $6 + 3x + 11$.

    b. Simplify the expression $2 + 7x - 6$.

    c. Solve the equation $3 + 5x - 10 = 13$.

d. Solve the equation $4 + 8x - 14 = -26$.

e. Translate the word problem below into an equation; then solve.

There were 2,400 stamps in the man's collection, but only 15 of them contained pictures of wagons. What percent of the stamps had pictures of wagons on them? (The answer to your equation will be in decimal form. Make sure your final answer is written as a percent.)

Problem Set 96

Tell whether each sentence below is True or False.

1. There's a rule (called the associative property of addition) which says that more than two numbers can be added in any order without affecting the total.

2. It is impossible to simplify an equation where one of the numbers is subtracted.

Multiply or divide each pair of numbers below. Make sure your answers are fully reduced.

3. $\dfrac{3}{10} \cdot \dfrac{20}{36}$

4. $32 \div \dfrac{8}{11}$

Add or subtract (as indicated) each pair of numbers below.

5. $50 + (-50)$

6. $34 - (-27)$

Multiply or divide (as indicated) each pair of numbers below.

7. $(-16)(3)$

8. $\dfrac{-18}{-2}$

9. $\left(\dfrac{1}{4}\right)(-20)$

Calculate the value of each expression below. (Make sure to do the operations in the correct order.)

10. $-9 + \dfrac{10}{5}$

11. $8 \cdot 4 - 12$

12. $-2(6 + 1)$

Translate each of the following phrases into a mathematical expression. (Don't calculate the answer.)

13. 6 multiplied by 5 first, and then 18 subtracted from that total.

14. -11 added to 3 first, and then that total divided 2.

Simplify each expression below.

15. $7x + 2 + 6$ **(a) 16.** $5 + 4x + 9$ **(b) 17.** $3 + 6x - 8$

Solve each equation below by undoing.

18. $\dfrac{x}{-11} = -8$ **19.** $\dfrac{x}{3} + 9 = 17$ **20.** $5(x - 4) = -45$

(c) 21. $4 + 2x - 6 = 16$ **(d) 22.** $3 + 4x - 11 = -32$

Translate the word problem below into an equation; then solve.

(e) 23. There were 9,600 tourists on the beach that day, but only 12 of them were buried up to their neck in sand. What percent of the tourists were buried up to their neck in sand? (The answer to your equation will be in decimal form. Make sure your final answer is written as a percent.)

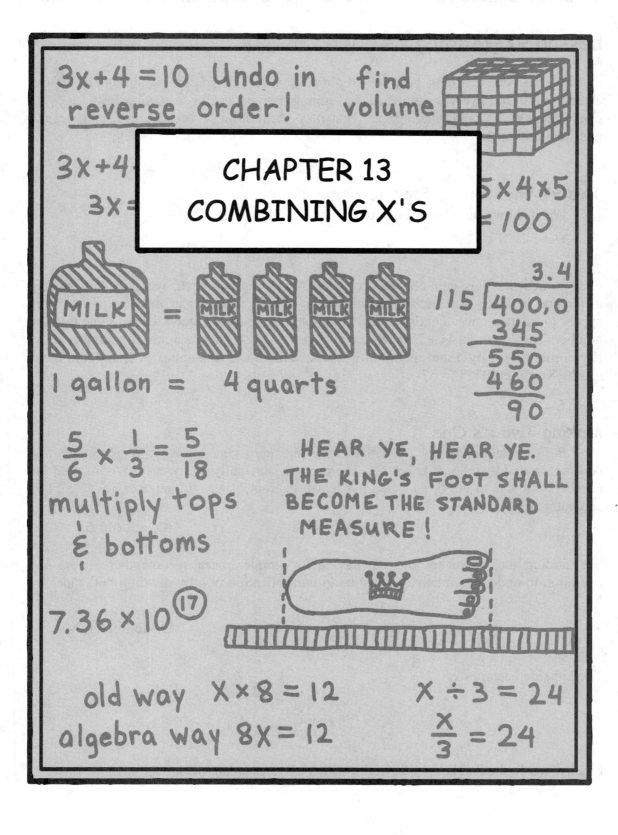

CHAPTER 13
COMBINING X'S

Lesson 97—Adding x's

We've been learning how to simplify equations first before undoing. In all our examples so far, we've simplified by adding numbers. But sometimes we need to simplify an equation by adding x's. That may seem strange, because how can we add missing numbers?

Two x's that Stand for the Same Thing

We'll show you with an example.

$$4x + 2x = 18$$

First, notice that this equation has two x's. A few lessons back, we said that one big difference between algebra and arithmetic is that in algebra the missing number can appear more than once. That's what is going on here. Both x's stand for the same missing number. The equation $4x + 2x = 18$ actually means this: "There's a missing number x and if you multiply it by 4 and then multiply that same missing number by 2 and add those results, you'll get 18."

Making Two x's One

Before undoing, we have to simplify the left side so that there's only one x showing. And we do that by adding $4x$ and $2x$. The process is actually pretty easy. We just add the numbers 4 and 2 to get 6, and then put that 6 in front of an x to get $6x$. So $4x + 2x$ is equivalent to $6x$.

$$6x = 18 \qquad \textbf{4x + 2x is 6x}$$

See, adding the x's makes our equation a lot simpler, because now there's just one operation to undo. From here, we just undo multiplication of 6 by dividing both sides by 6.

$$\frac{6x}{6} = \frac{18}{6} \qquad \textbf{Undo normally}$$

The left side becomes x.

$$x = \frac{18}{6}$$

Finally, we do the division on the right, which gives us an answer of 3.

$$x = 3$$

How It Works

We really should explain how $4x$ and $2x$ can be added to get $6x$. First, remember that 4 times 3 means $3+3+3+3$. And 2 times 3 equals $3+3$. Well, then, shouldn't $4x$ (which is just 4 times x) mean $x+x+x+x$? And shouldn't $2x$ mean $x+x$? Yes. So $4x+2x$ is really just $x+x+x+x+x+x$. But that's six x's added, which is the same as $6x$.

$$
\begin{array}{ccccc}
4x & + & 2x & = & 18 \\
\downarrow & & \downarrow & & \\
\underbrace{x+x+x+x}+\underbrace{x+x} & = & 18 \\
\underbrace{} & & \\
6x & & = & 18
\end{array}
$$

That's why we can change $4x + 2x$ to $6x$. And the great thing is that no matter what numbers are multiplied by the x's, to add them all we have to do is add the numbers in front (and put the total in front of an x). Here are a few other examples.

5x + 3x is equivalent to 8x
2x + 7x is equivalent to 9x
10x + 12x is equivalent to 22x

Some Important Terms

We should also define some new technical terms for you. As it turns out, the numbers that are multiplied by the x's are actually called **coefficients**. So, for example, the coefficient of $7x$ is 7, and the coefficient of $3x$ is 3. Also, instead of saying "add the x's," some people say **combine** the x's. But adding and combining mean basically the same thing, so use whichever word you like. The main point of this lesson, though, is that to solve an equation with more than one x, we simplify first by adding (combining) the x's and then undoing normally.

Practice 97

a. Translate the following word problem into an equation: There's some number that if you add 7 to it first, and then multiply that total by -2, the result is 36. (Do not attempt to solve the equation that you write.)

b. Simplify the expression $6x + 2x$.

c. Solve the equation $4x + 3x = 14$.

d. Solve the equation $2x + 8x = 30$.

e. Translate the word problem below into an equation; then solve.

The rocket flew for 15 seconds, traveling a total of 11,250 meters. How fast did the rocket travel in meters per second?

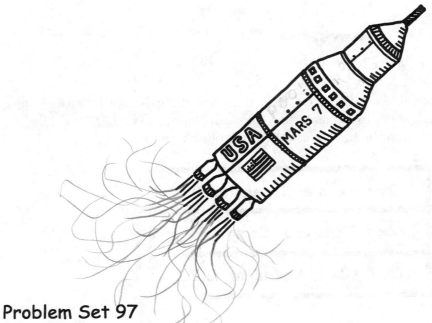

Problem Set 97

Tell whether each sentence below is True or False.

1. Some equations need to be simplified by adding x's (instead of numbers).

2. A number multiplied by an x is called a "coefficient."

3. To add (combine) x's, you just add their coefficients.

Answer each question below.

4. How far will a sports car traveling at 78 miles per hour go in $4\frac{1}{2}$ hours?

5. How far will a tree growing at 6 inches per year grow in 3 years?

Add or subtract (as indicated) each pair of numbers below.

6. $1-(-6)$ **7.** $-95+(-105)$

Multiply or divide (as indicated) each pair of numbers below.

8. $(13)(-9)$ **9.** $\dfrac{-42}{-7}$

Calculate the value of each expression below. (Make sure to do the operations in the correct order.)

10. $\dfrac{3-27}{2}$ **11.** $25-(5)(3)$

Translate each of the following word problems into an equation. (Don't solve.)

12. There's some number that if you divide it by -7 first, and then subtract 11 from that total, the result is 53.

(a) 13. There's some number that if you add 5 to it first, and then multiply that total by -3, the result is 40.

Simplify each expression below.

14. $1+5x+4$ **(b) 15.** $5x+4x$

Solve each equation below.

16. $\dfrac{2}{3}-x=\dfrac{5}{6}$ **17.** $\dfrac{1}{2}x=6$ **18.** $\dfrac{x-4}{3}=10$

19. $-2x+3+4=25$ **(c) 20.** $2x+3x=15$ **(d) 21.** $5x+3x=16$

Translate the word problem below into an equation; then solve.

(e) 22. The satellite had been on its own for 45 seconds, traveling a total of 5,400 meters. How fast did the satellite travel in meters per second?

Lesson 98—Subtracting x's

In the last lesson, we learned how to solve equations that have more than one x, and if you'll remember the process turned out to be pretty simple. All we did was add (or combine) the x's and then undo. Well, now we're going to look at some other equations with more than one x, but this time the x's are subtracted instead of added. Here's an example.

$$8x - 3x = 15$$

Subtracting Coefficients

Before solving this by undoing, we have to subtract the x's. And you can probably guess how it's done. We just *subtract* the coefficients 8 and 3 (remember, the numbers multiplied by x are called "coefficients"). Since $8 - 3$ equals 5, the left side simplifies to $5x$.

$$5x = 15.$$ **8 – 3 is 5**

Now there's just one operation left to undo. Dividing both sides by 5, we get

$$x = \frac{15}{5}.$$

Finally, we simplify on the right.

$$x = 3$$

So to subtract x's, we just subtract the coefficients (the numbers in front of the x's). Here are a few other examples.

11x - 4x is equivalent to 7x
5x - 2x is equivalent to 3x
18x - 10x is equivalent to 8x

How It Works

You may be wondering how the method of subtracting coefficients works. Basically, it works the same way as adding coefficients. Let's go back to our original example of $8x - 3x$. Doesn't $8x$ mean eight x's added? Of course it does. And doesn't $3x$ equal three x's added? Yes. So if we take away three x's from eight x's, that just leaves five x's, or $5x$.

Here's something else worth mentioning. Adding x's is called "combining x's," as you know. Well, it turns out that subtracting x's can also be called combining. So we can say that we "combined" $8x - 3x$ to get $5x$. Generally, the word combining applies to both addition and subtraction of x's.

More than One Method

You may have already realized this, but there's actually another way to subtract x's. We'll show what we mean on the equation $8x - 3x = 15$. Instead of subtracting the coefficients, we can change the subtraction to addition of the opposite first like this.

$$8x + (-3x) = 15.$$ **Change subtraction to addition**

Now since the x's on the left are being added, we can combine them by adding their coefficients. But watch what happens when we do that: $8 + (-3) = 5$. We still end up with $5x$.

$$5x = 15$$

So when combining x's that are subtracted, you can either subtract the coefficients or change the subtraction to addition first and then add. Use whichever method you think is easier. Just remember to add coefficients when the x's are added and subtract coefficients when the coefficients are subtracted. It doesn't matter whether the numbers involved are positive or negative.

Negative Coefficients from the Start

Here's an example of an equation where the coefficients are negative to begin with.

$$-9x + (-3x) = 48$$

Of course, before undoing, we have to add (combine) the x's. To do that, we just add the coefficients -9 and -3 to get $-12x$.

$$-12x = 48$$ **Add the coefficients**

That leaves us with just one operation to undo. Dividing both sides by -12 we have

$$\frac{-12x}{-12} = \frac{48}{-12}.$$

The left side now becomes just x.

$$x = \frac{48}{-12}$$

Finally, we do the division on the right to get our answer of -4. The main point here is that even when the coefficients are negative, we combine the x's in the same way.

Practice 98

    a. Simplify the expression $7x - 3x$.

    b. Solve the equation $11 + 3x - 7 = 19$.

    c. Solve the equation $4x + 7x = 88$.

    d. Solve the equation $12x - 8x = 24$.

    e. Translate the word problem below into an equation; then solve.

        There is a number that if you subtract 3 from it first, and then divide that total by 8, you get 4. What's the number?

Problem Set 98

Tell whether each sentence below is True or False.

    1. To subtract x's, you subtract their coefficients.

    2. Another way to subtract x's is to change the subtraction to addition of the opposite first.

Convert each fraction below into decimal form. Give exact answers (no rounding).

    3. $\dfrac{2}{3}$ **4.** $\dfrac{1}{100}$

Add or subtract (as indicated) each pair of numbers below.

    5. $-20 + (-17)$ **6.** $-52 - 18$

Multiply or divide (as indicated) each pair of numbers below.

    7. $(-2)(-23)$ **8.** $\dfrac{82}{-41}$

Calculate the value of each expression below. (Make sure to do the operations in the correct order.)

9. $8 + \dfrac{10}{2}$

10. $4(26 - 19)$

Translate each of the following phrases into a mathematical expression. (Don't calculate the answer.)

11. 16 divided by 4 first, and that total subtracted from 31.

12. 15 added to 8 first, and then that total multiplied by 6.

Simplify each expression below.

13. $6 + 2x - 9$

14. $7x + 5x$

(a) 15. $8x - 2x$

Solve each equation below.

16. $\dfrac{x}{2.4} = 15.1$

17. $8(x - 2) = 96$

18. $5x - 14 = 31$

(b) 19. $15 + 4x - 9 = 18$

(c) 20. $3x + 6x = 54$

(d) 21. $10x - 4x = 42$

Translate the word problem below into an equation; then solve.

(e) 22. There is a number that if you subtract 6 from it first, and then divide that total by 3, you get 5. What's the number?

Lesson 99—x and 1x

We've been learning how to combine x's, and so far it hasn't been too tough. Remember, all we have to do is add the coefficients if the x's are added or subtract the coefficients if the x's are subtracted. But now take a look at this equation.

$$2x + x = -24$$

This says that there's a missing number and if we multiply it by 2 and then add the same missing number to that total we'll get -24. To solve, we need to combine the x's and then undo as always. But notice that if we try to combine the x's by adding their coefficients, we won't be able to, because the second x doesn't have a coefficient. What do we do?

Let's think about this. Since $2x$ means $x + x$, the left side of our equation is really the same as $x + x + x$. But aren't three x's added the same as $3x$? Yes, so we can change $2x + x$ to $3x$.

$$3x = -24$$

Now we can solve by undoing. The multiplication can be undone by dividing both sides by 3.

$$\frac{3x}{3} = \frac{-24}{3}$$

That gives us just x on the left.

$$x = \frac{-24}{3}$$

Finally, we divide -24 by 3 to get $x = -8$, which is our answer.

Changing x to 1x

We were able to deal with the x that didn't have a coefficient fairly easily. But wouldn't it be nice if we could use the shortcut of adding the coefficients, even in equations like $2x + x = -24$? Actually, we can. The mathematicians figured out a way to add coefficients even in an equation with just a plain x. Here's how they did it. Any number times 1 is just the number itself. For example, 5 times 1 equals 5, 3 times 1 equals 3, 8 times 1 equals 8 and so on. Now, think about it. Shouldn't 1 times x equal x? Absolutely. Then why not change $2x + x$ to $2x + 1x$? That won't change the value of the left side one bit, because $1x$ and x are equal.

$$2x + 1x = -24 \qquad \textbf{Change x to 1x}$$

But now *both* x's have a coefficient, which means we can use the shortcut of adding the coefficients. Since $2+1$ is 3, the left side becomes $3x$, which we know is right.

Of course, you don't have to write the coefficient of 1 down on paper. You can just do it in your head. (Every time you see an x, just think $1x$.) The important thing, though, is that you can still use the shortcut of adding the coefficients, even when there's a plain x. You just have to change x to $1x$ first. Here are a few other examples of how to do that.

7x + x is equivalent to 8x
5x + x is equivalent to 6x
10x + x is equivalent to 11x

Subtracting x

It should come as no surprise that we can also *subtract* plain x's. Take a look at this example.

$$5x - x = 9$$

First, we change x to $1x$ again.

$$5x - 1x = 9 \qquad \qquad \textbf{Change x to 1x}$$

Now we subtract the coefficients. Since $5-1$ is 4, the left side becomes $4x$, and that leaves just one operation to undo.

$$4x = 9$$

Dividing both sides by 4 gives us this.

$$\frac{4x}{4} = \frac{9}{4}$$

$$x = \frac{9}{4}$$

So anytime you have a single x subtracted, just change it to $1x$.

Another way to handle $5x - x = 9$ is to change the subtraction to addition of the opposite.

$$5x + (-x) = 9.$$

That gives us $-x$, but what is the coefficient of $-x$? Well, from the rules for multiplying negatives, we know that −1 multiplied by any number is equal to its opposite. For instance, -1 times 6 is -6, -1 times -8 is $+8$, and so on. So −1 times x must be the same as $-x$. Why not change $-x$ to $-1x$ then? That would leave us with this.

$$5x + (-1x) = 9 \qquad \textbf{Change –x to -1x}$$

Now both x's have a coefficient, and we can combine normally by adding their coefficients. Since $5 + (-1)$ equals 4, the left side becomes $4x$, which we know is right. Remember, then, that if you need to combine $-x$, you can always change it to $-1x$, in your head or on paper. It's up to you.

Practice 99

    a.   Simplify the expression $8x + x$.

    b.   Simplify the expression $3x - x$.

    c.   Solve the equation $-3x + (-5x) = 64$.

    d.   Solve the equation $5x - x = -28$.

    e.   Translate the word problem below into an equation; then solve.

        There is a number that if you multiply it by 4 first, and then subtract 10 from the result, you get 14. What's the number?

Problem Set 99

Tell whether each sentence below is True or False.

    1.   You can change a single x to $1x$ in order to use the adding coefficients shortcut.

    2.   You can change a $-x$ to $-1x$ in order to use the adding coefficients shortcut.

Add or subtract each pair of numbers below. Make sure your answers are fully reduced.

    3. $\dfrac{3}{10} + \dfrac{4}{5}$ **4.** $9 - 3\dfrac{1}{4}$

Add or subtract (as indicated) each pair of numbers below.

5. $82 + (-49)$

6. $-41 - (-25)$

Multiply or divide (as indicated) each pair of numbers below.

7. $(-6)(9)$

8. $\dfrac{40}{-8}$

Calculate the value of each expression below. (Make sure to do the operations in the correct order.)

9. $-3 + (5)(3)$

10. $\dfrac{5-13}{-2}$

Translate each of the following word problems into an equation. (Don't solve.)

11. There's some number that if you subtract 14 from it first, and then divide that total by 2, the result is -1.

12. There's some number that if you multiply it by 10 first, and then add 6 to that total, the result is 27.

Simplify each expression below.

13. $2x + 13x$

(a) 14. $4x + x$

(b) 15. $7x - x$

Solve each equation below.

16. $\dfrac{3}{5}x = \dfrac{7}{10}$

17. $3 + 8x + 2 = 37$

18. $13x + 5x = -18$

19. $9x - 6x = 21$

(c) 20. $-2x + (-7x) = 81$

(d) 21. $9x - x = -16$

Translate the word problem below into an equation; then solve.

(e) 22. There is a number that if you multiply it by 7 first, and then subtract 12 from the result, you get 23. What's the number?

Lesson 100—Work Problems

For several lessons now, we've been solving equations with x's that are added or subtracted. But are there any real-world problems that have equations like that? Well, as a matter of fact, there are lots of them. In this lesson, we'll show you one of the simplest (and most common) kinds. Here's an example.

> Gina can paint 3 porcelain dolls per hour and Rosalie can paint 4 porcelain dolls per hour. How long will it take the two of them working together to paint 21 dolls?

This is what's called a work problem, because it involves people doing a job. In a work problem, we're told how long it takes a person to do a certain task. In this case, Gina can make 3 porcelain dolls per hour. That's called a rate, by the way. A different work problem might be about a person who licks 2 stamps per hour (definitely a slow worker) or a person who digs 5 ditches per day. Those are also rates. Obviously, rates come up all the time in the real world, because it's often necessary to calculate how long it will take to get a job done.

Writing the Equation

Now for some bad news. Work problems are useful but they can be tough. In fact, they're too tough for most people to solve using just basic arithmetic. Fortunately, they can be solved quickly with a little algebra. To see what we mean, let's translate our work problem about Gina and Rosalie into an algebra equation.

Since we're trying to find the number of hours it will take the two of them together to paint 21 dolls, that's what we should set equal to x.

x = number of hours it will take them to paint dolls

After this amount of time (x) the number of dolls Gina has painted plus the number Rosalie has painted should equal 21. So the equation should be set up like this.

number of dolls Gina painted + number of dolls Rosalie painted = 21.

Next, we need to put in the x's and numbers. If Gina can paint 3 dolls per hour, then in 2 hours she can paint 3 times 2, or 6 dolls. In 5 hours she can paint 3 times 5 or 15 dolls. In 7 hours she can paint 3 times 7 or 21 dolls. Get the picture? The rate multiplied by the time always equals the total amount of work done.

Rate x time = total amount of work done

So how many dolls should Gina be able to paint in x hours? That's the amount of time we're trying to find, isn't it? Well, in x hours shouldn't Gina be able to paint 3 times x, or

$3x$ dolls. So we need to put $3x$ in for the number of dolls Gina painted. We can just follow the same process to figure out how many dolls Rosalie painted. Since she can paint 4 dolls per hour, in x hours she can paint $4x$ dolls. That finishes our equation.

$$3x + 4x = 21$$

Solving the Equation

This equation looks familiar, doesn't it? It has two x's that are added. Work problems almost always translate into equations like this. To solve the equation, we first have to simplify the left side by combining the x's. All we have to do is add the coefficients. Since $3 + 4$ is 7, that gives us $7x$.

$$7x = 21$$

Now we can undo the multiplication by dividing both sides by 7.

$$\frac{7x}{7} = \frac{21}{7}$$

Simplifying on the left, we end up with

$$x = \frac{21}{7}.$$

Since 21 divided by 7 is 3, we end up with an answer of $x = 3$. That means it will take Gina and Rosalie 3 hours working together to paint 21 dolls. You'll be doing a lot of problems like this throughout the rest of this book. But don't worry. They'll get easier and easier.

Practice 100

a.   How many square feet are in 4 square yards?

b.   Simplify the expression $-4x + (-10x)$.

c.   Solve the equation $6x - x = 35$.

d.   Solve the equation $-x + (-4x) = 25$.

e.   Translate the word problem below into an equation; then solve.

Toby can make 4 shelves per hour and Brett can make 5 per hour. Working together, how many hours will it take them to make 18 shelves?

Problem Set 100

Tell whether each sentence below is True or False.

1. Work problems usually translate into an equation with more than one x.

2. In a work problem, the rate multiplied by the time equals the total amount of work a person does.

Multiply or divide each pair of numbers below. Write any remainders in decimal form.

3.
$$\begin{array}{r} 250 \\ \times 6.8 \\ \hline \end{array}$$

4. $22\overline{)14{,}322}$

Do each unit conversion below.

5. Convert 14 meters into millimeters.

(a) 6. How many square feet are in 2 square yards?

Add or subtract (as indicated) each pair of numbers below.

7. $-19 + (-65)$

8. $0 - (-5)$

Multiply or divide (as indicated) each pair of numbers below.

9. $\left(-\dfrac{1}{2}\right)(12)$

10. $\dfrac{-46}{23}$

Calculate the value of each expression below. (Make sure to do the operations in the correct order.)

11. $8 + \dfrac{100}{50}$

12. $-9(4 + 3)$

Translate each of the following phrases into a mathematical expression. (Don't calculate the answer.)

13. -7 added to -3 first, and that total divided by 5.

14. 16 multiplied by 2 first, and then 21 subtracted from that total.

Simplify each expression below.

15. $5 + 2x + 8$ **16.** $19x - x$ **(b) 17.** $-5x + (-11x)$

Solve each equation below.

18. $\dfrac{\frac{x}{2}}{7} = 49$ **19.** $24 - x = -6$ **20.** $8x + 12x = 100$

(c) 21. $5x - x = 44$ **(d) 22.** $-x + (-3x) = 32$

Translate the word problem below into an equation; then solve.

(e) 23. Scott can deliver 10 pizzas per hour and Kenneth can deliver 12 per hour. How many hours will it take them to deliver 110 pizzas?

Lesson 101—Fancy Distance Problems

In the last lesson, we learned about work problems. As it turned out, we were able to solve those with equations having more than one x. There are also quite a few distance problems that can be solved with equations with more than one x. Since these distance problems are more complicated than the ones you've been doing, we call them "fancy distance problems." Here's an example.

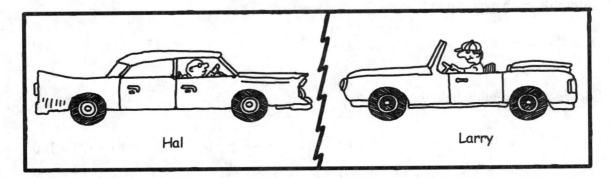

Hal   Larry

Hal and Larry are headed straight toward each other. Hal is driving at a safe speed of 55 mph, but Larry is driving recklessly at a speed of 75 mph. If the two are 260 miles apart, how many hours will it be before they meet (assuming Larry can keep his car on the road)?

Drawing a Picture then Writing an Equation

What makes this problem a little more complicated is that there are two drivers. Since we're trying to find the number of hours it will take the two to meet, let's make that equal to x.

x = number of hours it will take them to meet

Hal and Larry have to meet somewhere, but it won't be in the middle because Larry's going faster than Hal.

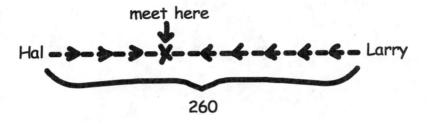

They'll meet somewhere over to the left, as the diagram shows. We don't know how far Hal and Larry will travel individually before meeting. But we do know that the total distance that both will travel must equal 260 miles. That's because Hal and Larry started

498

out 260 miles apart. That's the key piece of information we need to set up the equation. We can add Hal's distance to Larry's distance to get 260. It looks like this.

$$\text{Hal's distance} + \text{Larry's distance} = 260$$

To finish the equation, we just need to put in the x's and numbers. The key to doing this step is to remember that distance is always equal to speed multiplied by time. Since Hal's speed is 55 mph and his time is x hours, speed multiplied by time for Hal is $55x$. We can figure out an expression for Larry's distance in the exact same way. His speed is 75 mph and he's going to drive for x hours. So Larry's distance is $75x$. Putting these two expressions into the equation gives us this.

$$55x + 75x = 260$$

Solving for x

Just as we promised, the equation has two x's. Of course, now that you've had a lot of practice combining x's by adding coefficients, solving this equation should be simple. First, we'll combine $55x$ and $75x$. Since $55 + 75 = 130$, we're left with

$$130x = 260.$$

Next, we can undo the multiplication by dividing both sides by 130.

$$\frac{130x}{130} = \frac{260}{130}$$

That makes the left side x.

$$x = \frac{260}{130}$$

And this turns the equation into an arithmetic problem. Finally, dividing on the right gives us

$$x = 2.$$

So the answer to our problem is that it will take 2 hours for Hal and Larry to meet.

To do fancy distance problems, you just have to set up expressions for the two people's distances. Those are always going to equal the speed multiplied by the time. Then you add these two distances together to get the total distance that they have to travel to come together (which was 260 miles for Hal and Larry).

Practice 101

    a. Simplify the expression $-5x + x$.

    b. Solve the equation $9 + 2x - 5 = 12$.

    c. Solve the equation $x + 15x = -80$.

    d. Solve the equation $-x + (-5x) = 48$.

    e. Translate the word problem below into an equation; then solve.

Train #1 and train #2 are headed straight toward each other. Train #1 is traveling at 60 mph, and train #2 is traveling at 68 mph. If the two trains are 512 miles apart, how many hours will it be before they meet?

Problem Set 101

Multiply or divide each pair of fractions below. Make sure your answers are fully reduced.

    1. $\dfrac{5}{12} \cdot \dfrac{3}{10}$ **2.** $\dfrac{3}{4} \div \dfrac{1}{16}$

Add or subtract (as indicated) each pair of numbers below.

    3. $-20 + 14$ **4.** $-8 - (-1)$

Multiply or divide (as indicated) each pair of numbers below.

    5. $\dfrac{-45}{-5}$ **6.** $(-8)(8)$

Calculate the value of each expression below. (Make sure to do the operations in the correct order.)

7. $4 \cdot 7 - 13$

8. $14 + \dfrac{12}{-4}$

9. $5(8 + 6)$

Translate each of the following word problems into an equation. (Don't solve.)

10. There's some number that if you multiply it by 9 first, and then subtract 7 from that total, the result is 10.

11. There's some number that if you subtract 2 from it first, and then divide that total by 14, the result is -33.

Simplify each expression below.

12. $-4 + 4x + 7$

13. $2x + 3x$

(a) 14. $-7x + x$

Solve each equation below.

15. $\dfrac{1}{2}x = 7$

(b) 16. $7 + 3x - 2 = 11$

17. $\dfrac{-x}{5} = 8$

18. $15x - 9x = 30$

(c) 19. $x + 17x = -54$

(d) 20. $-x + (-6x) = 49$

Translate the word problem below into an equation; then solve.

(e) 21. Cyclist #1 and cyclist #2 are headed straight toward each other. Cyclist #1 is traveling at 15 mph, and cyclist #2 is traveling at 20 mph. If the two cyclists are 70 miles apart, how many hours will it be before they meet?

Lesson 102—x's on Both Sides

Now that you're getting more comfortable solving equations with two x's, it's time for something new. As it turns out, in some equations the x's are on different sides. Take a look.

$$7 + 5x = 16 + 2x$$

See, there's a $5x$ on the left side, and then a $2x$ on the right. This equation says that there's a missing number, x, and if we multiply it by 5, then add that to 7, the result is equal to 16 plus the product of 2 and that same missing number. We know that the x's have to be combined before undoing. But how do we combine the x's when they're on different sides? What we have to do is move the $2x$ over to the left side so that both of the x's are together.

Getting the x's on the Same Side

To get the x's on the same side, we can just subtract $2x$ from both sides, like this.

$$7 + 5x - 2x = 16 + 2x - 2x$$
Subtract 2x from both sides

You may be wondering if this step is legal. We subtract *numbers* from both sides of an equation all the time. But can we subtract a $2x$? Absolutely. Even though we don't know the value of $2x$ (since x is an unknown number), we're still subtracting the same amount from both sides ($2x$ and $2x$). And that doesn't violate the golden rule of algebra. So subtracting $2x$ is just fine.

The next step is to simplify the right side. Since the subtraction of $2x$ undoes the addition of $2x$, we end up with just 16.

$$7 + 5x - 2x = 16$$
2x is now on the left

Now do you see why we subtracted $2x$? That step eliminated the $2x$ from the right side completely and caused it to pop up on the left side, with the $5x$, which is exactly what we wanted. The only thing that's changed, really, is that the $2x$ is now subtracted instead of added. So by subtracting $2x$ from both sides, we were able to move the $2x$ from the right to the left. The next step is to combine $5x$ and $2x$ by subtracting their coefficients. Since $5 - 2 = 3$, we get $3x$.

$$7 + 3x = 16$$

Switch and Undo

This leaves only two operations to undo: a multiplication by 3 and an addition of 7. But since we're not used to seeing a $3x$ written on the inside (near the equals sign) and a plain number on the outside, let's switch the order of the 7 and $3x$ before undoing.

$$3x + 7 = 16$$ **Switch 7 and 3x**

In this case, switching is allowed since the 7 and $3x$ are added, and we can always add two things in any order. It's no different, really, than changing $7 + x$ to $x + 7$, and we do that all the time.

Now we're ready to undo. Since the multiplication is done before the addition, we should undo the addition first by subtracting 7 from both sides.

$$3x + 7 - 7 = 16 - 7$$

The left side becomes $3x$ and the right side 9.

$$3x = 9$$

Next, we undo the multiplication by dividing both sides by 3.

$$\frac{3x}{3} = \frac{9}{3}$$

That makes the left side equal to x.

$$x = \frac{9}{3}$$

Our algebra equation has been turned into a simple arithmetic problem. The last step is to divide 9 by 3 for our answer.

$$x = 3$$

Moving a Subtracted x Term

Just to make sure you're catching on, let's do one more problem.

$$5 + 7x = 25 - 3x$$

Notice we have x's on both sides again: a $7x$ on the left and a $3x$ on the right. In order to combine the x's, we need to get them on the same side of the equation. Let's move the $3x$ over to the left side. But look. The $3x$ is subtracted. Can we still move it by undoing? Sure we can, and here's how. Instead of subtracting, we just add $3x$ to both sides, like this.

$$5 + 7x + 3x = 25 - 3x + 3x$$ **Add 3x to both sides**

On the right side, the addition of $3x$ undoes the subtraction of $3x$, leaving just 25.

$$5 + 7x + 3x = 25$$

Now the x's are on the same side, and we can combine them by adding their coefficients. Since $7 + 3 = 10$, we end up with $10x$ on the left.

$$5 + 10x = 25$$

Next, let's switch the order of the 5 and $10x$ before undoing.

$$10x + 5 = 25$$

Finally, we're ready to undo. The x is multiplied by 10 first and then 5 is added second, so we need to undo the addition first, by subtracting 5 from both sides.

$$10x + 5 - 5 = 25 - 5$$

That makes the left side equal to $10x$ and the right side 20.

$$10x = 20$$

From here, we undo the multiplication by dividing both sides by 10.

$$\frac{10x}{10} = \frac{20}{10}$$

Naturally, the left side becomes just x.

$$x = \frac{20}{10}$$

The algebra equation has become an arithmetic equation, and the last step is to divide on the right to get an answer of 2.

$$x = 2$$

Practice 102

   a. Simplify the expression $-x + (-6x)$.

   b. Solve the equation $5 + 9x = 19 + 2x$.

   c. Solve the equation $2 + 6x = 7 + 5x$.

   d. Solve the equation $3 + 2x = 21 - 4x$.

e. Translate the word problem below into an equation; then solve.

There is a number that if you add 4 to it, and then multiply the result by 5, you get 60. What's the number?

Problem Set 102

Tell whether each sentence below is True or False.

1. To solve an equation with x's on both sides, you have to move the x's to the same side first.

2. Undoing can be used to move an x to the other side of an equation.

Add or subtract each group of numbers below.

3.
$$5.384$$
$$+9.027$$

4.
$$7,305$$
$$-4,018$$

Add or subtract (as indicated) each pair of numbers below.

5. $-41+(-9)$

6. $-84-67$

Multiply or divide (as indicated) each pair of numbers below.

7. $(11)(-12)$

8. $\dfrac{-70}{-10}$

Calculate the value of each expression below. (Make sure to do the operations in the correct order.)

9. $8-3 \cdot 9$

10. $\dfrac{-56}{5+2}$

Translate each of the following phrases into a mathematical expression. (Don't calculate the answer.)

11. 15 divided by 3 first, and 21 added to that total.

12. 6 minus 4 first, and then that total multiplied by -5.

Simplify each expression below.

13. $25x + 5 + 11$ **14.** $18x - 7x$ **(a) 15.** $-x + (-4x)$

Solve each equation below.

16. $9 - x = 11$ **17.** $5x + 3 = 38$ **18.** $\dfrac{x + 6}{2} = -7$

(b) 19. $6 + 8x = 21 + 3x$ **(c) 20.** $1 + 5x = 7 + 4x$ **(d) 21.** $4 + 3x = 12 - 5x$

Translate the word problem below into an equation; then solve.

(e) 22. There is a number that if you add 7 to it, and then multiply the result by 9, you get 81. What's the number?

Lesson 103—Refrigerator Repairs

As we've said before, there's no point in learning algebra if we can't use it to solve real-world problems. But what kinds of problems have equations with x's on both sides (which we learned about in the last lesson)? Well, here's an example from the not-so-glamorous (yet certainly important) world of refrigerator repairs.

> Poor Richard's Refrigerator Repair Service only charges $25 for a service call (just to come to the house) plus $40 per hour to do the repair job. Snooty Rudy's Refrigerator Repair Service charges $50 for a service call plus $35 per hour to do the repair job. How many hours would a job have to take for the bill of both repair services to be the same?

This problem is asking us to figure out which repair service will be cheaper to use on a particular job. To solve, we need to first make x equal the thing we're trying to find. We want to know how many hours a job has to take for Rudy's and Richard's bills to be the same. So that's x.

x = number of hours the job has to take for bills to be the same

Writing the Equation

Next, let's set up the equation. We're interested in a job where Richard and Rudy will charge the same amount. That means the equation can be set up like this.

Poor Richard's bill = Snooty Rudy's bill.

Now we have to put in the x's and numbers. How can we write an expression for Poor Richard's bill, though? He charges $25 just to come out to the house plus $40 per hour to do the repair work. That means if a job takes 2 hours, then his bill will be $25+40(2)$. If a job takes 3 hours, his bill will be $25+40(3)$. But we're interested in a job that takes x hours (that's what we're trying to find). For that job, Richard's bill will be 25 plus 40 times x, or $25+40x$. That's the expression we need.

To finish the other side of the equation, we need an expression for Snooty Rudy's bill. If Snooty Rudy charges $50 to come out to the house plus $35 per hour to do the work, his bill for a job taking x hours must be $50+35x$. It's the same thinking we used for Poor Richard. Putting both expressions in the equation gives us this.

Poor Richard's bill   Snooty Rudy's bill

$$25 + 40x \quad = \quad 50 + 35x$$

Getting the x's on the Same Side

This equation has x's on both sides, just as we said it would. We know how to solve it, after the last lesson. We have to move the x's to the same side. Let's move $35x$ to the left side by subtracting $35x$ from both sides.

$$25 + 40x - 35x = 50 + 35x - 35x$$

The subtraction undoes the addition (of $35x$) on the right, leaving just 50.

$$25 + 40x - 35x = 50$$

This step has moved the $35x$ over to the left side (only now it's being subtracted). From here, we can combine the x's by subtracting their coefficients. Since $40 - 35 = 5$, we end up with a $5x$ on the left.

$$25 + 5x = 50$$

To get ready to undo, let's switch the order of 25 and $5x$.

$$5x + 25 = 50$$

Since addition is the last operation being performed on x, it's the first thing we should undo. So we subtract 25 from both sides.

$$5x + 25 - 25 = 50 - 25$$

That leaves $5x$ on the left and 25 on the right.

$$5x = 25$$

Next, we undo the multiplication by dividing both sides by 5.

$$\frac{5x}{5} = \frac{25}{5}$$

And that gives us x on the left.

$$x = \frac{25}{5}$$

Dividing 25 by 5 on the right gives us this: $x = 5$. That means Poor Richard's and Snooty Rudy's bill will be exactly the same for a job that takes 5 hours. This was an example of a real-world problem that can be solved with an equation that has x's on both sides.

Practice 103

a. What is $\dfrac{3}{4}$ of $\dfrac{8}{9}$?

b. Simplify the expression $4x - 6x$.

c. Solve the equation $2 + 8x = 6 + 3x$.

d. Solve the equation $12 + x = 2 - 4x$.

e. Translate the word problem below into an equation; then solve.

Palatial Plumbing only charges $35 for a service call (just to come to the house) plus $50 per hour to do the repair job. Perfecto Plumbing charges $60 for a service call plus $45 per hour to do the repair job. How many hours would a job have to take for the bills of both plumbing services to be the same?

Problem Set 103

Convert each percent below into decimal form.

1. 42%

2. 75.25%

Answer each question below.

3. What is 38% of 275?

(a) 4. What is $\dfrac{5}{6}$ of $\dfrac{7}{10}$?

Add or subtract (as indicated) each pair of numbers below.

5. $-17 + 31$

6. $-25 - (-43)$

Multiply or divide (as indicated) each pair of numbers below.

7. $\dfrac{42}{-7}$

8. $(-7.5)(4)$

Calculate the value of each expression below. (Make sure to do the operations in the correct order.)

9. $-3(8+5)$

10. $\dfrac{54}{6}-9$

Translate each of the following word problems into an equation. (Don't solve.)

11. There's some number that if you divide it by 4 first, and then add 26 to that total, the result is 89.

12. There's some number that if you subtract 3 from it first, and then multiply that total by -7, the result is 21.

Simplify each expression below.

13. $9+x-4$

14. $x+8x$

(b) 15. $2x-5x$

Solve each equation below.

16. $2(x+7)=24$

17. $\dfrac{x}{5}-9=3$

18. $8x+11=27$

19. $3x+6x=-81$

(c) 20. $2+7x=4+2x$

(d) 21. $9+x=3-5x$

Translate the word problem below into an equation; then solve.

(e) 22. Alaskan Air Conditioning only charges $20 for a service call (just to come to the house) plus $30 per hour to do the repair job. Antarctic Air Conditioning charges $40 for a service call plus $25 per hour to do the repair job. How many hours would a job have to take for the bills of both air conditioning services to be the same?

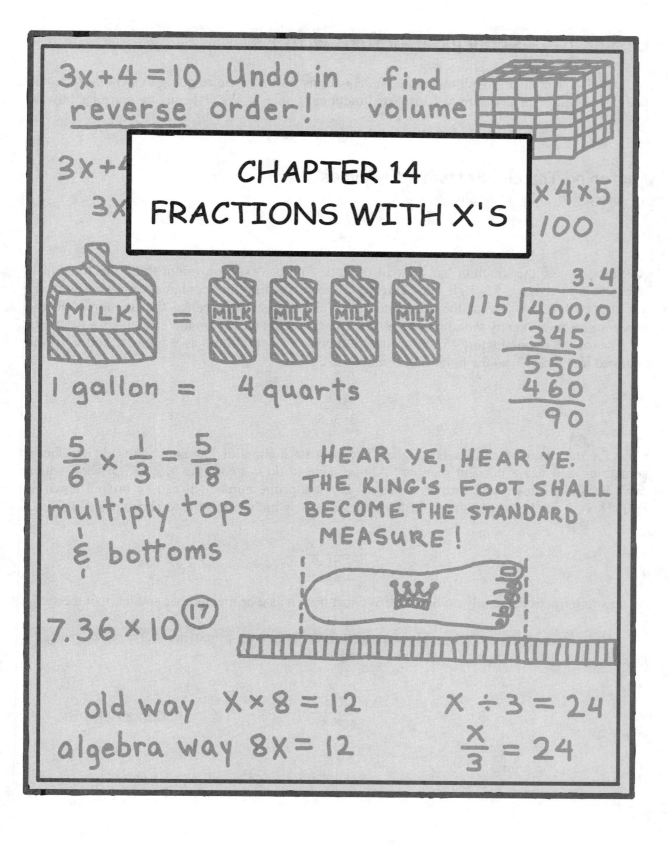

$3x + 4 = 10$ Undo in reverse order! find volume

$3x +$ ...

$3x$ ...

$\times 4 \times 5$
100

MILK = MILK MILK MILK MILK

1 gallon = 4 quarts

$$\frac{5}{6} \times \frac{1}{3} = \frac{5}{18}$$

multiply tops & bottoms

$7.36 \times 10^{\textcircled{17}}$

$$\begin{array}{r} 3.4 \\ 115\overline{\smash)400,0} \\ 345 \\ \hline 550 \\ 460 \\ \hline 90 \end{array}$$

HEAR YE, HEAR YE. THE KING'S FOOT SHALL BECOME THE STANDARD MEASURE!

CHAPTER 14
FRACTIONS WITH X'S

old way $X \times 8 = 12$

algebra way $8X = 12$

$X \div 3 = 24$

$$\frac{X}{3} = 24$$

Lesson 104—Reducing Fractions with x's

We've been learning all about algebra equations. But now we're going to switch gears, and learn about algebra fractions. Those are fractions with x's. We'll begin by learning how to reduce them.

Factoring Top and Bottom into Primes

Here's our first example.

$$\frac{18x}{45}$$

As you can see, this fraction has an x in the top. And at first, you might think the fraction is impossible to reduce. After all, how can we reduce a fraction that contains a missing number? We don't even know what the numerator is. Well, we can still reduce the fraction. And the process is almost exactly the same one we use in arithmetic: we factor and cancel. As a first step, let's factor the denominator, 45, into prime numbers: 45 is the same as 9 times 5, and 9 can be changed to 3 times 3, so the bottom becomes $3 \cdot 3 \cdot 5$.

$$\frac{18x}{3 \cdot 3 \cdot 5}$$

Now for the numerator. This is tougher, because the numerator has an x. How do we factor something that has a missing number? All we have to do is treat x as a prime number, which can't be broken down any further. Since 18 is *not* a prime number, it can be broken down as $9 \cdot 2$. Next, 9 can be broken down further to get $3 \cdot 3 \cdot 2$, which means the top becomes $3 \cdot 3 \cdot 2 \cdot x$.

$$\frac{3 \cdot 3 \cdot 2 \cdot x}{3 \cdot 3 \cdot 5}$$

So an x in a fraction is really no big deal. We just treat it as a prime number and let it sit there.

With both the numerator and denominator factored into prime numbers, we're ready to cancel. There are two pairs of 3s that can be canceled.

$$\frac{\cancel{3} \cdot \cancel{3} \cdot 2 \cdot x}{\cancel{3} \cdot \cancel{3} \cdot 5} \qquad \textbf{Cancel the 3s.}$$

That leaves us with this.

$$\frac{2 \cdot x}{5} \quad \text{or} \quad \frac{2x}{5}.$$

So $\dfrac{2x}{5}$ is the fully reduced fraction.

The thing to remember from this first example is that we reduce fractions with x's in basically same way that we reduce fractions in arithmetic: We factor everything into prime numbers and then cancel. Just remember to treat x as a prime number.

Reducing with an x in the Bottom

Let's do another example.

$$\frac{8}{24x}$$

This fraction has an x in the bottom. That's no problem, though. We're still going to treat it as a prime number. To reduce the fraction, we factor the top and bottom into prime numbers first. On top, 8 can be broken down as $2 \cdot 2 \cdot 2$.

$$\frac{2 \cdot 2 \cdot 2}{24x}$$

On bottom, 24 breaks down as $8 \cdot 3$, but then 8 can be broken down further as $2 \cdot 2 \cdot 2$. And then x is just x. So that gives us $2 \cdot 2 \cdot 2 \cdot 3 \cdot x$.

$$\frac{2 \cdot 2 \cdot 2}{2 \cdot 2 \cdot 2 \cdot 3 \cdot x}$$

Now we're ready to cancel. There are three pairs of 2s that can be crossed out.

$$\frac{\cancel{2} \cdot \cancel{2} \cdot \cancel{2}}{\cancel{2} \cdot \cancel{2} \cdot \cancel{2} \cdot 3 \cdot x} \qquad \textbf{Cancel the 2s.}$$

That leaves us with a $3x$ on bottom. But what about the top? Everything canceled up there, so we put a 1 in the numerator. That's because canceling is the same as dividing, remember. So by canceling those 2s, we were really dividing the top and bottom by 2 three times, which is the same as dividing by 8. And $8 \div 8$ equals 1. So we end up with 1 on top and $3x$ on bottom.

$$\frac{1}{3x}$$

Practice 104

   a.   How many feet are in 3.7 miles?

   b.   Reduce the fraction $\dfrac{20x}{44}$.

   c.   Reduce the fraction $\dfrac{9}{45x}$.

   d.   Solve the equation $3 + 7x = 15 + 5x$.

   e.   Translate the word problem below into an equation; then solve.

   Eric can paint 4 postcards an hour and Jeremy can paint 5. Working together, how many hours will it take them to paint 54 postcards?

Problem Set 104

Tell whether each sentence below is True or False.

   1.   To reduce fractions with x's, you need a completely different method from the one used in basic math. T

   2.   An x is treated as a prime number when factoring. F

Do each unit conversion below.

   3.   Convert 5,700 centimeters to meters.

   (a) 4.   How many feet are in 2.4 miles?

Add or subtract (as indicated) each pair of numbers below.

   5. $-10 + 29$ 39

   6. $-62 - (-23)$ -41

Multiply or divide (as indicated) each pair of numbers below.

7. $\left(\dfrac{1}{4}\right)(-12)$ -2

8. $\dfrac{35}{-7}$

Calculate the value of each expression below. Make sure to do the operations in the correct order.

9. $14 - 2 \cdot 3$

10. $\dfrac{-5 + 17}{2}$

Translate each of the following phrases into a mathematical expression. (Don't calculate the answer.)

11. 31 minus 4 first, and that total divided by 9.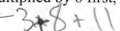

12. -3 multiplied by 8 first, and then 11 added to that total.

$-3 * 8 + 11$

Simplify each expression below.

13. $7x + 2 + 5$

14. $20x - 11x$

Reduce each fraction below.

(b) 15. $\dfrac{12x}{42}$

(c) 16. $\dfrac{4}{28x}$

17. $\dfrac{5x}{35}$

Solve each equation below.

18. $\dfrac{x + 15}{2} = 13$

19. $\dfrac{1}{3}x = \dfrac{5}{9}$

20. $7 + 3x + 5 = -15$

21. $6x + 3x = 18$

(d) 22. $6 + 8x = 18 + 5x$

Translate the word problem below into an equation; then solve.

(e) 23. Lucy can assemble 6 care packages to the troops overseas in an hour. Debra can assemble 10 care packages in an hour. Working together, how many hours will it take them to assemble 128 care packages?

Lesson 105—Canceling x's

In the previous lesson, we learned how to reduce fractions with x's. But did you notice that each of our examples had just one x? Some fractions have more than one x, though. Here's an example.

$$\frac{9x}{15x}$$

See, this fraction has an x on top and another on bottom. The question is how do we reduce in a case like this? We just factor and cancel, as usual. The numerator, $9x$, can be factored by breaking down 9 as $3 \cdot 3$ and then treating x as a prime number. That gives us $3 \cdot 3 \cdot x$ on top.

$$\frac{3 \cdot 3 \cdot x}{15x} \qquad \textbf{Factor the top.}$$

Now we do the same thing with the bottom. Fifteen can be factored as $3 \cdot 5$. Then with the x, we have $3 \cdot 5 \cdot x$ on bottom.

$$\frac{3 \cdot 3 \cdot x}{3 \cdot 5 \cdot x} \qquad \textbf{Factor the bottom.}$$

Cancel x's Like Numbers

With everything factored, we're ready to cancel. We'll start by canceling a pair of 3s.

$$\frac{\cancel{3} \cdot 3 \cdot x}{\cancel{3} \cdot 5 \cdot x} \qquad \textbf{Cancel the 3s.}$$

What about the x's? Can they be canceled? Absolutely. After all, x just stands for a missing number. And it's the same missing number on top as it is on bottom. So we can cancel x's just as we would any other number. Just cross them out.

$$\frac{\cancel{3} \cdot 3 \cdot \cancel{x}}{\cancel{3} \cdot 5 \cdot \cancel{x}} \qquad \textbf{Cancel the xs.}$$

That leaves 3 on top and 5 on bottom. So our fully reduced answer is $\frac{3}{5}$.

Another example

Let's do one more example.

$$\frac{5x}{30x}$$

The first step is to factor the numerator and the denominator. In this case, the top has just a 5 and an x, so nothing can be factored any further there. We'll put a dot in between the 5 and the x, just to show that the top is factored.

$$\frac{5 \cdot x}{30x} \qquad \text{Factor the top.}$$

Next, the $30x$ in the denominator can be changed to $6 \cdot 5 \cdot x$. But then 6 can be broken down further as 2 times 3 to get $2 \cdot 3 \cdot 5 \cdot x$ on bottom.

$$\frac{5 \cdot x}{2 \cdot 3 \cdot 5 \cdot x} \qquad \text{Factor the bottom.}$$

Now we're ready to cancel. We can cancel a pair of 5s and x's, like this.

$$\frac{\cancel{5} \cdot \cancel{x}}{2 \cdot 3 \cdot \cancel{5} \cdot \cancel{x}} \qquad \text{Cancel the 5s and xs.}$$

Since everything on top has canceled, we need to put a 1 up there. On the bottom, we have 2 times 3, or 6. So we end up with $\frac{1}{2 \cdot 3}$, or $\frac{1}{6}$, which is fully reduced.

The main point of this lesson, then, is that we can cancel x's just as we would any other number.

Practice 105

a. Reduce the fraction $\frac{9x}{21x}$.

b. Reduce the fraction $\frac{7x}{63x}$.

c. Solve the equation $8 + 2x = 7 - 5x$.

d. Solve the equation $10 + 11x = -14 + 3x$.

e. Translate the word problem below into an equation; then solve.

Dump truck #1 and dump truck #2 are headed straight toward each other. Truck #1 is traveling at 55 mph, and truck #2 is traveling at 58 mph. If the two are 339 miles apart, how many hours will it be before they meet?

Problem Set 105

Convert each fraction below into decimal form. Give exact answers (no rounding).

1. $\dfrac{1}{100}$

2. $\dfrac{2}{9}$

Add or subtract (as indicated) each pair of numbers below.

3. $-\dfrac{1}{5}+\left(-\dfrac{2}{5}\right)$

4. $74-(-59)$

Multiply or divide (as indicated) each pair of numbers below.

5. $(-7)(14)$

6. $\dfrac{-52}{13}$

Calculate the value of each expression below. (Make sure to do the operations in the correct order.)

7. $\dfrac{60}{12}+18$

8. $6(1-8)$

Translate each of the following word problems into an equation. (Don't solve.)

9. There's some number that if you multiply it by -3 first, and then add 15 to that total, the result is 29.

10. There's some number that if you subtract 7 from it first, and then divide that total by 20, the result is -100.

Simplify each expression below.

11. $3x + (-5x)$ **12.** $-x + 4x$

Reduce each fraction below.

(a) 13. $\dfrac{4x}{10x}$ **(b) 14.** $\dfrac{3x}{12x}$ **15.** $\dfrac{16}{36x}$

Solve each equation below.

16. $-14x = 378$ **17.** $\dfrac{x}{3} + 7 = -3$ **18.** $-4(x+9) = -16$

19. $5x + 2x = 63$ **(c) 20.** $6 + 2x = 5 - 7x$ **(d) 21.** $3 + 10x = -9 + 4x$

Translate the word problem below into an equation; then solve.

(e) 22. Motorcycle #1 and motorcycle #2 are headed straight toward each other. Motorcycle #1 is traveling at 55 mph, and motorcycle #2 is traveling at 70 mph. If the two motorcycles are 500 miles apart, how many hours will it be before they meet?

Lesson 106—Fractions and Parentheses—Part 1

We've been learning how to reduce fractions with x's, and so far it probably seems pretty easy. We just treat the x's as numbers, and everything else works just like fractions from arithmetic. Well, in this lesson, things get a little more complicated. Take a look at our first example.

$$\frac{2(x+5)}{4}$$

What's different about this fraction is that it has parentheses in the numerator. Basically, the fraction takes a missing number (x) and adds 5 to it; then 2 is multiplied by that result, and finally that total is divided by 4.

The Top Really is Factored

The question is how do we reduce the fraction? Well, the good news is that we can still use our same method: factor and cancel. As a first step, let's factor the denominator: 4 breaks down as $2 \cdot 2$.

$$\frac{2(x+5)}{2 \cdot 2}$$ **Factor the bottom.**

Now for the numerator. It may seem like the numerator isn't factored, because it has an addition: $x+5$. But actually the numerator is factored. That's because the $x+5$ is inside parentheses. Here's why that matters. The rule says that any quantity that's inside parentheses should be treated as a single number. So we can think of $2(x+5)$ as the number 2 multiplied by another number $(x+5)$. That's a multiplication, so the numerator is technically factored. That means we have both bottom and top factored, and we're ready to cancel.[1]

$$\frac{2 \cdot (x+5)}{2 \cdot 2}$$ **The top is already factored.**

We have a 2 and an $(x+5)$ on top and two 2s on bottom. The only thing to cancel is a pair of 2s.

$$\frac{\cancel{2} \cdot (x+5)}{\cancel{2} \cdot 2}$$ **Cancel the 2s.**

All we have left now is the quantity $x+5$ on top (remember, that's supposed to be treated as a

---

[1] We put a dot between the 2 and the $(x + 5)$ to show that it's been broken down into its factors (just as we did with the 4 on bottom)

single number) and one 2 on bottom. So there's nothing else to cancel. Our final fully reduced answer, then, is

$$\frac{x+5}{2}.$$

Notice that we took off the parentheses. Those can be dropped, because $x+5$ isn't being multiplied by anything anymore.

Subtraction in Parentheses

Here's a slightly tougher example.

$$\frac{6(x-5)}{12}$$

This fraction also has a quantity inside parentheses, but it's a subtraction instead of an addition. That doesn't change a thing, though. The $x-5$ should be treated as a single number, as in the previous example. And we should start by factoring the top and bottom, as usual. In the bottom, 12 factors as $2 \cdot 2 \cdot 3$.

$$\frac{6(x-5)}{2 \cdot 2 \cdot 3} \qquad \textbf{Factor the bottom.}$$

On top, we have 6 times the quantity inside parentheses, $(x-5)$. The $(x-5)$ has to be treated like a single number, remember. So we have 6 times $(x-5)$, which is factored. But we can break the top down a little further by changing 6 to $2 \cdot 3$.

$$\frac{2 \cdot 3 \cdot (x-5)}{2 \cdot 2 \cdot 3}$$

Now the top is factored as far as it will go, and we're ready to cancel. There's a pair of 2s that will cancel, and there's also a pair of 3s.

$$\frac{\cancel{2} \cdot \cancel{3} \cdot (x-5)}{\cancel{2} \cdot 2 \cdot \cancel{3}} \qquad \textbf{Cancel the 2s and 3s.}$$

Since $x-5$ is no longer multiplied by anything, we can drop the parentheses. And on bottom, we have just a 2 left.

$$\frac{x-5}{2}.$$

The main point is that when reducing fractions, quantities inside parentheses are treated as a single number.

Practice 106

a. Reduce the fraction $\dfrac{2(x+7)}{4}$.   **b.** Reduce the fraction $\dfrac{8(x-3)}{16}$.

c. Solve the equation $6 + 7x = 8 + 2x$.

d. Solve the equation $9 + x = 3 - 4x$.

e. Translate the word problem below into an equation; then solve.

There is a number that if you divide it by 3, and then add 7 to the result, you get 13. What's the number?

Problem Set 106

Tell whether each sentence below is True or False.

1. The method used to reduce fractions with x's is basically the same one used to reduce fractions that have just numbers.

2. When reducing fractions, any quantity in parentheses should be treated as a single number.

Add or subtract each group of numbers below.

3.   297.5
        $+931.04$

4.   0.6359
        -0.4836

Add or subtract (as indicated) each pair of numbers below.

5. $12 + (-25)$ **6.** $-9 - (-13)$

Multiply or divide (as indicated) each pair of numbers below.

7. $(10)(-3.5)$ **8.** $\dfrac{-36}{-4}$

Calculate the value of each expression below. (Make sure to do the operations in the correct order.)

9. $7 \cdot 3 - 5$

10. $\dfrac{2-14}{-4}$

Translate each of the following phrases into a mathematical expression. (Don't calculate the answer.)

11. -7 added to 6 first, and that total multiplied by 20.

12. -42 divided by 6 first, and then 8 subtracted from that total.

Simplify each expression below.

13. $8x + x$

14. $-5x + 4x$

Reduce each fraction below.

15. $\dfrac{3x}{24x}$

16. $\dfrac{27x}{18}$

(a) 17. $\dfrac{3(x+4)}{9}$

(b) 18. $\dfrac{10(x-3)}{20}$

Solve each equation below.

19. $4x - 7 = 13$

20. $\dfrac{x+11}{2} = -14$

(c) 21. $2 + 6x = 6 + 3x$

(d) 22. $9 + x = 2 - 5x$

Translate the word problem below into an equation; then solve.

(e) 23. There is a number that if you divide it by 6, and then add 4 to the result, you get 12. What's the number?

Lesson 107—Fractions and Parentheses—Part 2

In the last lesson, we learned how to reduce fractions with parentheses. Well, here's another example.

$$\frac{15}{3(x+1)}$$

Notice that this time the parentheses are in the bottom of the fraction. This just means 15 divided by 3 times the sum of x and 1 (in other words, the addition is done before the multiplication). To reduce the fraction, we follow the same method we always use: factor and cancel.

The top factors as 3 times 5.

$$\frac{3 \cdot 5}{3(x+1)}$$

The bottom is already factored, because the quantity in parentheses has to be treated as a single number. So the bottom is the number 3 times some other quantity $(x+1)$.

$$\frac{3 \cdot 5}{3 \cdot (x+1)}$$

With both top and bottom factored, we're ready to cancel. We can cross out a pair of 3s.

$$\frac{\cancel{3} \cdot 5}{\cancel{3} \cdot (x+1)}$$ **Cancel the 3s.**

That leaves us with 5 on top and $(x+1)$ on bottom. But we don't need parentheses around the $x+1$. Our final, fully reduced answer, then is

$$\frac{5}{x+1}.$$

Parentheses in Top and Bottom

Now, for the next example.

$$\frac{8(x-7)}{24(x-7)}$$

This fraction has parentheses in both the top and bottom. But we can still use our standard method for reducing: factor and cancel. The top is already factored, since 8 is multiplied by the quantity $(x-7)$ (which is treated as a single number). But we can factor the top even further by breaking down 8 as $2 \cdot 2 \cdot 2$.

$$\frac{2 \cdot 2 \cdot 2 \cdot (x-7)}{24(x-7)}$$

On the bottom, we have 24 multiplied by the quantity $(x-7)$, which is factored. But we can go further by breaking 24 down as $2 \cdot 12$. Then 12 can be changed to $2 \cdot 2 \cdot 3$. So we end up with $2 \cdot 2 \cdot 2 \cdot 3 \cdot (x-7)$ on bottom.

$$\frac{2 \cdot 2 \cdot 2 \cdot (x-7)}{2 \cdot 2 \cdot 2 \cdot 3 \cdot (x-7)}$$

Now we're ready to cancel. There are actually three pairs of 2s that can be canceled.

$$\frac{\cancel{2} \cdot \cancel{2} \cdot \cancel{2} \cdot (x-7)}{\cancel{2} \cdot \cancel{2} \cdot \cancel{2} \cdot 3 \cdot (x-7)}$$ **Cancel three pairs of 2s.**

Canceling Quantities in Parentheses

But what about the $(x-7)$'s? Can they be canceled? Well, remember, anything inside parentheses has to be treated as a single number, so what we have is some number on top, $(x-7)$, and that same number on bottom. Since they're the same, we can cancel them.

$$\frac{\cancel{2} \cdot \cancel{2} \cdot \cancel{2} \cdot \cancel{(x-7)}}{\cancel{2} \cdot \cancel{2} \cdot \cancel{2} \cdot 3 \cdot \cancel{(x-7)}}$$ **Cancel the (x-7)'s too.**

By the way, what we really did by canceling the $(x-7)$'s was divide the top and bottom by $(x-7)$. Since everything on top has been canceled, we have to put a 1 up there (as always). And there's just a 3 left on bottom. Amazingly, our original messy fraction, $\frac{8(x-7)}{24(x-7)}$, has reduced all the way down to $\frac{1}{3}$.

$$\frac{1}{3}$$

The main points of this lesson are that quantities in parentheses can be in the top and bottom of a fraction. And, since they're treated as single numbers, they can be canceled just like anything else.

Practice 107

a. Reduce the fraction $\dfrac{15}{5(x+4)}$.

b. Reduce the fraction $\dfrac{6(x-9)}{42(x-9)}$.

c. Solve the equation $-x-4x=55$.

d. Solve the equation $7+9x=5+2x$.

e. Translate the word problem below into an equation; then solve.

Sunshine Electrical Repair Service only charges $20 for a service call (just to come to the house) plus $30 per hour to do the repair job. Rainy Day Electrical Repair Service charges $40 for a service call plus $25 per hour to do the repair job. How many hours would a job have to take for the bills of both repair services to be the same?

Problem Set 107

Answer each question below.

1. What is 50% of 1,274?   **2.** What is $\dfrac{3}{4}$ of 230?

Add or subtract (as indicated) each pair of numbers below.

3. $-83+(-55)$ **4.** $-29-14$

Multiply or divide (as indicated) each pair of numbers below.

5. $(-5)(-16)$ **6.** $\dfrac{43}{-43}$

Calculate the value of each expression below. (Make sure to do the operations in the correct order.)

7. $30 + \dfrac{20}{4}$

8. $9(-11+4)$

Translate each of the following word problems into an equation. (Don't solve.)

9. There's some number that if you divide it by 8 first, and then subtract 37 from that total, the result is -91.

10. There's some number that if you add 4 to it first, and then multiply that total by -13, the result is 50.

Simplify each expression below.

11. $7 + 4x + 21$

12. $6x + 9x$

Reduce each fraction below.

13. $\dfrac{18}{6x}$

14. $\dfrac{5x}{25x}$

15. $\dfrac{4(x-2)}{12}$

(a) 16. $\dfrac{14}{7(x+1)}$

(b) 17. $\dfrac{4(x-5)}{24(x-5)}$

Solve each equation below.

18. $5(x-8) = 30$

19. $\dfrac{x}{4} + 21 = 19$

(c) 20. $-x - 3x = 48$

(d) 21. $5 + 11x = 3 + 2x$

Translate the word problem below into an equation; then solve.

(e) 22. Four Eyes Computer Repair Service only charges \$40 for a service call (just to come to the house) plus \$25 per hour to do the repair job. File Savers Computer Repair Service charges \$50 for a service call plus \$20 per hour to do the repair job. How many hours would a job have to take for the bills of both repair services to be the same?

Lesson 108—Multiplying Fractions with x's

We've learned to reduce fractions with x's. But what about multiplying, dividing, adding, and subtracting fractions with x's? We need to learn to do that too. So for the next few lessons, we'll concentrate on that, and we'll start in this lesson with multiplication.

Multiply the Tops and Bottoms

Here's our first example.

$$\frac{6x}{15} \cdot \frac{5}{14x}$$

See, we have two fractions multiplied and both contain x's. As it turns out, we can multiply these in the same way that we multiply fractions with just numbers. We factor and cancel first and then multiply the tops and the bottoms. The only thing we have to remember is to treat x as a prime number, which means it can't be broken down any further.

As a first step, then, let's factor everything in the top and bottom of both fractions. Remember, when multiplying fractions we always want to factor and cancel first, because it's faster. The top of the first fraction factors as $2 \cdot 3 \cdot x$, and the bottom factors as $3 \cdot 5$.

$$\frac{2 \cdot 3 \cdot x}{3 \cdot 5} \cdot \frac{5}{14x} \qquad \textbf{Factor first fraction.}$$

Now for the second fraction. On top, we have the prime number, 5, which can't be broken down any further. On bottom, we can factor $14x$ as $2 \cdot 7 \cdot x$.

$$\frac{2 \cdot 3 \cdot x}{3 \cdot 5} \cdot \frac{5}{2 \cdot 7 \cdot x} \qquad \textbf{Factor second fraction.}$$

With everything factored in both fractions, we're ready to cancel. And, remember, as with fractions that have only numbers, we can cancel anything on top with anything on bottom, in either fraction. There's a pair of 2s, a pair of 3s, a pair of 5s, and a pair of x's that will cancel.

$$\frac{\overset{1}{\cancel{2} \cdot \cancel{3} \cdot \cancel{x}}}{\underset{1}{\cancel{3} \cdot \cancel{5}}} \cdot \frac{\overset{1}{\cancel{5}}}{\cancel{2} \cdot 7 \cdot \cancel{x}} \qquad \textbf{Cancel first.}$$

Every factor has been canceled on top and bottom of the first fraction, so we need to put 1s there. And a 1 goes in place of the canceled 5. Here's what is left in both fractions.

$$\frac{1}{1} \cdot \frac{1}{7}$$

The final step is to multiply the tops and bottoms to get $\frac{1}{7}$, which is fully reduced. The great thing about factoring and canceling before multiplying is that we know that our answer is always fully reduced.

One More Time

Let's do one more multiplication example.

$$\frac{9x}{20} \cdot \frac{4x}{18x}$$

The first step is to factor everything in both fractions. The top of the first fraction factors as $3 \cdot 3 \cdot x$, and the 20 on bottom factors as $2 \cdot 2 \cdot 5$.

$$\frac{3 \cdot 3 \cdot x}{2 \cdot 2 \cdot 5} \cdot \frac{4x}{18x} \qquad \textbf{Factor the first fraction.}$$

Now for the second fraction. On top, $4x$ factors as $2 \cdot 2 \cdot x$ and on bottom $18x$ factors as $2 \cdot 3 \cdot 3 \cdot x$.

$$\frac{3 \cdot 3 \cdot x}{2 \cdot 2 \cdot 5} \cdot \frac{2 \cdot 2 \cdot x}{2 \cdot 3 \cdot 3 \cdot x} \qquad \textbf{Factor the second fraction.}$$

Next, we're ready to cancel. There are two pairs of 2s and two pairs of 3s that will cancel. A pair of x's can be canceled too.

$$\frac{\overset{1}{\cancel{3} \cdot \cancel{3} \cdot \cancel{x}}}{\cancel{2} \cdot \cancel{2} \cdot 5} \cdot \frac{\cancel{2} \cdot \cancel{2} \cdot x}{2 \cdot \cancel{3} \cdot \cancel{3} \cdot \cancel{x}} \qquad \textbf{Cancel in both fractions.}$$

Here are the remaining factors.

$$\frac{1}{5} \cdot \frac{x}{2}$$

The last step is to multiply the tops and bottoms to get the fully reduced answer.

$$\frac{x}{10}$$

The main point is that fractions with x's are multiplied in basically the same way that we multiply fractions with just numbers: factor and cancel, then multiply the tops and bottoms.

Practice 108

a.   Reduce the fraction $\dfrac{15(x-7)}{20(x-7)}$.

b.   Multiply the fractions $\dfrac{4x}{24}\cdot\dfrac{8}{16x}$. (Make sure your answer is fully reduced.)

c.   Multiply the fractions $\dfrac{12x}{26}\cdot\dfrac{13x}{24x}$. (Make sure your answer is fully reduced.)

d.   Solve the equation $5+4x=-19-4x$.

e.   Translate the word problem below into an equation; then solve.

Wendy and Sue are doubles partners. Wendy usually hits about 4 aces per hour, and Sue usually hits about 5 per hour. Together, how many hours should it take them to hit 27 aces?

Problem Set 108

Tell whether each sentence below is True or False.

1.   To multiply fractions with x's, you factor and cancel first.

2.   When multiplying fractions with x's, you factor, cancel, and then add the numerators.

Convert each fraction below into decimal form. Give exact answers (no rounding).

3. $\dfrac{3}{5}$

4. $\dfrac{1}{9}$

Add or subtract (as indicated) each pair of numbers below.

5. $-15+8$

6. $10-(-10)$

Multiply or divide (as indicated) each pair of numbers below.

7. $(9)(-9)$

8. $\dfrac{-60}{-4}$

Calculate the value of each expression below. (Make sure to do the operations in the correct order.)

9. $10 + 4(-3)$

10. $\dfrac{-15}{4-7}$

Translate each of the following phrases into a mathematical expression. (Don't calculate the answer.)

11. -7 multiplied by 16 first, and 22 added to that total.

12. 11 minus 4 first, and then that total divided by -3.

Simplify each expression below.

13. $5 + 10x - 11$

14. $-8x + (-5x)$

Reduce each fraction below.

15. $\dfrac{35}{5(x+11)}$

(a) 16. $\dfrac{14(x-4)}{21(x-4)}$

Multiply each pair of fractions below. (Make sure your answers are fully reduced.)

(b) 17. $\dfrac{4x}{18} \cdot \dfrac{6}{12x}$

(c) 18. $\dfrac{10x}{28} \cdot \dfrac{6x}{15x}$

Solve each equation below.

19. $\dfrac{x-5}{8} = -2$

20. $25x - 17x = -64$

(d) 21. $4 + 5x = -16 - 5x$

Translate the word problem below into an equation; then solve.

(e) 22. Bud and Lou are on the same bowling team. Bud usually bowls about 6 strikes per hour, and Lou usually bowls about 8 per hour. Together, how many hours should it take them to bowl 56 strikes?

Lesson 109—Dividing Fractions with x's

We've been combining fractions with x's, and in the last lesson we covered multiplication. Now we're going to learn how to divide fractions with x's. Here's our first example.

$$\frac{3x}{10} \div \frac{21x}{8}$$

The Old Division Symbol

First of all, notice that we've used the old arithmetic division symbol. Dividing fractions is one of the few places in algebra where this symbol is still used. It's also okay to use the fraction bar on this kind of problem. With the fraction bar, the problem looks like this.

$$\frac{\dfrac{3x}{10}}{\dfrac{21x}{8}}$$

So you can write it that way too. But most of the time, when fractions with x's are divided, the problem will be written with the old division symbol.

Invert and Multiply

Now let's do the division. It's actually really easy. Everything works the same way as it does when dividing fractions with only numbers. All we have to do is invert the second fraction (which just means flip it over) and then multiply. Flipping over $\dfrac{21x}{8}$, gives us this.

$$\frac{3x}{10} \cdot \frac{8}{21x} \qquad \textbf{Invert second fraction.}$$

If the division had been written with the fraction bar, then we would have inverted the bottom fraction and multiplied.

From here, we just multiply in the usual way. First, we factor everything in both fractions. On top of the first fraction, 3 and x can't be broken down any further. On bottom, 10 can be factored as $2 \cdot 5$.

$$\frac{3 \cdot x}{2 \cdot 5} \cdot \frac{8}{21x} \qquad \textbf{Factor first fraction.}$$

Now for the second fraction. On bottom, $21x$ can be factored as $3 \cdot 7 \cdot x$, and on top, 8 can be factored as $2 \cdot 2 \cdot 2$.

$$\frac{3 \cdot x}{2 \cdot 5} \cdot \frac{2 \cdot 2 \cdot 2}{3 \cdot 7 \cdot x} \qquad \textbf{Factor second fraction.}$$

With everything factored, we're ready to cancel. As usual, we can cancel any factor on top with any factor on bottom in either fraction. We can cancel one pair of 2s, a pair of 3s, and a pair of x's.

$$\frac{\overset{1}{\cancel{3}} \cdot \cancel{x}}{\cancel{2} \cdot 5} \cdot \frac{\cancel{2} \cdot 2 \cdot 2}{\cancel{3} \cdot 7 \cdot \cancel{x}} \qquad \textbf{Cancel in both fractions.}$$

That leaves us with this.

$$\frac{1}{5} \cdot \frac{2 \cdot 2}{7}$$

The last step is to multiply the tops and bottoms to get $\dfrac{4}{35}$. And even though these numbers are pretty big, we don't need to bother trying to reduce our answer. Since we factored and canceled before multiplying, we know the answer has to be fully reduced. So dividing fractions with x's is exactly like dividing fractions in arithmetic. (At least for the fractions that we'll be dividing in this book. It gets a little harder in *Algebra 1*.)

Practice 109

a. Multiply $(-2)(-5)(-6)$.

b. Multiply the fractions $\dfrac{5x}{12x} \cdot \dfrac{14x}{10x}$. (Make sure your answer is fully reduced.)

c. Divide the fractions $\dfrac{4x}{18} \div \dfrac{16x}{9}$. (Make sure your answer is fully reduced.)

d. Divide the fractions $\dfrac{\dfrac{5}{6x}}{\dfrac{10}{16x}}$. (Make sure your answer is fully reduced.)

e. Translate the word problem below into an equation; then solve.

Riding lawnmower #1 and riding lawnmower #2 are headed straight toward each other. Mower #1 is traveling at 3 feet per second, and mower #2 is traveling at 4 feet per second. If the two mowers are 77 feet apart, how many seconds will it be before they meet?

Problem Set 109

Answer each question below.

1. How far will a roller blader skating at 28 miles per hour go in $2\frac{1}{4}$ hours?

2. How long will a strand of blonde hair growing at 10 inches per year grow in $\frac{1}{2}$ year?

Add or subtract (as indicated) each pair of numbers below.

3. $-70-(-58)$

4. $-100+82$

Multiply or divide (as indicated) each group of numbers below.

5. $\dfrac{-1,000}{-50}$

(a) 6. $(-2)(-3)(-4)$

Calculate the value of each expression below. (Make sure to do the operations in the correct order.)

7. $\dfrac{-45}{5}-7$

8. $10(12-8)$

Translate each of the following word problems into an equation. (Don't solve.)

9. There's some number that if you multiply it by 14 first, and then add 23 to that total, the result is 101.

10. There's some number that if you subtract 41 from it first, and then divide that total by -5, the result is 26.

Simplify each expression below.

11. $17x+59x$

12. $10x+(-x)$

Reduce each fraction below.

13. $\dfrac{21}{7(x+5)}$

14. $\dfrac{10(x-2)}{18(x-2)}$

Multiply each pair of fractions below. (Make sure your answers are fully reduced.)

15. $\dfrac{32}{27x} \cdot \dfrac{9x}{8}$

(b) 16. $\dfrac{3x}{14x} \cdot \dfrac{7x}{5x}$

Divide each pair of fractions below. (Make sure your answers are fully reduced.)

(c) 17. $\dfrac{2x}{15} \div \dfrac{8x}{10}$

(d) 18. $\dfrac{\frac{4}{9x}}{\frac{2}{3x}}$

Solve each equation below.

19. $-9(x+3)=18$

20. $4x-10=6$

21. $21x-13x=56$

Translate the word problem below into an equation; then solve.

(e) 22. Electric scooter #1 and electric scooter #2 are headed straight toward each other. Scooter #1 is traveling at 5 feet per second, and scooter #2 is traveling at 8 feet per second. If the two scooters are 52 feet apart, how many seconds will it be before they meet?

Lesson 110—Adding Fractions with x's

We've covered multiplying and dividing fractions with x's. What about adding them?

Same Denominators
Look at this example.

$$\frac{4}{3x} + \frac{2}{3x}$$

See, these two fractions are added together. But for the first time, the denominators have x's. The good news, though, is that all we have to do to add these is add the numerators. It works just like adding fractions that have only numbers. Since our denominators are the same ($3x$), we can just add the numerators.

$$\frac{4+2}{3x} \quad \text{or} \quad \frac{6}{3x} \qquad \textbf{Add numerators.}$$

Now, we have to make sure our answer is fully reduced. And this is where addition of fractions is different from multiplication and division. When multiplying or dividing fractions, we reduce first, which means we don't have to worry about reducing our answer. But when adding fractions the reducing step comes last. So after getting our answer, we always have to try to reduce it. So let's see if we can reduce $\frac{6}{3x}$. The top factors as $2 \cdot 3$ and the bottom is already broken down as far as it will go as $3 \cdot x$.

$$\frac{2 \cdot 3}{3 \cdot x} \qquad \textbf{Factoring top and bottom.}$$

From here, we can cancel the 3s.

$$\frac{2 \cdot \cancel{3}}{\cancel{3} \cdot x} \qquad \textbf{Cancel the 3s.}$$

That leaves $\frac{2}{x}$, which is our fully reduced answer.

Different Denominators
Let's try another one.

$$\frac{5}{2x} + \frac{6}{x}$$

We have x's in each denominator again. But what's different about this example is that the denominators are not the same. As always, we need to make the denominators the same before adding. All we have to do is multiply the bottom and top of the second fraction by 2.

$$\frac{5}{2x} + \frac{2 \cdot 6}{2 \cdot x} \qquad \text{Multiply top and bottom by 2.}$$

$$\frac{5}{2x} + \frac{12}{2x}$$

Now we're ready to add the numerators.

$$\frac{17}{2x} \qquad \text{Add the numerators}$$

Since we're adding (and not multiplying or dividing), we need to make sure that our answer is fully reduced by trying to factor and cancel. On top, 17 is a prime number, so it can't be broken down any further. Nothing can be done on bottom either. It just has the factors 2 and x.

$$\frac{17}{2 \cdot x} \qquad \text{Nothing cancels}$$

Since nothing will cancel, $\frac{17}{2x}$ is fully reduced, and that's our final answer.

Let's do another example.

$$\frac{3}{5x} + \frac{1}{2x}$$

The denominators are different here too, so we have to make them the same before adding. Only this time, we need to multiply both fractions. The lowest common denominator is $10x$, which means we need to multiply the top and bottom of the first fraction by 2 and the top and bottom of the second fraction by 5.

$$\frac{2 \cdot 3}{2 \cdot 5 \cdot x} + \frac{5 \cdot 1}{5 \cdot 2 \cdot x} \qquad \text{Change bottoms to 10x.}$$

Now we can simplify in both fractions to get this.

$$\frac{6}{10x} + \frac{5}{10x}$$

With both denominators the same, we can now add the numerators to get $\frac{11}{10x}$.

We're not finished yet, though. We still need to try to reduce our answer. Since 11 is a prime number, it can't be broken down. On bottom, $10x$ factors as $2 \cdot 5 \cdot x$.

$$\frac{11}{2 \cdot 5 \cdot x}$$

Since nothing will cancel, $\frac{11}{10x}$ is fully reduced.

So adding fractions with x's is pretty simple. First, we make sure the denominators are the same. If they're not we multiply the top and bottom of one or both fractions by the right numbers. Second, we add the numerators. Last, we reduce the answer (if possible). It's the same exact process we use in arithmetic.

Practice 110

a. Reduce the fraction $\frac{28(x-6)}{49(x-6)}$.

b. Multiply the fractions $\left(\frac{16x}{21x}\right)\left(\frac{7}{24x}\right)$. (Make sure your answer is fully reduced.)

c. Add the fractions $\frac{2}{5x} + \frac{3}{x}$. (Make sure your answer is fully reduced.)

d. Add the fractions $\frac{1}{3x} + \frac{2}{7x}$. (Make sure your answer is fully reduced.)

e. Translate the word problem below into an equation; then solve.

There is a number that if you subtract 4 from it, and then multiply the result by 7, you get 42. What's the number?

Problem Set 110

Tell whether each sentence below is True or False.

1. To add fractions with x's, you factor and cancel first.

2. When adding fractions with x's, once the denominators are the same, you add the numerators.

Multiply or divide each pair of numbers below. Write any remainders in decimal form.

3.
$$15.3$$
$$\times 4.6$$

4. $12\overline{)34{,}254}$

Add or subtract (as indicated) each group of numbers below.

5. $-4+(-7)+(-8)$

6. $-19-20$

Multiply or divide (as indicated) each pair of numbers below.

7. $(6)(-9)$

8. $\dfrac{-68}{-17}$

Calculate the value of each expression below. (Make sure to do the operations in the correct order.)

9. $(9)(3)-14$

10. $\dfrac{7+15}{2}$

Translate each of the following phrases into a mathematical expression. (Don't calculate the answer.)

11. 12 added to 21 first, and that total multiplied by 3.

12. 42 divided by 7 first, and then 5 added to that total.

Reduce each fraction below.

13. $\dfrac{20(x+7)}{60}$

(a) 14. $\dfrac{32(x-3)}{40(x-3)}$

Multiply or divide (as indicated) each pair of fractions below. (Make sure your answers are fully reduced.)

15. $\dfrac{4x}{12} \div \dfrac{8x}{6}$

(b) 16. $\left(\dfrac{20x}{15x}\right)\left(\dfrac{5}{16x}\right)$

Add each pair of fractions below. (Make sure your answers are fully reduced.)

17. $\dfrac{5}{2x} + \dfrac{3}{2x}$

(c) 18. $\dfrac{5}{3x} + \dfrac{3}{x}$

(d) 19. $\dfrac{7}{2x} + \dfrac{1}{3x}$

Solve each equation below.

20. $-x + (-x) = 14$

(d) 21. $6 + 7x = -4 + 2x$

Translate the word problem below into an equation; then solve.

(e) 22. There is a number that if you subtract 5 from it, and then multiply the result by 8, you get 72. What's the number?

Lesson 111—Subtracting Fractions with x's

We've covered multiplying, dividing, and adding fractions with x's. That just leaves subtraction.

Same Denominators
So let's look at a subtracting fractions example.

$$\frac{9}{8x} - \frac{5}{8x}$$

Since the denominators are already the same, we can just subtract the numerators.

$$\frac{4}{8x} \qquad \textbf{Subtract the tops.}$$

See, the process works just like subtracting fractions in arithmetic. We're not finished yet, though. We still need to make sure that our answer is fully reduced. (Subtracting fractions is just like adding fractions in this way too: we have to reduce at the end.) The top factors as $2 \cdot 2$ and the bottom factors as $2 \cdot 2 \cdot 2 \cdot x$.

$$\frac{2 \cdot 2}{2 \cdot 2 \cdot 2 \cdot x} \qquad \textbf{Factor on top and bottom.}$$

Now we can cancel. There are two pairs of 2s that will cancel.

$$\frac{\overset{1}{\cancel{2} \cdot \cancel{2}}}{\cancel{2} \cdot \cancel{2} \cdot 2 \ x} \qquad \textbf{Cancel the 2s.}$$

That leaves $\dfrac{1}{2x}$, which is fully reduced. So subtracting fractions with x's is pretty easy. It's the same method you learned in basic math.

Different Denominators
Let's do another example that's a little harder.

$$\frac{1}{3x} - \frac{5}{2x}$$

See, this is harder because the denominators are different. But all we have to do is make the denominators the same before subtracting. The lowest common denominator for these two fractions is $6x$. That means we're going to have to multiply both fractions. We should multiply the top and bottom of the first fraction by 2 and the top and bottom of the second fraction by 3.

$$\frac{2\cdot1}{2\cdot3x}-\frac{3\cdot5}{3\cdot2x}$$ **Make bottoms equal 6x.**

Let's simplify by multiplying everything.

$$\frac{2}{6x}-\frac{15}{6x}$$

Now you can see another reason why this example is a little harder. Subtracting the numerators is going to give us a negative result (since $2-15$ is negative). That's no big deal, though. The numerator comes out to -13.

$$\frac{-13}{6x}$$ **Subtracting tops.**

Next, we have to make sure our answer is fully reduced. Since 13 is a prime number, the top factors only as $(-1)(13)$. On bottom, $6x$ factors as $2\cdot3\cdot x$.

$$\frac{(-1)(13)}{2\cdot3\cdot x}$$ **Factoring top and bottom.**

Everything's factored, but there isn't anything to cancel. So $\frac{-13}{6x}$ is fully reduced. There's still one last step, though. We need to figure out the sign of the fraction as a whole. Since a negative divided by a positive equals a negative, we can put the negative sign out in front of the entire fraction like this.

$$-\frac{13}{6x}$$

And that's our final answer.

x's on Top and Bottom

We'll do one more example, and this one has something new.

$$\frac{7x}{4}-\frac{3x}{2}$$

As you can see, there are x's in the numerators instead of the denominators. At first that might seem hard, but it's really not. We can subtract these fractions in the same way—by subtracting the numerators. We already know how to subtract x's, so those shouldn't be a problem. But before subtracting, we have to make the denominators the same. This time, we only have to multiply the top and bottom of the second fraction by 2.

$$\frac{7x}{4} - \frac{2 \cdot 3x}{2 \cdot 2}$$ **Making bottoms the same.**

And we can simplify by multiplying.

$$\frac{7x}{4} - \frac{6x}{4}$$

Now we're ready to subtract the tops: $7x$ minus $6x$ equals just x. That gives us this.

$$\frac{x}{4}$$ **Subtracting the tops.**

We can try to reduce this answer. But it's pretty obvious that it won't reduce. The x on top can't be broken down at all, and 4 is $2 \cdot 2$, so there's nothing to cancel. Our fully reduced answer, then, is $\frac{x}{4}$.

Practice 111

a. Add the fractions $\frac{1}{2x} + \frac{2}{6x}$. (Make sure your answer is fully reduced.)

b. Subtract the fractions $\frac{8}{3x} - \frac{5}{3x}$. (Make sure your answer is fully reduced.)

c. Subtract the fractions $\frac{11x}{9} - \frac{2x}{3}$. (Make sure your answer is fully reduced.)

d. Solve the equation $4 + 5x = 20 - 3x$.

e. Translate the word problem below into an equation; then solve.

The Sound Doctor, an on-site stereo repair service, charges $15 for a service call (just to come to the house) plus $15 per hour to do the repair job. The Audio Cure, another on-site stereo fixer-upper, charges $25 for a service call plus $10 per hour to do the repair job. How many hours would a job have to take for the bills of both repair services to be the same?

Problem Set 111

Convert each percent below into decimal form.

1. 3.5%

2. 182%

Add or subtract (as indicated) each pair of numbers below.

3. $-13 + (-4)$

4. $-11 - (-8)$

Multiply or divide (as indicated) each group of numbers below.

5. $\dfrac{62}{-2}$

6. $(4)(-6)(5)$

Calculate the value of each expression below. (Make sure to do the operations in the correct order.)

7. $\dfrac{15}{3} + 14$

8. $2(6 + 8)$

Translate each of the following word problems into an equation. (Don't solve.)

9. There's some number that if you subtract 7 from it first, and then multiply that total by 5, the result is -3.

10. There's some number that if you divide it by 9 first, and then add 28 to that total, the result is 40.

Simplify each expression below.

11. $14x + 5x$

12. $-3x + (-7x)$

Multiply or divide (as indicated) each pair of fractions below. (Make sure your answers are fully reduced.)

13. $\dfrac{3x}{25} \cdot \dfrac{10x}{9x}$

14. $\dfrac{4x}{3} \div \dfrac{16x}{6}$

Add each pair of fractions below. (Make sure your answers are fully reduced.)

15. $\dfrac{3}{12x} + \dfrac{1}{12x}$ **(a) 16.** $\dfrac{1}{2x} + \dfrac{3}{8x}$

Subtract each pair of fractions below.

(b) 17. $\dfrac{7}{2x} - \dfrac{5}{2x}$ **(c) 18.** $\dfrac{13x}{6} - \dfrac{4x}{3}$

Solve each equation below.

19. $\dfrac{x+3}{2} = 5$ **20.** $4x + 2x = -30$ **(d) 21.** $1 + 8x = 11 - 2x$

Translate the word problem below into an equation; then solve.

(e) 22. The Roof Rescue Squad, a roofing repair service, charges $35 for a service call (just to come to the house) plus $35 per hour to do the repair job. The Shingle Masters, another roofing repair service, charges $55 for a service call plus $30 per hour to do the repair job. How many hours would a job have to take for the bills of both repair services to be the same?

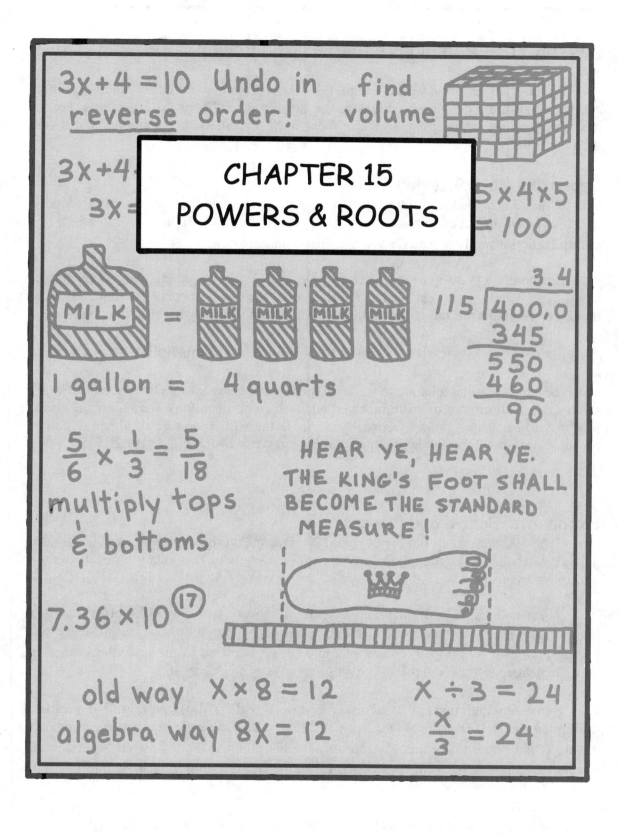

CHAPTER 15
POWERS & ROOTS

Lesson 112—Raising a Number to a Power

So far, we've only worked with the four operations of basic math—addition, subtraction, multiplication, and division. But algebra actually has six operations. For the next few lessons, we're going to learn about the fifth and sixth operations. We'll start with the fifth.

Repeated Multiplication

You already know that multiplication is a short way to write the same number added to itself several times. For example, $(3)(5)$ is really just three 5s added or $5+5+5$. So multiplication is really repeated addition. That's nothing new.

But here's a good question. Is it ever necessary to *multiply* the same number over and over? The answer is yes. We have to do that all the time, especially in more advanced math. For example, we might have to multiply the number 3 seven times, like this.

$$(3)(3)(3)(3)(3)(3)(3) \qquad \textbf{3 multiplied seven times}$$

The problem is that it's a hassle to write all those 3s. It takes up a lot of space too. So just as we have a short way to write repeated addition (multiplication), we also have a short way to write repeated multiplication. And this is the fifth operation of algebra. You've probably seen it before, but here's the short way to write 3 multiplied seven times.

$$3^7$$

Exponents, Bases, and Powers

The little number in the upper right (the 7) is called the **exponent**; the big number down below (the 3) is called the **base.** The exponent tells us how many times the base is multiplied by itself.

When a repeated multiplication is written this way (with an exponent) we say that the number (the base) has been **raised to a power.** So the fifth operation of algebra is raising a number to a power. In our example (3^7) 3 is raised to the seventh power. The entire expression (the 3 and the 7) is also sometimes called a **power**.

Here's another power: 2^5. This is 2 raised to the fifth power. And it means 2 multiplied by itself five times or $(2)(2)(2)(2)(2)$ or 32. The little number, the exponent, always tells us how many times to multiply the big number, the base. Here's yet another example of a power: 4^3. This is 4 raised to the third power, and it means 4 multiplied by itself three times, or $(4)(4)(4)$ or 64.

There are several advantages to writing a repeated multiplication as a power. We already mentioned two: It saves pencil lead and it takes up a lot less space. But another advantage is that we don't have to count a bunch of numbers that are being multiplied repeatedly. We can just read it off the exponent. With really long repeated multiplications this last advantage can be important. Imagine that we had to multiply not seven 3s, as we did above, but seventeen 3s. Without being able to use powers, we would have to write it like this.

$$(3)(3)(3)(3)(3)(3)(3)(3)(3)(3)(3)(3)(3)(3)(3)(3)(3)$$

Not only is this incredibly long, but you can't even figure out how many 3s there are without counting them. But now look at the same thing written as a power: 3^{17}. It's so nice and short, and we don't have to count how many 3s are multiplied, because the exponent tells us.

x's and Powers

We're already learning algebra, so we should mention that it's even possible to raise an x to a power. Here's an example: x^2. This is x raised to the second power, and it means two x's multiplied or $x \cdot x$. We can't actually calculate the value of this because x stands for an unknown number. But whatever that number is, x^2 is that number multiplied twice. And x^3 is x raised to the third power. It means three x's multiplied or $x \cdot x \cdot x$. We can also raise other letters like y or z to powers. It works exactly the same way as with plain numbers. The exponent always tells us how many times the unknown letter is multiplied by itself.

Math Nicknames

Second powers (with 2 in the exponent) and third powers (with 3 in the exponent) have special nicknames. A second power is also called a **square**. So to multiply 8 two times by writing it as a power (8^2), most people don't say "8 raised to the second power." It's okay to say it that way. But most people say "8 squared" or "the square of 8." The nickname for a third power is **cube**. For example, 7^3 is not usually called "7 raised to the third power." It's more often called "7 cubed" or "the cube of 7."

The reasons for these nicknames goes way back into history. In ancient times, people used exponents primarily to calculate areas of squares and volumes of cubes. As you know, the area of a square is its length multiplied by its width.

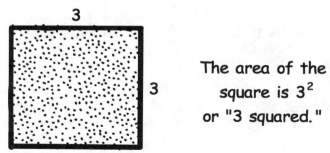

The area of the square is 3^2 or "3 squared."

Of course, all of the sides of a square are equal. That means the area, which is the length times the width, requires us to multiply the side length by itself. The area of the square above is 3 times 3 or 3^2. Since this used to be just about the only time second powers were ever used—to calculate areas of squares—people called 3 raised to the second power "3 squared."

And the same thing happened with cubes. The volume of a cube is its length times its width times its height. And all those lengths are equal, so the volume calculation involves multiplying a number by itself three times, which is a third power. Here's a cube with sides equal to 5, and the volume is (5)(5)(5) or 5^3.

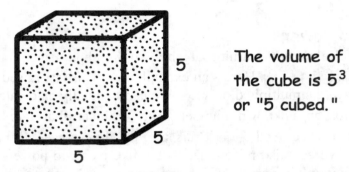

The volume of the cube is 5^3 or "5 cubed."

Since in ancient times, this was the only time people used third powers (to calculate volumes of cubes), they called 5^3 "5 cubed."

Of course, today we use powers for lots of other things besides calculating areas of squares and volumes of cubes. But the old nicknames are still really popular. So if you hear somebody say 4 squared or 6 cubed, you'll know they mean 4^2 and 6^3.

Practice 112

    a.   Calculate the value of 2^6.

    b.   Write $5 \cdot 5 \cdot 5 \cdot 5 \cdot 5 \cdot 5 \cdot 5$ as a power. (Don't calculate the answer.)

    c.   Divide the fractions $\dfrac{\frac{2}{5x}}{\frac{16}{15x}}$. (Make sure your answer is fully reduced.)

    d.   Subtract the fractions $\dfrac{2}{5x} - \dfrac{3}{x}$. (Make sure your answer is fully reduced.)

e. Translate the word problem below into an equation; then solve.

Bored listener #1 fidgets 12 times each minute. Bored listener #2 fidgets 18 times each minute. Together, how many minutes will it take them to fidget 600 times?

Problem Set 112

Tell whether each sentence below is True or False.

1. Raising a number to a power is a short way to write the same number multiplied repeatedly.

2. In a power (like 5^3) the little number in the upper right is called the "exponent" and the big number below is called the "base."

Do the indicated operation with each group of numbers below.

3. $45 - (-38)$ 4. $-15 + (-7) + 9$ 5. $(-20)(3)$

Calculate the value of each expression below. (Make sure to do the operations in the correct order.)

6. $11 - 8 \cdot 6$ 7. $\dfrac{28}{9-2}$

Calculate the value of each power below.

8. 2^4 (a) 9. 3^5

Write each of the following as a power. (Don't calculate the answer.)

10. 9 squared   (b) 11. $4 \cdot 4 \cdot 4 \cdot 4 \cdot 4 \cdot 4$

Translate each of the following phrases into a mathematical expression. (Don't calculate the answer.)

12. 5 multiplied by -19 first, and 22 subtracted from that total.

13. 6 added to 14 first, and then that total divided by -3.

Reduce each fraction below.

14. $\dfrac{3(x-1)}{9}$

15. $\dfrac{18(x+5)}{24(x+5)}$

Multiply or divide (as indicated) each pair of fractions below. (Make sure your answers are fully reduced.)

16. $\dfrac{12x}{20} \cdot \dfrac{15x}{24x}$

(c) 17. $\dfrac{\frac{3}{8x}}{\frac{9}{10x}}$

Add or subtract (as indicated) each pair of fractions below. (Make sure your answers are fully reduced.)

18. $\dfrac{4x}{13} + \dfrac{5x}{13}$

(d) 19. $\dfrac{3}{7x} - \dfrac{2}{x}$

Solve each equation below.

20. $\dfrac{x}{9} + 14 = 17$

21. $-x + 5x = 36$

Translate the word problem below into an equation; then solve.

(e) 22. Nervous speaker #1 says the word "um" 8 times each minute. Nervous speaker #2 says the word "um" 10 times each minute. Working together, how many minutes will it take them to say the word "um" 270 times?

Lesson 113—Scientific Notation

In this lesson, we're going to see how powers are used in science. Scientists have to deal with really huge numbers all the time. For instance, an astronomer might have to do a calculation involving the distance from the sun to the planet Pluto. Actually, that's nearly 4 *billion* miles.[1]

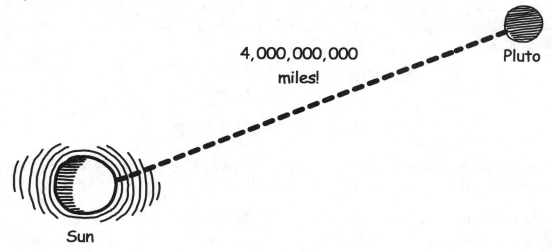

Shorter and Simpler

The bad thing about big numbers, though, is that all those zeros take up too much space. Another problem is that you have to count the zeros to figure out how big the number is. Otherwise it would have been hard to tell whether 4,000,000,000 was in billions or millions. Scientists got so tired of wrestling with big numbers that they invented a new way to write them. And this new way uses powers.

Instead of writing the distance from the sun to Pluto as 4,000,000,000, a scientist would write it like this.

$$4 \times 10^9$$

See, the number contains a 10 raised to the ninth power. If you do the calculation, 4 times 10 to the ninth power has the exact same value as 4,000,000,000, but it's shorter. Plus we don't have to count zeros at all, because the exponent tells us how many zeros go after the 4. The exponent is 9 and 4 billion has exactly 9 zeros.

This way of writing large numbers is called **scientific notation** (because scientists use it so much). Technically, for a number to be in scientific notation it needs to be in the following form:

A number between 1 and 10 times a power with a base of 10

---

[1] This picture is not drawn to scale. In reality, Pluto would be much smaller compared to the sun and the space between them would be far greater.

The number 4×10^9 is in proper scientific notation, then, since 4 is between 1 and 10 and 10^9 has a base of 10.

If you're not convinced that 4×10^9 equals 4,000,000,000, we can prove it to you. As you know, when any number is multiplied by 10, its decimal point will move one place to the right (for example 3.2 times 10 is 32.0 or 32). The number 4×10^9 is just 4 or 4.0 multiplied by 10 nine times. If we move the decimal point in 4.0 nine places to the right, one for each multiplication by 10, we end up with the original number, 4,000,000,000.

4.000000000   **Move 9 places**
                 to the right

4,000,000,000.   **to get 4 billion.**

That's why the exponent is equal to the number of zeros. The exponent 9 is really telling you how many times to multiply by 10 to get back to the original number 4 billion.

Another thing you may have noticed about scientific notation is that it uses the old multiplication symbol from arithmetic: 4×10^9. It's not absolutely necessary to write it this way. We could write 4×10^9 like this: $(4)(10^9)$. Or we could use a dot. But most people use the old multiplication symbol.

Writing a Number in Scientific Notation

In order to use scientific notation, you have to be able to put any number that might come up into scientific notation form. How do you actually do that? Well, let's go through the process on another large number. Here it is.

$$7,200,000,000,000,000,000$$

This is a gigantic number; it's a lot bigger than the distance from the sun to Pluto. This number would definitely be easier to work with if it were in scientific notation. Here's what we do. We know there's really a decimal point to the right of the last zero. Let's put it in.

Putting in the decimal point.
$$7,200,000,000,000,000,000.0$$

Now all we have to do is move that decimal point to the left. Every place we move it will make the number smaller. So we just move the point until the number gets to be between 1 and 10. That means it should go between the 7 and 2, which makes the number equal to 7.2.

7,200,000,000,000,000,000.

That's 18 places.

Move the decimal point to between the 7 and 2.

The important thing about this step, though, is that we need to count how many places we've moved the decimal point. We had to move the decimal point 18 places.

The next step is easy. We take 7.2 and multiply it by a power with a base of 10 and an exponent equal to however many places we moved that decimal point, which was 18. That gives us this.

$$7.2 \times 10^{18}$$

That's our gigantic number, 7,200,000,000,000,000,000, in scientific notation.

So scientific notation is a great way to write really large numbers. Not only are numbers in scientific notation shorter and easier to read, they're also easier to calculate with. We won't do any calculations with them in this book, though. That's saved for *Algebra 1*.

To finish off the lesson, let's review the two steps for changing a number to scientific notation.

1.	Move the decimal point in the original number to the left as many times as necessary for the number to be between 1 and 10 (and count the number of places).
2.	Take the new smaller number and multiply it by a power of 10 with an exponent equal to the number of places you moved the decimal point.

Practice 113

a. Rewrite 83,000,000,000,000 in scientific notation.

b. Write "8 cubed" as a power. (Don't calculate the answer.)

c. Add the fractions $\frac{5x}{12} + \frac{7x}{12}$. (Make sure your answer is fully reduced.)

d. Solve the equation $-3(x+5)=-15$.

e. Translate the word problem below into an equation; then solve.

Runaway firework #1 and runaway firework #2 are headed straight toward each other. Firework #1 is traveling at 20 feet per second, and firework #2 is traveling at 25 feet per second. If the two fireworks are 405 feet apart, how many seconds will it be before they meet?

Problem Set 113

Tell whether each sentence below is True or False.

1. Scientific notation is a short way to write very large numbers that is used by scientists.

2. Scientific notation never includes powers.

Rewrite each number below in scientific notation.

3. 8,000,000,000 **(a) 4.** 57,000,000,000,000

Do the indicated operation with each pair of numbers below.

5. $-32-44$ **6.** $\dfrac{-75}{-25}$

Calculate the value of each expression below. (Make sure to do the operations in the correct order.)

7. $15-\dfrac{8}{2}$ **8.** $5(3+4)$

Calculate the value of each power below.

9. 7^2 **10.** 5^4

Write each of the following as a power. (Don't calculate the answer.)

11. $9 \cdot 9 \cdot 9 \cdot 9 \cdot 9$ **(b) 12.** 7 cubed

Translate each of the following word problems into an equation. (Don't solve.)

13. There's some number that if you multiply it by 26 first, and then add 15 to that total, the result is 305.

14. There's some number that if you subtract 4 from it first, and then divide that total by 8, the result is 0.

Simplify each expression below.

15. $4 + 7x + 16$ 16. $-5x + (-18x)$

Multiply or divide (as indicated) each pair of fractions below. (Make sure your answers are fully reduced.)

17. $\dfrac{5x}{14} \div \dfrac{15x}{7}$ 18. $\dfrac{8x}{11x} \cdot \dfrac{22}{24x}$

Add or subtract (as indicated) each pair of fractions below. (Make sure your answers are fully reduced.)

19. $\dfrac{5}{3x} + \dfrac{1}{x}$ (c) 20. $\dfrac{3x}{10} + \dfrac{7x}{10}$

Solve each equation below.

21. $-9x + 13 = -5$ (d) 22. $-4(x + 3) = -12$

Translate the word problem below into an equation; then solve.

(e) 23. Test missile #1 and test missile #2 are headed straight toward each other. Missile #1 is traveling at 950 feet per second, and missile #2 is traveling at 1,000 feet per second. If the two missiles are 7,800 feet apart, how many seconds will it be before they meet?

Lesson 114—Order and Powers

We've been learning about raising a number to a power, which is the fifth operation of algebra. It goes along with the other four: addition, subtraction, multiplication, and division. But if we want to mix powers with the other operations, we need to include powers in our order of operations rules. Otherwise, we'll create a lot of confusion.

Which Way is Right?

For instance, take the expression $2 \cdot 3^2$, which mixes a power with a multiplication. There are actually two ways we might calculate this. We could start on the left and multiply 2 and 3 first to get 6^2. Then we could raise 6 to the second power to get 36. The other way to do the calculation, though, is to do the power first. We could raise 3 to the second power first to get $2 \cdot 9$. Then we could multiply second to get 18.

Multiply first?	Raise power first?
$2 \cdot 3^2$	$2 \cdot 3^2$
6^2	$2 \cdot 9$
36	18

See what happened. We did the operations in a different order and got two different answers: 36 and 18. So to clear up any confusion, we need to include powers in our rules for the order of operations. Here are the new rules with powers included.

Updated Order of Operations Rules

1.	*All powers are calculated first.*
2.	All multiplications and divisions are done second.
3.	All additions and subtractions are done third.
4.	If a different order is needed, the operations that are supposed to be done first must be put in parentheses (or inside a fraction).

Powers come first, before all the other operations, even before multiplication and division.

With these rules, there's no more confusion about how to calculate $2 \cdot 3^2$. The power should be done first: 3^2 is 9. That gives us $2 \cdot 9$. Then the multiplication is done second to get 18. The correct answer is 18, not 36.

Parentheses and Powers

Notice in rule 4 that if we want to change the usual order so that some other operation is done before a power, we need to use parentheses. For instance, to write our example so that the multiplication of 2 and 3 was first, we would have to use parentheses: $(2 \cdot 3)^2$. The correct way to do this calculation is to multiply 2 and 3 first to get 6^2. Then we calculate the power second to get 36. Written as $(2 \cdot 3)^2$, the correct answer is 36, not 18.

$$(2 \cdot 3)^2 \qquad \textbf{Multiply first.}$$

We can use parentheses to put any of the other operations ahead of a power too. For example, look at this expression: $1 + 2^3$. Since powers are supposed to be done before additions, the correct way to calculate this is to raise 2 to the third power first to get $1 + 8$. Then the addition is done second to get 9. But if we wanted the addition to be done before the power, we would need to put parentheses around the addition: $(1 + 2)^3$. The correct way to calculate this one is to add 1 and 2 first to get 3^3. Then the power is done second to get 27 ($3 \cdot 3 \cdot 3$ equals 27).

Raise power first	Add first
$1 + 2^3$	$(1 + 2)^3$
$1 + 8$	3^3
9	27

x's Too

Of course, all of these rules still apply when x's are involved. Take $6x^2$ for example. Because of the rule that powers are calculated before multiplications, this means x multiplied by itself first and that total multiplied by 6 second. If we want to show the multiplication first, we would have to put it in parentheses like this: $(6x)^2$. Now the expression means 6 multiplied by x first and then that total raised to the second power.

So the order of operations rules are powers first, multiplications and divisions second, additions and subtractions third. To change that order, we have to use parentheses (or a fraction bar).

Practice 114

    a. Rewrite 340,000,000,000 in scientific notation.

    b. Calculate the value of $(2 \cdot 3)^3$. (Make sure to do the operations in the correct order.)

    c. Calculate the value of $(4+3)^2$. (Make sure to do the operations in the correct order.)

    d. Reduce the fraction $\dfrac{4(x-5)}{12}$.

    e. Translate the word problem below into an equation; then solve.

    There is a number that if you multiply it by 3 first, and then add 7 to the result, you get 43. What's the number?

Problem Set 114

Tell whether each sentence below is True or False.

    1. If they're going to be mixed with other operations, powers need to be included in the order of operations rules.

    2. In the new order of operations rules, powers are done first unless parentheses (or a fraction) indicate otherwise.

Rewrite each number below in scientific notation.

    3. 2,000,000   **(a) 4.** 560,000,000,000

Do the indicated operation with each group of numbers below.

    5. $(5)(2)(-8)$ **6.** $7+(-16)$

Calculate the value of each expression below. (Make sure to do the operations in the correct order.)

7. $24 - 2 \cdot 5$

8. $\dfrac{8 + 12}{4}$

9. $5 \cdot 2^3$

(b) 10. $(2 \cdot 4)^3$

(c) 11. $(3 + 1)^2$

Write each of the following as a power. (Don't calculate the answer.)

12. 4 raised to the fifth power

13. $(8)(8)(8)(8)(8)(8)(8)(8)(8)$

Translate each of the following phrases into a mathematical expression. (Don't calculate the answer.)

14. 22 added to 16 first, and that total multiplied by 7.

15. 42 divided by 6 first, and then that total added to 19.

Reduce each fraction below.

16. $\dfrac{27x}{45x}$

(d) 17. $\dfrac{9(x - 7)}{18}$

Add or subtract (as indicated) each pair of fractions below. (Make sure your answers are fully reduced.)

18. $\dfrac{2}{x} - \dfrac{3}{4x}$

19. $\dfrac{1}{2x} + \dfrac{4}{5x}$

Solve each equation below.

20. $\dfrac{x - 8}{4} = 5$

21. $2 + 5x + 4 = 21$

Translate the word problem below into an equation; then solve.

(e) 22. There is a number that if you multiply it by 5 first, and then add 6 to the result, you get 91. What's the number?

Lesson 115—Adding and Subtracting Powers

A few lessons ago, we learned to add x's. Remember $3x + 2x$ is equal to $5x$. Well, it turns out that it's also possible to add x's that are raised to a power.

Adding Coefficients Again

Here's an example.

$$3x^2 + 2x^2$$

To add these, all we have to do is add the 3 and 2 to get $5x^2$. Three and 2 are called coefficients, as you know.

$$3x^2 + 2x^2 \text{ is equivalent to } 5x^2 \qquad \textbf{Add coefficients.}$$

So the method is to add the coefficients. It's just like adding plain x's.

You may be wondering why we can add the coefficients even when the x's are raised to powers. Well, $3x^2$ is 3 multiplied by x^2. But that's the same as $x^2 + x^2 + x^2$, because multiplication is just repeated addition. And $2x^2$ is the same as $x^2 + x^2$ for the same reason. So $3x^2 + 2x^2$ is really just $x^2 + x^2 + x^2 + x^2 + x^2$, which is five x^2's added, or $5x^2$. That's why it works.

$$3x^2 \qquad + \qquad 2x^2 \qquad = \qquad 5x^2$$
$$\underbrace{x^2 + x^2 + x^2} + \underbrace{x^2 + x^2} \quad = \quad 5x^2$$

The same as five x²'s added.

Subtracting Too

We can also subtract x's that are raised to powers in the same way that we subtract plain x's. Here's an example of that.

$$7x^3 - 4x^3$$

All we have to do is subtract the coefficients: $7 - 4$ equals 3. So that gives us $3x^3$. And the reason this works is that $7x^3$ is seven x^3's added, and if we take four of those away, we're left with three x^3's, which is $3x^3$.

Sometimes when we're adding or subtracting x's raised to a power, one of them won't have a coefficient showing. Here's an example of that.

$$5x^2 + x^2 \qquad \textbf{No coefficient showing}$$

You already know how to handle this. The second x^2 can be written as $1x^2$, so it actually does have a coefficient of 1. Then we can go ahead and add the coefficients to get $6x^2$. It's all exactly like combining plain x's again. (Remember, you can also say "combine" instead of add or subtract x's.)

Like Terms

The only thing we really have to watch out for when combining x's with powers is to make sure that both x's have the same exponent. For instance, we can't add these two powers.

$$3x^4 + 2x^5 \qquad \textbf{These can't be added}$$

The reason is that one of the x's has an exponent of 4 and the other has an exponent of 5. $3x^4 + 2x^5$ really means $x^4 + x^4 + x^4 + x^5 + x^5$. Obviously, there's not five of any one thing. There are three x^4's and two x^5's, so there's no way to combine.

Actually, x's that have the same exponent are called "like terms". For instance, $3x^2 + 2x^2$ are like terms, since both x's are squared. But $3x^4 + 2x^5$ are not like terms, because the exponents on the x's are different. The formal rule for adding and subtracting x's raised to a power, then, is that we can only combine like terms. And the method we use is to add or subtract their coefficients.

Practice 115

a. Calculate the value of $15 - 3^2$. (Make sure to do the operations in the correct order.)

b. Simplify the expression $3x^2 + 4x^2$.

c. Simplify the expression $13x^5 + x^5$.

d. Solve the equation $9 + 7x = 14 - 6x$.

e. Translate the word problem below into an equation; then solve.

Better Than Spotless, a carpet cleaning service, charges $50 for a service call (just to come to the house) plus $45 per hour to do the cleaning job. Whiter Than White, another carpet cleaning service, charges $80 for a service call plus $30 per hour to do the cleaning job. How many hours would a job have to take for the bill of both cleaning services to be the same?

Problem Set 115

Tell whether each sentence below is True or False.

1. To add x's raised to a power, you add their coefficients.

2. Like terms are x's with the same exponents.

Rewrite each number below in scientific notation.

3. 90,000

4. 1,800,000,000

Do the indicated operation with each pair of numbers below.

5. $\dfrac{-24}{6}$

6. $-5-(-12)$

Calculate the value of each expression below. (Make sure to do the operations in the correct order.)

7. $\dfrac{32}{2}-14$

8. $3(11-6)$

9. $(3\cdot4)^2$

(a) 10. $19-2^3$

Translate each of the following word problems into an equation. (Don't solve.)

11. There's some number that if you subtract 29 from it first, and then multiply that result by 3, the result is 41.

12. There's some number that if you divide it by 20 first, and then add 52 to that total, the result is 98.

Simplify each expression below.

13. $2x+15x$

(b) 14. $4x^2+5x^2$

(c) 15. $10x^5+x^5$

Multiply or divide (as indicated) each pair of fractions below. (Make sure your answers are fully reduced.)

16. $\dfrac{9x}{22} \cdot \dfrac{11x}{18x}$

17. $\dfrac{3}{20x} \div \dfrac{6}{15x}$

Add or subtract (as indicated) each pair of fractions below. (Make sure your answers are fully reduced.)

18. $\dfrac{5}{3x} + \dfrac{7}{6x}$

19. $\dfrac{7}{20x} - \dfrac{9}{20x}$

Solve each equation below.

20. $4(x+7) = 20$

(d) 21. $7 + 8x = 13 - 3x$

Translate the word problem below into an equation; then solve.

(e) 22. Dependable Maids, a housecleaning service, charges $20 for a service call (just to come to the house) plus $15 per hour to do the cleaning job. Clean as a Whistle, another housecleaning service, charges $35 for a service call plus $12 per hour to do the cleaning job. How many hours would a job have to take for the bill of both cleaning services to be the same?

Lesson 116—Multiplying Powers

We've learned how to add and subtract powers. In this lesson, we're going to learn how to multiply powers. Let's start with a simple example.

$$4^3 \cdot 4^2$$

We could just follow the order of operations rules. First, we calculate the value of each power.

$$64 \cdot 16$$

Next, we multiply 64 and 16.

$$1,024$$

And that gives us our answer of 1,024.

Just Add the Exponents

But there's another way to do $4^3 \cdot 4^2$. We can just add the exponents. We take $3+2$ which is 5, and that total becomes the exponent of the answer.

$$4^3 \cdot 4^2$$

$$4^{3+2} = 4^5 \qquad \text{adding the exponents}$$

If you multiply out 4 to the fifth, you'll see that it equals 1,024, which is right. So a really easy way to multiply powers is just to add their exponents. Here are some other examples of this technique.

$$2^4 \cdot 2^3 = 2^7 \qquad 3^5 \cdot 3^4 = 3^9 \qquad 5^6 \cdot 5^2 = 5^8$$

You may be wondering why this technique works. To explain, let's go back to the first example.

$$4^3 \cdot 4^2$$

We know that 4^3 means $4 \cdot 4 \cdot 4$ and 4^2 means $4 \cdot 4$. So $4^3 \cdot 4^2$ is really just a string of five 4's multiplied or $4 \cdot 4 \cdot 4 \cdot 4 \cdot 4$.

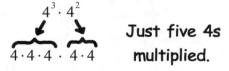

Just five 4s multiplied.

But that's the same as 4^5. So that's why we can always add the exponents. By adding the exponents, we're really just counting the number of 4s that are being multiplied.

With x's Too

But why would anyone bother multiplying $4^3 \cdot 4^2$ by adding their exponents? After all, once you get 4^5, you still have to calculate its value and that takes awhile. So the adding exponents method doesn't really seem any faster. But for anybody who knows algebra, adding the exponents still has a big advantage. You can use it to multiply x's that have exponents. Look at this example.

$$x^3 \cdot x^2$$

See, these powers both have a base (x) that's an unknown number. So we can't calculate the value of each of these powers and then multiply them together. But with the adding exponents method, we can still multiply, even though the bases are unknowns.

$$x^{3+2} = x^5$$

The answer is x^5. The real advantage, then, of the adding exponents method is that it works on x's as well as numbers. Only a person who understands algebra could appreciate that. Here are a few other examples of multiplying x's with exponents.

$$x^2 \cdot x^5 = x^7 \qquad x^3 \cdot x^6 = x^9 \qquad x^4 \cdot x^7 = x^{11}$$

A Warning

Before finishing this lesson, we need to give you an important warning. The adding exponents method can only be used to multiply powers when the powers have the same base. That's the way it was with all of our examples. In $4^3 \cdot 4^2$, both powers had a base of 4. In $2^4 \cdot 2^3$, both powers had a base of 2. In $3^5 \cdot 3^4$, the bases were both 3. And, of course, in the examples with x's, (like $x^3 \cdot x^2$) the powers all had a base of x. But if we had powers with different bases, like $4^3 \cdot 7^2$, it would be totally wrong to try and multiply them by adding their exponents to get 4^5 or 7^5. The reason this won't work is that $4^3 \cdot 7^2$ actually means $4 \cdot 4 \cdot 4 \cdot 7 \cdot 7$.

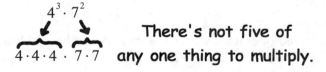

There's not five of any one thing to multiply.

As you can see, we don't have five of any one number being multiplied. So don't forget that in order to multiply powers by adding their exponents, those powers have to have the same base.

Practice 116

    a. How many square inches are in 8 square feet?

    b. Simplify $-5x^4 + (-3x^4)$ by adding or subtracting the powers.

    c. Simplify $6^5 \cdot 6^7$ by multiplying the powers. (Don't calculate the answer.)

    d. Simplify $x^5 \cdot x^3$ by multiplying the powers.

    e. Translate the word problem below into an equation; then solve.

    Insomniac #1 can count 55 sheep each minute. Insomniac #2 can count 58 sheep each minute. Working together, how many minutes will it take them to count 791 sheep?

Problem Set 116

Tell whether each sentence below is True or False.

    1. One way to multiply powers is to add their exponents.

    2. Only powers with the same base can be multiplied with the adding exponents method.

Do each unit conversion below.

    3. Convert 4.8 kilometers to dekameters.

  (a) 4. How many square inches are in 16 square feet?

Do the indicated operation with each pair of numbers below.

    5. $-17 + (-26)$ **6.** $(-31)(4)$

Calculate the value of each expression below. (Make sure to do the operations in the correct order.)

    7. $\dfrac{16}{5-1}$ **8.** $(2+6)^3$ **9.** $5 \cdot 4^2$

Translate each of the following phrases into a mathematical expression. (Don't calculate the answer.)

10. 3 multiplied by 7 first, and 15 subtracted from that total.

11. 14 minus 8 first, and that total divided by 2.

Reduce each fraction below.

12. $\dfrac{18}{24x}$

13. $\dfrac{15(x-6)}{10(x-6)}$

Add or subtract (as indicated) each pair of fractions below. (Make sure your answers are fully reduced.)

14. $\dfrac{3x}{16}+\dfrac{7x}{16}$

15. $\dfrac{2}{5x}-\dfrac{4}{x}$

Simplify each expression below by adding or subtracting (as indicated) the powers.

16. $8x^3+4x^3$

(b) 17. $-7x^4+(-2x^4)$

Simplify each expression below by multiplying the powers. (Don't calculate the answer.)

(c) 18. $4^7 \cdot 4^4$

(d) 19. $x^4 \cdot x^2$

Solve each equation below.

20. $4x-11=13$

21. $\dfrac{x+5}{4}=-7$

Translate the word problem below into an equation; then solve.

(e) 22. Ultra chef #1 can ice 42 cakes each hour. Ultra chef #2 can ice 47 cakes each hour. Working together, how many hours will it take them to ice 1,068 cakes?

Lesson 117—Multiplying Powers: Tougher Cases

In the last lesson, we learned to multiply powers by adding their exponents. It turns out that we can use that method to multiply even in tougher cases.

Multiply Numbers, Multiply x's

Here's our first example.

$$(5x^3)(6x^2)$$

This is a little tougher because it has both powers with x's and numbers. But all we have to do is multiply the numbers first: 5 times 6 is 30.

$$(30)(x^3)(x^2)$$

Next, we multiply the x's by adding their exponents: $3 + 2$ is 5, so $(x^3)(x^2)$ equals x^5. That gives us

$$30x^5.$$

Why it Works

It's always important to understand why a method works, so we'll explain what we just did. The expression $(5x^3)(6x^2)$ really means $5 \cdot x \cdot x \cdot x \cdot 6 \cdot x \cdot x$.

$$5x^3 \cdot 6x^2$$

$$\underbrace{5 \cdot x \cdot x \cdot x} \cdot \underbrace{6 \cdot x \cdot x}$$

Remember the commutative property of multiplication? That's the rule which says we can multiply two numbers in any order ($3 \cdot 4$ is the same as $4 \cdot 3$, for instance). Well, there's another rule that applies when there are more than two numbers. So actually it's possible to multiply a string of numbers, no matter how long, in any order and the answer will come out the same. You can try it for yourself on $(3)(8)(2)$. No matter how you multiply, the answer is always be 48. This new rule is called the **associative property of multiplication**, by the way, and the mathematicians write it as $(ab)c = a(bc)$.

But getting back to our problem, it's because of the associative property of multiplication that we can multiply the numbers first and then the x's in $(5x^3)(6x^2)$, even though they aren't right next to each other.

Another Example

Just to make sure you've got the hang of it, let's try another example.

$$(7x^9)(3x^8)$$

The exponents on these x's are pretty big, but that doesn't matter. Our adding exponents method will still work just fine. We can multiply in any order, so let's multiply the numbers first: 7 times 3 is 21.

$$(21)(x^9)(x^8)$$

Now we can multiply the x's by adding their exponents ($9+8$ is 17) to get $21x^{17}$.

Practice 117

a. Divide the fractions $\dfrac{6x}{30x} \div \dfrac{15}{40x}$. (Make sure your answer is fully reduced.)

b. Subtract the fractions $\dfrac{4}{3x} - \dfrac{5}{2x}$. (Make sure your answer is fully reduced.)

c. Simplify $(7x^3)(8x^4)$ by multiplying the powers.

d. Solve the equation $6 + 7x = 19 + 2x$.

e. Translate the word problem below into an equation; then solve.

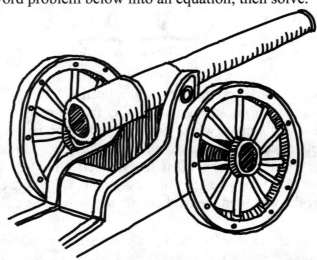

Cannonball #1 and cannonball #2 are headed straight toward each other. Cannonball #1 is traveling 40 meters each second, and cannonball #2 is traveling 45 meters each second. If the two cannonballs are 680 meters apart, how many seconds will it be before they meet?

Problem Set 117

Rewrite each number below in scientific notation.

    1.   200,000,000,000   **2.**   93,000,000

Do the indicated operation with each pair of numbers below.

    3. $\dfrac{-96}{-8}$ **4.** $-13-(-13)$

Calculate the value of each expression below. (Make sure to do the operations in the correct order.)

    5. $2(5+4)$ **6.** $(2\cdot6)^2$ **7.** 8^2+15

Translate each of the following word problems into an equation. (Don't solve.)

    8.   There's some number that if you multiply it by 8 first, and then add -14, the result is 95.

    9.   There's some number that if you subtract 3 from it first, and then divide that total by 24, the result is 17.

Multiply or divide (as indicated) each pair of fractions below. (Make sure your answers are fully reduced.)

    10. $\dfrac{14x}{24}\cdot\dfrac{6}{7x}$ **(a) 11.** $\dfrac{4x}{20x}\div\dfrac{10}{30x}$

Add or subtract (as indicated) each pair of fractions below. (Make sure your answers are fully reduced.)

    12. $\dfrac{1}{2x}+\dfrac{3}{7x}$ **(b) 13.** $\dfrac{5}{4x}-\dfrac{7}{2x}$

Simplify each expression below by adding or subtracting (as indicated) the powers.

    14. $10x^2+9x^2$ **15.** $4x^8-x^8$

Simplify each expression below by multiplying the powers.

16. $x^3 \cdot x^7$ 　　　　　　　**17.** $x^5 \cdot x^9$ 　　　　　**(c) 18.** $(4x^5)(9x^2)$

19. $(5x^9)(4x^7)$

Solve each equation below.

20. $\dfrac{x}{8} - 1 = -6$ 　　　　**(d) 21.** $5 + 8x = 20 + 2x$

Translate the word problem below into an equation; then solve.

(e) 22. Meteoroid #1 and meteoroid #2 are headed straight toward each other. Meteoroid #1 is traveling 980 meters each second, and meteoroid #2 is traveling 1,100 meters each second. If the two meteoroids are 6,240 meters apart, how many seconds will it be before they meet?

Lesson 118—Dividing Powers

We've learned how to multiply powers. Now we're going to see how to divide them. Let's start with a numbers-only example. Let's divide 9^5 by 9^3. Since we always show division with a fraction bar, we'll write it like this.

$$\frac{9^5}{9^3}$$

One way to divide here is to write each power as a repeated multiplication. On top, 9^5 just means five 9's multiplied. And on bottom, 9^3 means three 9's multiplied. So that gives us

$$\frac{9 \cdot 9 \cdot 9 \cdot 9 \cdot 9}{9 \cdot 9 \cdot 9}.$$

Now we can cancel. There are three pairs of 9s that can be canceled.

$$\frac{\cancel{9} \cdot \cancel{9} \cdot \cancel{9} \cdot 9 \cdot 9}{\cancel{9} \cdot \cancel{9} \cdot \cancel{9}}$$ **Cancel the 9s.**

That leaves $\dfrac{9 \cdot 9}{1}$ or $9 \cdot 9$, which can also be written as 9^2. So the answer is 9^2 or 81. That's the long way to divide 9^5 by 9^3.

Just Subtract the Exponents

But if there's a long way to divide powers, there has to be a short way. In the last lesson, we learned to multiply powers by adding their exponents. As it turns out, we can divide powers by subtracting their exponents. On $\dfrac{9^5}{9^3}$, all we do is take 5, the exponent on top, and subtract 3, the exponent on bottom. The result becomes the exponent of the answer.

$$\frac{9^5}{9^3} = 9^{5-3} = 9^2$$ **Subtract the exponents.**

That gives us 9^2, which we know is right.

Wasn't that fast? And the reason it works is pretty obvious. The exponent on top tells us how many 9s are in the numerator and the exponent on bottom tells us how many 9s are in the denominator. By subtracting, we're figuring out how many 9s are going to be left after canceling. So the short method for dividing powers is to subtract their exponents. Here are a few other examples.

$$\frac{3^8}{3^2} = 3^6 \qquad\qquad \frac{5^7}{5^3} = 5^4 \qquad\qquad \frac{8^{11}}{8^6} = 8^5$$

Subtracting Exponents with x's

Of course, we can also use this method to divide powers with x's. And this is where it's really useful. Look at this example.

$$\frac{x^7}{x^2}$$

To divide here, all we have to do is subtract the exponents: $7 - 2 = 5$. Then we make the result, 5, the exponent of our answer.

$$\frac{x^7}{x^2} = x^5$$

It's incredibly easy. Here are a few other examples with x's.

$$\frac{x^{10}}{x^4} = x^6 \qquad\qquad \frac{x^8}{x^5} = x^3 \qquad\qquad \frac{x^{15}}{x^6} = x^9$$

Bases Must be the Same

There's one other really important point that you've probably already figured out. We can only subtract exponents when the bases are the same. It's just like multiplying, where we can only add exponents when the bases are the same. Here's why the bases have to be the same to divide. What if we had a division problem like this.

$$\frac{7^5}{4^2}$$

It would make no sense to try and subtract the exponents, $5 - 2 = 3$, and then make the answer 7^3 or 4^3. That would be crazy, because $\frac{7^5}{4^2}$ really means $\frac{7 \cdot 7 \cdot 7 \cdot 7 \cdot 7}{4 \cdot 4}$. This fraction can't be reduced at all, since there's nothing in the numerator and denominator that can be canceled. So there's no way $\frac{7^5}{4^2}$ equals 7^3 or 4^3. Don't forget, then, that to divide powers by subtracting exponents, the bases have to be the same. And to multiply powers by adding exponents, the bases have to be the same as well.

Practice 118

    a. Subtract the fractions $\dfrac{5x}{2} - \dfrac{7x}{3}$. (Make sure your answer is fully reduced.)

    b. Simplify $(-6x^5)(7x^8)$ by multiplying the powers.

    c. Divide the powers $\dfrac{x^9}{x^6}$.

    d. Solve the equation $4 + (-3x) = 9 - 4x$.

    e. Translate the word problem below into an equation; then solve.

        When Ginger special-ordered a book recently, she agreed to pay an 8% shipping and handling charge. If Ginger paid \$2.72 in shipping and handling, how much must the book have cost?

Problem Set 118

Tell whether each sentence below is True or False.

    1. The short method for dividing powers is to subtract their exponents.

    2. Only powers with the same base can be divided with the subtracting exponents method.

Convert each fraction below into decimal form. Give exact answers (no rounding).

    3. $\dfrac{7}{6}$ **4.** $\dfrac{1}{25}$

Calculate the value of each expression below. (Make sure to do the operations in the correct order.)

    5. $15 - 3 \cdot 2$ **6.** $(3-1)^4$

Translate each of the following phrases into a mathematical expression. (Don't calculate the answer.)

    7. 8 added to 4 first, and that total multiplied by 3.

8. 28 divided by 7 first, and 12 subtracted from that total.

Multiply or divide (as indicated) each pair of fractions below. (Make sure your answers are fully reduced.)

9. $\dfrac{8}{14x} \cdot \dfrac{21x}{12x}$

10. $\dfrac{6}{45x} \div \dfrac{15x}{9x}$

Add or subtract (as indicated) each pair of fractions below. (Make sure your answers are fully reduced.)

11. $\dfrac{7}{20x} + \dfrac{9}{20x}$

(a) 12. $\dfrac{3x}{7} - \dfrac{2x}{5}$

Simplify each expression below.

13. $4 + 5x - 9$

14. $3x^5 + (-7x^5)$

15. $8x^7 + 11x^7$

Simplify each expression below by multiplying the powers.

16. $x^{10} \cdot x^4$

17. $(2x^3)(8x^5)$

(b) 18. $(-4x^7)(5x^9)$

Simplify each expression below by dividing the powers. (Don't calculate the answer.)

19. $\dfrac{4^9}{4^4}$

(c) 20. $\dfrac{x^8}{x^2}$

Solve each equation below.

21. $-5x + (-7x) = 48$

(d) 22. $1 + (-5x) = 7 - 6x$

Translate the word problem below into an equation; then solve.

(e) 23. When Marcia bought an umbrella over the Internet, she agreed to pay a 12% shipping and handling charge. If Marcia paid \$3.36 in shipping and handling, how much must the umbrella have cost?

Lesson 119—Fractions with Powers

Now that we've learned to divide powers by subtracting their exponents, we can use the method to reduce some pretty complicated fractions.

The Long Way
Look at this example.

$$\frac{4x^7}{4x^2}$$

This fraction has both numbers and x's. And one way to reduce it is to factor everything first. On top, 4 factors as $2 \cdot 2$ and x^7 is the same as seven x's multiplied.

$$\frac{2 \cdot 2 \cdot x \cdot x \cdot x \cdot x \cdot x \cdot x \cdot x}{4x^2} \qquad \textbf{Factor everything on top}$$

On bottom, 4 factors as $2 \cdot 2$ again, and x^2 is the same as two x's multiplied.

$$\frac{2 \cdot 2 \cdot x \cdot x \cdot x \cdot x \cdot x \cdot x \cdot x}{2 \cdot 2 \cdot x \cdot x} \qquad \textbf{and bottom.}$$

The next step is to cancel. We can cancel two pairs of 2s and two pairs of x's.

$$\frac{\cancel{2} \cdot \cancel{2} \cdot \cancel{x} \cdot \cancel{x} \cdot x \cdot x \cdot x \cdot x \cdot x}{\underset{1}{\cancel{2} \cdot \cancel{2} \cdot \cancel{x} \cdot \cancel{x}}} \qquad \textbf{Cancel the 2s and x's.}$$

That leaves $\dfrac{x \cdot x \cdot x \cdot x \cdot x}{1}$ or $\dfrac{x^5}{1}$, which is just x^5.

The Short Way
So that's one method for reducing $\dfrac{4x^7}{4x^2}$. But another, faster method is to just factor the numbers.

$$\frac{2 \cdot 2 \cdot x^7}{2 \cdot 2 \cdot x^2} \qquad \textbf{Just factor numbers.}$$

Now we can cancel the pairs of 2s.

$$\frac{\cancel{2}\cdot\cancel{2}\cdot x^7}{\cancel{2}\cdot\cancel{2}\cdot x^2}$$

Cancel the 2s.

That gives us $\frac{x^7}{x^2}$. Next, instead of factoring x^7 and x^2 by writing out a bunch of x's, we can just divide them by subtracting their exponents: $7-2=5$, so we end up with x^5. That's the same answer we got before. Only by using the subtracting exponents shortcut, we didn't have to write all those x's!

Let's do one more example.

$$\frac{3x^9}{15x^5}$$

First, we factor the numbers: 3 is a prime number, so it can't be broken down any further; 15 factors as 3 times 5.

$$\frac{3\cdot x^9}{3\cdot 5\cdot x^5}$$

Factor the numbers.

There is one pair of 3s that will cancel.

$$\frac{\cancel{3}\cdot x^9}{\cancel{3}\cdot 5\cdot x^5}$$

Cancel the 3s.

That leaves $\frac{x^9}{5\cdot x^5}$. Next, instead of having to write out a bunch of x's, we'll use the subtracting exponents method: $9-5=4$, so we end up with x^4, which goes on top.

$$\frac{x^4}{5}$$

Subtracting exponents

And that's fully reduced. The main point, then, is that dividing powers by subtracting exponents can be a big time saver when reducing more complicated fractions.

Practice 119

a. What is $\frac{2}{5}$ of $\frac{7}{8}$?

b. Reduce the fraction $\frac{8x^7}{8x^5}$.

c. Reduce the fraction $\dfrac{5x^6}{30x^3}$.

d. Solve the equation $2x + 3x + 3 = 18$.

e. Translate the word problem below into an equation; then solve.

There is a number that if you subtract 6 from it first, and then divide that total by 4, you get 2. What's the number?

Problem Set 119

Rewrite each number below in scientific notation.

1. 8,000

2. 650,000,000,000,000,000

Answer each question below.

3. What is 70% of 490?

(a) 4. What is $\dfrac{2}{3}$ of $\dfrac{5}{8}$?

Do the indicated operation with each pair of numbers below.

5. $(-6)(-12)$

6. $35 + (-43)$

Calculate the value of each expression below. (Make sure to do the operations in the correct order.)

7. $9(2 + 5)$

8. $14 - 3^2$

Translate each of the following word problems into an equation. (Don't solve.)

9. There's some number that if you subtract 28 from it first, and then multiply that total by 7, the result is 0.

10. There's some number that if you divide it by 50 first, and then add 41 to that total, the result is -183.

Multiply or divide (as indicated) each pair of fractions below. Make sure your answers are fully reduced.

11. $\dfrac{5x}{24} \cdot \dfrac{21}{35x}$ **12.** $\dfrac{8}{3x} \div \dfrac{2}{9x}$

Simplify each expression below.

13. $17x + 13x$ **14.** $25x^4 - 14x^4$

Simplify each expression below by multiplying the powers.

15. $x^4 \cdot x^4$ **16.** $(9x^2)(5x^4)$ **17.** $(-4x^8)(12x^2)$

Reduce each fraction below.

18. $\dfrac{9(x+2)}{15(x+2)}$ **(b) 19.** $\dfrac{6x^9}{6x^5}$ **(c) 20.** $\dfrac{4x^8}{28x^3}$

Solve each equation below.

21. $4(x-9) = 20$ **(d) 22.** $4x + 3x + 5 = 19$

Translate the word problem below into an equation; then solve.

(e) 23. There is a number that if you subtract 5 from it first, and then divide that total by 3, you get 7. What's the number?

Lesson 120—Taking a Root

Well, we've learned all about the fifth operation of algebra, which is raising a number to a power. Now it's time for the sixth operation, which is called **taking a root**. Here's how it works. To take the "second" root of 16, we find the number which when raised to the second power equals 16. Can you think of what number that is? It's 4, because 4 to the second power (or $4 \cdot 4$) is 16.

Roots and Radical Signs

A root is shown with a funny symbol called a **radical sign**. Here's what it looks like.

$$\sqrt[2]{} \qquad\qquad \text{A radical sign}$$

The little 2 means that this is a second root. So we write the second root of 16 as $\sqrt[2]{16} = 4$. Roots are also sometimes called **radicals**, since they're written with radical signs.

Higher Roots

Roots aren't limited to just second roots. There are also third roots. To show you, let's take the "third" root of 27. We just find the number which, when raised to the "third" power, equals 27. That turns out to be 3, since 3^3 equals 27. In mathematical form, the third root of 27 is written like this: $\sqrt[3]{27} = 3$. The little 3 in the upper left means that it's a third root. Second roots and third roots are also called **square roots** and **cube roots**. You already know where those names come from. So we could also say that the square root of 16 is 4, and the cube root of 27 is 3.

There are also fourth roots. Let's do one of those. We'll take the fourth root of 16. That's the number that when raised to the fourth power is equal to 16. Since 2^4 equals 16, the fourth root of 16 must be 2. This is written mathematically like this: $\sqrt[4]{16} = 2$. Of course, the little 4 means fourth root. Are you getting the concept? It's just like powers. There are lots of different powers—second powers, third powers, fourth powers, and all the way up. In the same way, there are lots of different roots—second roots, third roots, fourth roots, and they go on up from there.

Leaving Off the 2

There's something else you should know about second roots (or square roots). These are by far the most common of all the roots. They're so common, in fact, that people usually don't bother to put the little two in the upper left corner of the radical sign. Instead of writing the square root of 16 as $\sqrt[2]{16}$, they just write it as $\sqrt{16}$.

$$\sqrt[2]{16} \text{ is usually written as } \sqrt{16}$$

That's just because people write square roots so much that they started leaving the 2 off. So when a radical sign doesn't have a little number at all, it is supposed to be a square root. That means if you want to show a third root or a fourth root, you'd better put in the little 3 or 4 ($\sqrt[3]{}$ and $\sqrt[4]{}$) or people will think it's a square root.

Practice 120

a. Simplify $3x^4 - 11x^4$ by subtracting the powers.

b. Reduce the fraction $\dfrac{8x^8}{48x^3}$.

c. Calculate the root $\sqrt{36}$.

d. Calculate the root $\sqrt[3]{64}$.

e. Translate the word problem below into an equation; then solve.

The experimental train traveled at a whopping speed of 297 miles per hour. At this speed, how many hours would it have taken it to travel 6,237 miles?

Problem Set 120

Tell whether each sentence below is True or False.

1. Taking a root is the sixth operation of algebra.

2. A root is shown with the symbol $\sqrt{}$, which is called a radical sign.

Calculate the value of each expression below. Make sure to do the operations in the correct order.

3. $8 \cdot 5 - 29$ 4. $(4 \cdot 2)^2$

Translate each of the following phrases into a mathematical expression. (Don't calculate the answer.)

5. 12 and 2 multiplied first, and 16 subtracted from that total.

6. 5 added to 94 first, and that total divided by 33.

Add or subtract (as indicated) each pair of fractions below. (Make sure your answers are fully reduced.)

7. $\dfrac{5}{18x} + \dfrac{11}{18x}$

8. $\dfrac{7}{6x} - \dfrac{1}{2x}$

Simplify each expression below by adding or subtracting (as indicated) the powers.

9. $4x^5 + 23x^5$

(a) 10. $4x^9 - 9x^9$

Simplify each expression below by multiplying the powers.

11. $x^{13} \cdot x^6$

12. $(-6x^7)(3x^5)$

Simplify each expression below by dividing the powers.

13. $\dfrac{x^{11}}{x^2}$

14. $\dfrac{x^9}{x^7}$

Reduce each fraction below.

15. $\dfrac{2x^5}{2x^2}$

(b) 16. $\dfrac{4x^9}{20x^5}$

Calculate each root below.

(c) 17. $\sqrt{25}$

(d) 18. $\sqrt[3]{8}$

19. $\sqrt[3]{27}$

Solve each equation below.

20. $-5x + 3 = 23$

21. $\dfrac{x-6}{9} = 3$

Translate the word problem below into an equation; then solve.

(e) 22. The primitive space capsule traveled at the rather unimpressive speed of 17,830 miles per hour. At this speed, how many hours would it have taken it to travel 160,470 miles?

Lesson 121—Undoing Powers and Roots

In the last lesson, we learned about the sixth operation of algebra: taking a root. But did you notice that taking a root was a lot like raising a number to a power backwards?

Inverse Operations Again

For example, when taking the second (square) root of 25, instead of multiplying the same number twice, we try to figure out what number has to be multiplied twice to get 25. That's going backwards.

The reason a root is like a power backwards is that roots and powers are inverse operations. Remember, inverse operations are operations that undo each other. Addition and subtraction are inverse operations, and so are multiplication and division. That's why we use one to undo the other when solving equations. It's also why subtraction is a lot like doing addition backwards (when subtracting $8-5$, we think "what number has to be added to 5 to get 8?") And division is like doing multiplication backwards too. They're inverse operations.

You already know how to show subtraction undoing addition. Let's say that 5 has 3 added to it: $5+3$. To undo the addition, we subtract 3 like this: $5+3-3$. That gets us back to 5 again. You also know how to show division undoing multiplication. If 8 is multiplied by 4, to undo the multiplication, we write it as $\dfrac{8\cdot4}{4}$. That gets us back to 8.

Well, since powers and roots are inverse operations, we can also show a root undoing a power. Let's say we have 5 squared: 5^2. To undo the power, we can just take the square root of 5^2. All we have to do is put a radical sign over the whole thing: $\sqrt{5^2}$.

$$\sqrt{5^2}=5 \qquad \textbf{Root undoes the power}$$

That equals 5, because the square root undoes the square. The other way to see this is to remember that 5 squared is 25, so we're really taking the square root of 25, which equals 5. The process would have worked the same way if it had been 4 or 3 or 8 or any other number that was squared (instead of 5). Basically, any square can be undone by taking the square root of the entire power. Here are a few other examples.

$$\sqrt{3^2}=3 \qquad \sqrt{7^2}=7 \qquad \sqrt{11^2}=11$$

Undoing Higher Powers

Just as second (square) roots can undo second powers (squares), so can third roots undo third powers. Look at this one: 2^3. To undo here, we just take the third root of the whole thing. It's written like this: $\sqrt[3]{2^3}$. And since the root undoes the power, the result is

2. You can also tell that this is right, because 2 cubed is 8, so we're really taking the third root of 8, which is 2. A fourth power can also be undone by a fourth root.

$$\sqrt[4]{5^4} = 5 \qquad \textbf{Root undoes the power}$$

See, the root undoes the power and gets us back to 5. Obviously, we could keep going all the way up: fifth roots will undo fifth powers, sixth roots will undo sixth powers, and so on. Therefore, a root will always undo the same degree (kind) of power.

Powers Also Undo Roots

But with inverse operations, both of the operations are supposed to undo each other. Remember, it's not just subtraction that undoes addition. Addition also undoes subtraction. Is the same thing true for powers and roots? Absolutely. If we have a square root, like $\sqrt{4}$, and you want to undo it, all we have to do is square the whole thing like this: $(\sqrt{4})^2$. Notice that we used parentheses to show that we're squaring the entire root. Since the square undoes the square root, the result is 4. It's obvious that that has to be true, because the square root of 4 is 2. So we're really just squaring 2, and that equals 4.

We can undo a third root with a third power, too. Here's an example like that: $\sqrt[3]{27}$. To undo the third root here, all we do is raise the whole thing to the third power.

$$(\sqrt[3]{27})^3 = 27 \qquad \textbf{Power undoes root}$$

You can see why this works, because the third root of 27 is actually 3. So we're really raising 3 to the third power, which is 27. Continuing upward, fourth roots can be undone with fourth powers. Here's a quick example of that.

$$(\sqrt[4]{16})^4 = 16 \qquad \textbf{Power undoes root}$$

See, raising the fourth root of 16 to the fourth power undoes the root and gets us back to 16. And we can continue all the way up. Fifth roots can be undone by fifth powers, and sixth roots can be undone by sixth powers, and so on.

The main point is that powers and roots are inverse operations so they will both undo each other.

Practice 121

a. Multiply the fractions $\dfrac{3}{6x^2} \cdot \dfrac{18x^5}{9}$. (Make sure your answer is fully reduced.)

b. Calculate the value of the root $\sqrt[4]{81}$.

c. Calculate the value of the expression $\sqrt{8^2}$.

d. Calculate the value of the expression $(\sqrt[3]{27})^3$.

e. Translate the word problem below into an equation; then solve.

There were 130 water slides in the whole state, but only 26 of them were open year-round. What percent of the water slides were open year-round? (The answer to your equation will be in decimal form. Make sure your final answer is written as a percent.)

Problem Set 121

Tell whether each sentence below is True or False.

1. Powers and roots are inverse operations.

2. Powers can undo roots, and roots can undo powers.

Do the indicated operation with each pair of numbers below.

3. $-37-(-28)$ **4.** $\dfrac{20}{-4}$

Calculate the value of each expression below. (Make sure to do the operations in the correct order.)

5. $14-\dfrac{35}{5}$ **6.** $(5-2)^4$

Translate each of the following word problems into an equation. (Don't solve.)

7. There's some number that if you multiply it by -4 first, and then add 29 to that total, the result is 45.

8. There's some number that if you subtract 3 from it first, and then divide that total by 17, the result is -11.

Simplify each expression below.

9. $23 + x - 18$ **10.** $-13x + (-41x)$

Simplify each expression below by multiplying the powers.

11. $x^4 \cdot x^9$ **12.** $(-15x^3)(-2x^5)$

Multiply or divide (as indicated) each pair of fractions below. Make sure your answers are fully reduced.

13. $\dfrac{4x}{9} \div \dfrac{8x}{27}$ **(a) 14.** $\dfrac{5}{4x^2} \cdot \dfrac{8x^4}{10}$

Reduce each fraction below.

15. $\dfrac{34x^6}{34x^3}$ **16.** $\dfrac{15x^7}{45x^2}$

Calculate each root below.

17. $\sqrt{49}$ **(b) 18.** $\sqrt[4]{16}$

Calculate the value of each expression below.

(c) 19. $\sqrt{9^2}$ **(d) 20.** $(\sqrt[3]{64})^3$

Solve each equation below.

21. $7x + 11x = -54$ **22.** $\dfrac{x}{9} - 6 = 2$

Translate the word problem below into an equation; then solve.

(e) 23.   There were 68 kinds of ice cream in the freezer, but only 17 of those were some kind of chocolate flavor. What percent were chocolate-flavored? (The answer to your equation will be in decimal form. Make sure your final answer is written as a percent.)

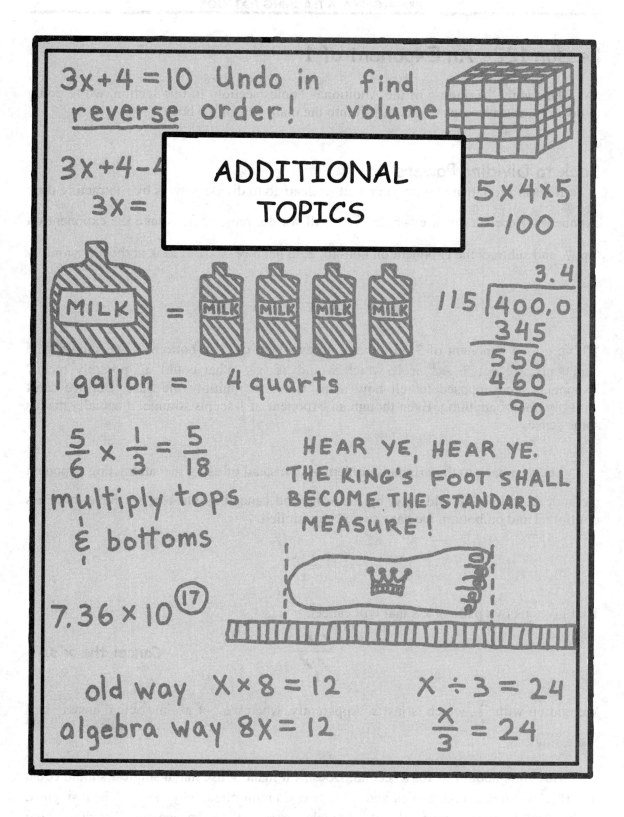

$3x + 4 = 10$ Undo in find
<u>reverse</u> order! volume

ADDITIONAL TOPICS

$3x + 4 - 4$

$3x =$

$5 \times 4 \times 5 = 100$

MILK $=$ MILK MILK MILK MILK

1 gallon $=$ 4 quarts

$$\frac{3.4}{115\overline{)400{,}0}}$$
$$\underline{345}$$
$$550$$
$$\underline{460}$$
$$90$$

$\dfrac{5}{6} \times \dfrac{1}{3} = \dfrac{5}{18}$

multiply tops
& bottoms

HEAR YE, HEAR YE.
THE KING'S FOOT SHALL
BECOME THE STANDARD
MEASURE!

$7.36 \times 10^{\text{⑰}}$

old way $X \times 8 = 12$ $X \div 3 = 24$

algebra way $8X = 12$ $\dfrac{X}{3} = 24$

Lesson 122—An Exponent of 1

This is the beginning of the Additional Topics section. In this section, we're going to do a few extra lessons that didn't fit into the main part of the book.

Back to Dividing Powers

It wasn't too many lessons ago that we learned to divide powers by subtracting their exponents. Here's a quick example: $\dfrac{x^7}{x^2}$. All we do, remember, is take the exponent on top, 7, and subtract the exponent on bottom, 2, to get 5 or x^5. But look at this division.

$$\frac{x^3}{x^2}$$

We've got an exponent of 3 on top and an exponent of 2 on bottom. If we subtract the exponents, we get $3 - 2$ or 1, which would be x^1. What could x^1 possibly mean? Exponents are supposed to tell how many times to multiply the base. But we can't multiply one of anything. Even though an exponent of 1 seems strange, it actually makes some sense.

Let's go back to the original problem $\dfrac{x^3}{x^2}$. Instead of using the subtracting exponent method, let's do it the old way, by factoring and canceling. On top, we have three x's multiplied and on bottom we have two x's multiplied.

$$\frac{x \cdot x \cdot x}{x \cdot x}$$

That gives us two pairs of x's that will cancel.

$$\frac{\cancel{x} \cdot \cancel{x} \cdot x}{\underset{1}{\cancel{x} \cdot \cancel{x}}} \qquad \textbf{Cancel the x's.}$$

We end up with $\dfrac{x}{1}$, which is just x. Apparently, when we got x^1, the actual answer was just a single x.

But think about this for a second. Doesn't it make sense that a single x should equal x^1? If x^3 is three x's multiplied and x^2 is two x's multiplied, why can't x^1 be a single x, all by itself? More importantly, if we make $x^1 = x$, then we can use the subtracting exponent method even on divisions like $\dfrac{x^3}{x^2}$, where the answer comes out to just a single *x*. That's exactly what the mathematicians decided to do. They made $x^1 = x$. Actually, they went further than that. They made any number raised to the first power equal to the number itself. Since this rule works for any number at all, powers with other bases can be handled this way too. Here are some examples with other bases.

$$\frac{2^5}{2^4} = 2^1 = 2 \qquad \frac{5^8}{5^7} = 5^1 = 5 \qquad \frac{7^4}{7^3} = 7^1 = 7.$$

Of course, you don't have to write out the exponent of 1. Once you get the hang of the concept, just do it in your head.

Multiplying with an Exponent of 1

Interestingly, an exponent of 1 isn't just useful for dividing powers. It can also help multiply powers. Look at this multiplication.

$$x^4 \cdot x$$

We know what the answer is here: x^4 represents four *x*'s multiplied. Then if we multiply by another *x*, we end up with five *x*'s multiplied or x^5. But what about using the method of adding the exponents? Remember, that's another, faster way to multiply powers. The problem with adding exponents here is that the second *x* doesn't seem to have an exponent. But if $x^1 = x$, why can't we change $x^4 \cdot x$ to $x^4 \cdot x^1$?

$$x^4 \cdot x \text{ can be changed to } x^4 \cdot x^1$$

That's perfectly legal. Now there are exponents on both *x*'s, and we can add them in the usual way: 4 + 1 is 5, so we get x^5, which we know is right.

$$x^4 \cdot x = x^4 \cdot x^1 = x^5 \qquad \textbf{Add the exponents}$$

Basically, we can put an exponent of 1 on anything if it helps us multiply. Here are a couple of other examples with different bases.

$$2^5 \cdot 2 = 2^5 \cdot 2^1 = 2^6 \qquad\qquad 8^3 \cdot 8 = 8^3 \cdot 8^1 = 8^4$$

Practice 122

a. Subtract the fractions $\frac{5}{2x} - \frac{8}{3x}$. (Make sure your answer is fully reduced.)

b. Simplify $\frac{3^8}{3^7}$ by dividing the powers.

c. Simplify $x^6 \cdot x$ by multiplying the powers.

d. Calculate the value of the expression $(\sqrt[4]{81})^4$.

e. Translate the word problem below into an equation; then solve.

Lickety-Split Emergency Care, a private ambulance service, charges $100 for a service call (just to come to the house) plus $60 per hour after that. Super Speedy Sirens, another ambulance firm, charges $120 for a service call plus $50 per hour after that. How many hours would a job have to take for the bill of both ambulance services to be the same?

Problem Set 122

Tell whether each sentence below is True or False.

1. Any number raised to the first power is equal to the number itself.

2. An exponent of 1 can be used to divide powers, but never to multiply powers.

Rewrite each number below in scientific notation.

3. 7,000,000,000

4. 31,800,000

Translate each of the following phrases into a mathematical expression. (Don't calculate the answer.)

5. 42 and 17 added first, and that total multiplied by 6.

6. 18 divided by 3 first, and 5 subtracted from that total.

Add or subtract (as indicated) each pair of fractions below. (Make sure your answers are fully reduced.)

7. $\dfrac{7x}{12} + \dfrac{2x}{12}$

(a) 8. $\dfrac{3}{2x} - \dfrac{8}{5x}$

Simplify each expression below by adding or subtracting (as indicated) the powers.

9. $7x^4 + 6x^4$

10. $9x^7 - 4x^7$

Simplify each expression below by dividing the powers.

11. $\dfrac{x^5}{x^3}$ **(b) 12.** $\dfrac{6^8}{6^7}$ **13.** $\dfrac{x^4}{x^3}$

Simplify each expression below by multiplying the powers.

14. $(9x^8)(4x^{11})$ **(c) 15.** $x^7 \cdot x$

Calculate each root below.

16. $\sqrt{100}$ **17.** $\sqrt[3]{125}$

Calculate the value of each expression below.

18. $\sqrt{7^2}$ **(d) 19.** $(\sqrt[4]{16})^4$

Solve each equation below.

20. $3(x-4)=15$ **21.** $-x+10x=72$

Translate the word problem below into an equation; then solve.

(e) 22. Gary's Green Thumb, a professional gardening service, charges $75 for a service call (just to come to the house) plus $60 per hour after that. Luscious Landscapes, another gardening firm, charges $95 for a service call plus $40 per hour after that. How many hours would a job have to take for the bill of both gardening services to be the same?

Lesson 123—An Exponent of 0

We learned about exponents of 1 in the last lesson. The idea probably seemed weird at first, but, if you remember, it turned out to be very useful. In this lesson, we're going to learn about an exponent that's even weirder.

Same Exponent on Top and Bottom

Here's an example.

$$\frac{x^3}{x^3}$$

We know this is equal to 1, since anything divided by itself equals 1. The other way to see that the answer has to be 1 is to factor and cancel. If we did that, all the x's on top would cancel with all the x's on bottom and that would give us an answer of 1. But watch what happens when we apply the subtracting exponents method here.

$$\frac{x^3}{x^3} = x^{3-3} = x^0$$

We end up with a 0 exponent. If you thought an exponent of 1 was weird, what do you think about this? But let's think this through. We know the real answer to our problem has to be 1. If we make x^0 equal 1, then we have the right answer. More importantly, we could use the shortcut of subtracting exponents to divide $\frac{x^3}{x^3}$. That's why the mathematicians decided to make a rule that any number with an exponent of 0 is automatically equal to 1. And since the rule applies to any number, it can also be used on other divisions. Here are a few examples with different bases.

$$\frac{2^5}{2^5} = 2^0 = 1 \qquad \frac{4^7}{4^7} = 4^0 = 1 \qquad \frac{9^2}{9^2} = 9^0 = 1$$

Notice that every time we get an exponent of 0, the actual answer to the division is 1. It has to be that way, because the only time the exponent will turn out to be 0 is when the exponent on top is the same as the exponent on bottom, which just means that all the factors are going to cancel.

Be careful, though. One of the most common mistakes that beginners make is thinking that a 0 exponent makes a power equal not 1 but 0. To a beginner, it's just common sense that 2^0 ought to equal 0. But common sense isn't always right. Once again, an exponent of 0 makes a power equal to 1, not 0.

Using a Zero Exponent to Multiply

Here's something else interesting about exponents of 0. They will also work when we're multiplying powers. Look at this example.

$$x^3 \cdot x^0$$

We have x^3 multiplied by x^0. If we multiply these by adding the exponents, we get this.

$$x^3 \cdot x^0 = x^{3+0} = x^3$$

Is that right? Yes it is, because any number with an exponent of 0 equals 1, remember. So $x^3 \cdot x^0$ is really just $x^3 \cdot 1$, which equals x^3. So an exponent of 0 even gives the right answer when it's used in a multiplication. The main point, then, is that any number with an exponent of 0 is automatically equal to 1. It doesn't matter whether it's an x or an actual number like 2 or 3.

Practice 123

    a. Simplify $\dfrac{4^9}{4^9}$ by dividing the powers.

    b. Simplify $x^4 \cdot x^0$ by multiplying the powers.

    c. Divide the fractions $\dfrac{4x^8}{7} \div \dfrac{8x^3}{14}$. (Make sure your answer is fully reduced.)

    d. Solve the equation $5 + 7x = 16 + 3x$

    e. Translate the word problem below into an equation; then solve.

        Carl can hand-toss 5 pizzas per hour. Eddie can hand-toss 7 pizzas per hour. Working together, how many hours would it take them to hand-toss 156 pizzas?

Problem Set 123

Tell whether each sentence below is True or False.

    1. Any number with an exponent of 0 is equal to 1.

    2. A number with an exponent of 0 cannot be used in any actual mathematical calculations.

Answer each question below.

3. How far will a chartered bus driving at 78 miles per hour go in 4 hours?

4. How far will a riding mower driving at 2 feet per second go in 30 seconds?

Calculate the value of each expression below. (Make sure to do the operations in the correct order.)

5. $7(9-1)$ **6.** $12 \cdot 2^3$

Translate each of the following word problems into an equation. (Don't solve.)

7. There's some number that if you subtract 2 from it first, and then multiply that total by 10, the result is 18.

8. There's some number that if you divide it by 5 first, and then add 22 to that total, the result is 350.

Simplify each expression below.

9. $3x + 14x$ **10.** $7 + 2x + (-5)$

Simplify each expression below by dividing the powers.

11. $\dfrac{x^{12}}{x^8}$ **(a) 12.** $\dfrac{2^9}{2^9}$ **13.** $\dfrac{x^4}{x^4}$

Simplify each expression below by multiplying the powers.

14. $x^2 \cdot x$ **(b) 15.** $x^6 \cdot x^0$

Multiply or divide (as indicated) each pair of fractions below. Make sure your answers are fully reduced.

16. $\dfrac{7x}{24x} \cdot \dfrac{20x}{14}$ **(c) 17.** $\dfrac{5x^7}{2} \div \dfrac{15x^3}{6}$

Calculate each root below.

18. $\sqrt{9}$

19. $\sqrt[3]{27}$

Calculate the value of each expression below.

20. $\sqrt{6^2}$

21. $(\sqrt[3]{64})^3$

Solve each equation below.

22. $7x + 19 = 23$

(d) 23. $3 + 5x = 11 + 2x$

Translate the word problem below into an equation; then solve.

(e) 24. Robert can do 12 belly-flops per hour. Timmy can do 16 belly-flops per hour. Together, how many hours would it take them to do 112 belly-flops?

Lesson 124—Measuring Mass

In this Additional Topics lesson, we're going to go all the way back to units of measurement. We covered those in the middle of the book. Remember, we learned about units of length, like inches and feet. We also learned about units of area for measuring flat surfaces, like square yards and square centimeters, and about units of volume, such as cubic feet, cubic meters, and liters, which are used for measuring 3-D spaces.

Measuring Solids

But what about measuring solid objects like a rock or a block of ice or a gold nugget? It turns out that solid objects can be measured by weighing them. The first weighing machine, or scale, was built in ancient times. It worked by comparing the weights of two objects. Here's a simple scale.

It has a horizontal rod with two pans suspended at either end. To compare the weights of two objects, we just put each object in a pan. As you can see, there's a big rock in the left and a smaller rock on the right. The pan holding the heavier object will be lower than the pan holding the lighter object. If the pans remain level, that would mean that the objects have the same weight. This is the way objects were weighed in ancient times.

Finding a Standard

The only problem with comparing weights like this was that you couldn't ever tell how much one object weighed on its own. That required a standard of measurement for weight. Eventually people got into the practice of using grains (which are just big seeds) as a standard. (They used grains that were the same size.) It worked like this. The object itself would be placed in one pan of the scale and then individual grains would be added to the other pan, one-by-one, until the two pans of the scale were level. Maybe somebody wanted to weigh a rock. Here's a rock in the right pan of the scale.

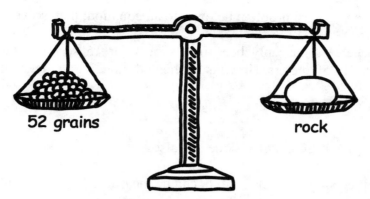

52 grains   rock

The rock weighs 52 grains

We would just keep putting more and more grains in the left pan until that side moves down and the right side moves up so that the pans are even. If it took 52 grains to make the scale balance, the rock weighed "52 grains." Many modern scales, even though they're a lot more sophisticated and precise, work in basically the same way.

Mass Instead of Weight

There is one difference between the ancient methods of weighing and our approach. Modern scientists have discovered that the weight of an object actually changes when you go into outer space. But another measure of an object's size, called its "mass," stays the same everywhere in the universe. Since scientists wanted their measurements for solid objects to stay the same throughout the universe, they decided to use units for mass instead of weight. So all of the units we're going to learn about in the next couple of lessons are actually units of mass and not weight. If you're a little confused about this, just think "weight" every time you see the word "mass" and you'll be all right. That's because on the surface of the earth (where we spend most of our time), mass and weight are tied together perfectly.

Practice 124

   a.   Simplify $-2x^2 + (-3x^2)$ by adding the powers.

   b.   Reduce the fraction $\dfrac{7x^4}{21x^3}$.

   c.   Calculate the value of the root $\sqrt[5]{243}$.

   d.   Solve the equation $13 + x = 8 - 5x$.

e. Translate the word problem below into an equation; then solve.

The space pod has only been on its own for 15 seconds, but it has already traveled 11,250 meters. How fast is the pod traveling in meters per second?

Problem Set 124

Tell whether each sentence below is True or False.

1. Solid objects, like a rock or gold, can be measured by weighing them on a scale.

2. The first known unit for weighing objects was the grain.

Add or subtract each group of numbers below.

3. $\begin{array}{r} 364.85 \\ + 729.21 \\ \hline \end{array}$

4. $\begin{array}{r} 62.03 \\ - 47.98 \\ \hline \end{array}$

Translate each of the following phrases into a mathematical expression. (Don't calculate the answer.)

5. 3 and 6 multiplied first, and 29 subtracted from that total.

6. 7 added to 8 first, and that total divided by 3.

Add or subtract (as indicated) each pair of fractions below. Make sure your answers are fully reduced.

7. $\dfrac{5}{9x} + \dfrac{1}{3x}$

8. $\dfrac{21}{30x} - \dfrac{11}{30x}$

Simplify each expression below by adding or subtracting (as indicated) the powers.

(a) 9. $-4x^2 + (-3x^2)$

10. $11x^3 - 2x^3$

Simplify each expression below by multiplying the powers.

11. $x^5 \cdot x^7$

12. $(-10x^9)(5x^4)$

Simplify each expression below by dividing the powers.

13. $\dfrac{x^7}{x}$ **14.** $\dfrac{15^8}{15^8}$

Reduce each fraction below.

15. $\dfrac{7x^{10}}{7x^2}$ **(b) 16.** $\dfrac{8x^3}{16x^2}$

Calculate each root below.

17. $\sqrt{81}$ **(c) 18.** $\sqrt[5]{32}$

Calculate the value of each expression below.

19. $\sqrt[6]{3^6}$ **20.** $\left(\sqrt{4}\right)^2$

Solve each equation below.

21. $\dfrac{x-10}{3}=-4$ **(d) 22.** $11+x=7-4x$

Translate the word problem below into an equation; then solve.

(e) 23. Although the woman has only been jogging for 65 seconds, she has already traveled 195 meters. How fast is the woman traveling in meters per second?

Lesson 125—Mass Units in the Common System

In the previous lesson, we learned that solid objects were first measured by comparing their weight (or mass) to the mass of little grains. That means that the grain was actually the first unit of measurement for mass.

Starting from the grain, several complete systems of units for mass were built up. The first one was for very small but valuable objects like gold and jewels. It's pretty obvious why it would be important to have units for valuable objects—measurements for those need to be very precise. One of the units in this system was the **carat** which you've probably heard of, because it's still used today to measure gold and diamond quality.

The Avoirdupois System

Another system of mass measurements was created for larger, less expensive objects. This is the one that's used most frequently today to measure mass (at least in English-speaking countries where common units are still popular) along with the common units for length, area, and volume (like inches, square miles, and cubic feet). But one of the interesting things about this system of mass for larger objects is its name. It's called the **avoirdupois (av-er-dew-POYZ) system**. The word "avoirdupois" comes from old French words for "goods of weight," which means bigger goods of greater weight, not tiny jewels.

Here is a table of some avoirdupois units of mass and how they relate.

Avoirdupois (Common) Units of Mass

$27\frac{11}{32}$ grains = 1 dram
16 drams = 1 ounce
16 ounces = 1 pound
100 pounds = 1 hundredweight
20 hundredweights = 1 ton

Notice that the number of grains in a dram is a messy number. That's because units of mass have been changed a lot over the years. Also, we should tell you that this ounce is not the same as the fluid ounce that we learned about before. The fluid ounce measures volume (empty space), but the avoirdupois ounce measures mass.[1] So we have the grain, dram, ounce, pound, hundredweight, and ton as the major common units for mass.

Important Conversion Factors

Actually, today the grain, dram, and hundredweight aren't used that much. But the other units—the ounce, pound, and ton—are still used a lot. That's why it's important to know the conversion factors between these units. As the table shows, there are 16 ounces in 1 pound. You should memorize that. Then, since there are 100 pounds in 1 hundredweight and 20 hundredweights in 1 ton, there have to be 2,000 pounds in 1 ton. (since you just multiply by 100 and then by 20, which is the same as multiplying by 2,000). So the conversion factor from pounds to tons is 2,000. That's one that you should memorize too.

Let's quickly go through a few examples of converting from one unit of mass to another.

How many ounces are in 7 pounds?

We're going from larger units (pounds) to smaller units (ounces), so we need to multiply. The rules about when to multiply and when to divide are exactly the same for conversions between units for mass as they are between units for length, area, or volume. Since there are 16 ounces in 1 pound, we multiply by 16.

$$(7)(16) = 112 \text{ ounces}$$ **Multiply by 16**

Here's another one.

Convert 4,500 pounds into tons.

This time, we're going from smaller units (pounds) to larger units (tons), so we need to divide. And since 2,000 pounds equals 1 ton, we need to divide by 2,000.

$$\frac{4,500}{2,000} = 2.25 \text{ tons}$$ **Divide by 2,000**

Practice 125

a. How many tons are in 8,600 pounds?

b. Convert 2.3 tons to ounces.

---

[1] It's confusing to have different units with the same name, but this is just another drawback of the common system.

c. Multiply the fractions $\dfrac{9}{5x^3} \cdot \dfrac{15x^7}{27}$. (Make sure your answer is fully reduced.)

d. Solve the equation $-x - 3x = -9$.

e. Translate the word problem below into an equation; then solve.

William loves to go backpacking on the weekends, and he usually carries about 24 ounces of energy bars with him. How many pounds is this?

Problem Set 125

Tell whether each sentence below is True or False.

1. The common units for mass come from the "avoirdupois" system, which is French for "goods of weight."

2. The most popular units from the avoirdupois system are the ounce, the pound, and the ton.

Do each unit conversion below.

3. Convert a mass of 38 pounds to ounces.

(a) 4. How many tons are in a mass of 10,400 pounds?

(b) 5. Convert a mass of 1.5 tons to ounces.

Translate each of the following word problems into an equation. (Don't solve.)

6. There's some number that if you multiply it by 7 first, and then add 16 to that total, the result is -31.

7. There's some number that if you subtract 54 from it first, and then divide that total by 3, the result is 26.

Simplify each expression below.

8. $6x - x$ 9. $12 + 4x + 7$

Simplify each expression below by dividing the powers.

10. $\dfrac{x^{11}}{x^{10}}$

11. $\dfrac{x^3}{x}$

Simplify each expression below by multiplying the powers.

12. $x^8 \cdot x^0$

13. $(12x^3)(13x^4)$

Multiply or divide (as indicated) each pair of fractions below. Make sure your answers are fully reduced.

14. $\dfrac{4x}{3x} \div \dfrac{2x}{9}$

(c) 15. $\dfrac{12}{13x^4} \cdot \dfrac{26x^9}{24}$

Calculate each root below.

16. $\sqrt{49}$

17. $\sqrt[3]{8}$

Calculate the value of each expression below.

18. $\sqrt[4]{5^4}$

19. $(\sqrt{16})^2$

Solve each equation below.

20. $7 + 3x + 4 = 20$

(d) 21. $-x - 2x = -7$

Translate the word problem below into an equation; then solve.

(e) 22. Griffin, the mountain climber, has a trusty sleeping bag which has never failed to keep him warm even at extremely high altitudes. The sleeping bag weighs exactly 40 ounces. How many pounds is this?

Lesson 126—Mass in the Metric System

In the last lesson, we learned about common (avoirdupois) units for mass. The main ones were the ounce, the pound, and the ton. But what about mass in the metric system?

The Gram

The main unit for mass in the metric system is the gram. A **gram** is equal to the mass of water that will fit into 1 milliliter of space. Just imagine a cube with side lengths equal to less than half an inch filled with water. That's a gram of mass. So a gram is actually really small. It's a lot smaller than an ounce.

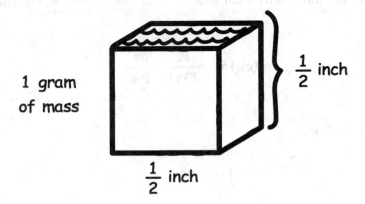

Smaller Metric Units for Mass

As always, the metric system organizes its units by 10s. And the prefixes of the mass units are the same ones we use with all the other metric units. That makes everything nice and simple. The next unit below the gram is the **decigram**. It's $\frac{1}{10}$ the mass of a gram, so 1 gram = 10 decigrams. Even smaller is the next unit down, which, as you can guess, is the centigram. The **centigram** is $\frac{1}{100}$ of a gram, so 1 gram = 100 centigrams. Then there's the extremely tiny unit, the **milligram**, which equals $\frac{1}{1,000}$ of a gram. That means 1 gram = 1,000 milligrams. A milligram is actually a lot smaller than a grain.

Larger Metric Units for Mass

Going up to the larger units, the next one just larger than the gram is the **dekagram**, which is, of course, 10 times the gram. Then there's the **hectogram**. It has a mass that's 100 times the gram. And that's followed by the **kilogram**, which equals 1,000 grams. The kilogram is quite a bit larger than a pound. Imagine a cube with 4-inch sides full of water. That's a kilogram. (A decimeter, remember, is about 4 inches long. So a kilogram is actually a mass equal to 1 liter full of water.)

Here are all the units together.

Major Metric Units for Mass

1,000 grams = 1 kilogram
100 grams = 1 hectogram
10 grams = 1 dekagram
1 gram = 10 decigrams
1 gram = 100 centigrams
1 gram = 1,000 milligrams

Some Conversions

As always, the great thing about metric units is that it's very easy to convert from one to another. All you have to do is multiply or divide by 10. Let's do some examples.

How many decigrams are in 13 grams?

We're going from larger to smaller units, so we need to multiply. And since there are 10 decigrams in 1 gram, we need to multiply by 10. There's no need for long multiplication or a calculator. All we have to do is move the decimal point in 13 one place to the right to get 130 decigrams. That's our answer.

Let's do another one.

Convert 825 hectograms to kilograms.

This time, we're going from smaller to larger units, so we need to divide. There are 10 hectograms in 1 kilogram, so we have to divide by 10. We can just move the decimal point in 825 one place to the left to get 82.5 kilograms. So that's the answer to that one.

We'll do one more.

How many grams are in 931 centigrams?

We're going from smaller to larger units, so we'll have to divide again. But this time, our conversion jumps through two units. There are two ways to do this. We could divide by 10 twice or we could just divide by 100, which is the same thing. Let's divide by 100. To do that, all we have to do is move the decimal point in 931 two places to the left to get 9.31 grams. That's our answer.

Practice 126

    a. Convert a mass of 285 decigrams to centigrams.

    b. How many kilograms are in a mass of 17,200 grams?

    c. Simplify $-8x^4 - 4x^4$ by subtracting the powers.

    d. Calculate the root $\sqrt{1}$.

    e. Translate the word problem below into an equation; then solve.

        There is a number that if you multiply it by 6 first, and then subtract 8 from the result, you get 106. What's the number?

Problem Set 126

Tell whether each sentence below is True or False.

    1. The main unit for mass in the metric system is the "gram."

    2. Mass units in the metric system use the same prefixes as all the other metric units.

Do each unit conversion below.

    3. Convert a mass of 96 ounces to pounds.

    4. How many ounces are in a mass of 2.3 tons?

  (a) 5. Convert a mass of 375 decigrams to centigrams.

  (b) 6. How many kilograms are in a mass of 14,500 grams?

Translate each of the following phrases into a mathematical expression. (Don't calculate the answer.)

7. 4 added to 19 first, and that total multiplied by 8.

8. 24 divided by 2 first, and 59 subtracted from that total.

Add or subtract (as indicated) each pair of fractions below. Make sure your answers are fully reduced.

9. $\dfrac{2x}{15} + \dfrac{7x}{15}$

10. $\dfrac{4}{3x} - \dfrac{1}{5x}$

Simplify each expression below by adding or subtracting (as indicated) the powers.

(c) 11. $-9x^4 - 2x^4$

12. $13x^5 + 6x^5$

Simplify each expression below by multiplying the powers.

13. $x^4 \cdot x^{10}$

14. $(25x^2)(4x^3)$

Simplify each expression below by dividing the powers.

15. $\dfrac{x^9}{x^3}$

16. $\dfrac{9^{12}}{9^{12}}$

Calculate each root below.

17. $\sqrt[4]{16}$

(d) 18. $\sqrt{1}$

Calculate the value of each expression below.

19. $\sqrt[3]{14^3}$

20. $(\sqrt{100})^2$

Solve each equation below.

21. $11(x - 3) = 44$ **22.** $9x + 5x = -28$

Translate the word problem below into an equation; then solve.

(e) 23. There is a number that if you multiply it by 7 first, and then subtract 9 from the result, you get 103. What's the number?